Yours

& Ours

**Just add love to make two
families become one!**

Yours, Mine & Ours

Miranda Lee
Debbie Macomber
Sandra Field

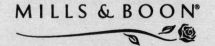

MILLS & BOON®

*MILLS & BOON and MILLS & BOON with the Rose Device
are registered trademarks of the publisher.
Harlequin Mills & Boon Limited,
Eton House, 18-24 Paradise Road, Richmond, Surrey, TW9 1SR*

YOURS, MINE & OURS
© *1998 by Harlequin Books SA*

An Obsessive Desire, Yours and Mine and *The Dating Game* were first
published in separate, single volumes by Mills & Boon Limited.
An Obsessive Desire in 1990, *Yours and Mine* in 1991
and *The Dating Game* in 1994.

An Obsessive Desire © Miranda Lee 1990
Yours and Mine © Debbie Macomber 1991
The Dating Game © Sandra Field 1994

ISBN 0 263 81085 2

05-9804

*Printed and bound in Great Britain
by Caledonian Book Manufacturing Ltd, Glasgow*

Miranda Lee is Australian, living near Sydney. Born and raised in the bush, she was boarding-school educated and briefly pursued a classical music career before moving to Sydney and embracing the world of computers. Happily married, with three daughters, she began writing when family commitments kept her at home, and had her first book published by Mills & Boon® in 1990. She likes to create stories that are believable, modern, fast-paced and sexy. Her interests include reading meaty sagas, doing word puzzles, gambling and going to the movies.

AN OBSESSIVE DESIRE
by
MIRANDA LEE

CHAPTER ONE

RHEA was late. She raced into the back of the church and opened the lid of the upright organ. Thank the Lord the bride was late as well! With a ragged sigh of relief she sat down and concentrated on sorting out the sheets of music she would need.

'Excuse me . . .'

Rhea controlled the surge of impatience at being interrupted and glanced up, only to have the blood drain from her face.

'I'm sorry to bother you,' the man standing on the other side of the organ said, 'but I have a message from the bride's mother.'

Rhea could not believe her eyes. It couldn't possibly be! Not the *same* man. Not *here*, at a small wedding on the outer fringes of Sydney, in an old, almost dilapidated church. This was the last place on earth such an individual would be!

But it *was* him! There was no doubt in her mind.

'. . . Miss . . .?'

He was puzzled, no doubt, by her open-mouthed surprise.

Surprise? That was a ridiculous word to use to describe her feelings, Rhea conceded. *Shock* better explained the sensations which even now threatened to embarrass her with devastating force. Her stomach was in instant knots. Her heart was pounding madly. And a mortifying heat was beginning to claim her normally cool cheeks.

His puzzlement became concern. 'Are you all right?' came the kind enquiry.

Rhea's mouth snapped shut. She struggled for composure and appeared to win. 'Sorry,' she apologised, though curtly, 'for a moment I thought you were someone else. But I was mistaken.'

A smile lit up his thoughtful face, lifting his straight black brows and transforming the cool grey eyes into warm wells of charm. It rocked Rhea considerably, but this time she didn't show it.

'I'm glad,' he returned. 'I wouldn't have wanted to be the man you thought I was. You looked positively terrified for a moment there!'

Terrified . . .

Yes, he was right—he did terrify her.

But *why*?

'Mrs Gabroni wanted to know,' he went on smoothly, 'if you could play Gounod's 'Ave Maria' while the couple are in the sacristy signing the register. It's a favourite of hers. Do you know it?'

Rhea's affirmative was made through dry lips.

'She also asked me to give you this envelope. It contains the agreed payment for today.'

He placed it on top of the organ, a flash of diamond and gold sparkling from one of his fingers. Rhea found her gaze travelling from his carefully manicured fingertips across the crisp white cuff of his shirt, then up the arm of the superbly cut black jacket.

No rented suit, that, she decided shakily. It had been made specially to fit his superb body so that not a crease formed around the strong neck and wide shoulders. And the material was a silk blend, of that she was certain. A rich man's dinner suit.

But then she had known he was well off, and successful, this man who terrified her.

'Thank you,' she managed with eyes already dropping. To gaze into that face again was out of the question. She had made enough of a fool of herself already.

But when he kept standing there, not moving away, obviously still staring down at her, she was forced to look up. 'Yes?' she asked, swallowing.

His eyes flicked assessingly over her, making her stomach muscles tighten again. Rhea knew what he was seeing, knew she was an attractive woman with her big blue eyes, shapely figure and dainty oval face. Her hair too was a drawcard, for it was long and thick and dark, given to fluffing out on to her shoulders before falling halfway down her back in a wild mass of loose curls. She usually tied it back some way, but she'd been running late, and had decided to leave it.

An unfortunate decision, she groaned silently, for the man standing before her was gazing at her abundant tresses with speculation in his eye. Was he wondering what it would look like spread out on his pillow?

Rhea was shocked by her train of thought, and the fantasy-like mental image she was having of herself in his bed. It rattled her, almost as much as the man himself. And yet he wasn't the first man to come on to her in the six years she had been widowed. Not by a long shot.

Till recently she had worked as a cashier in the local supermarket—the only job she could get as an untrained ex-housewife—where she had endured countless propositions from the sales representatives who called. At first she had been upset by their blatant attempts at familiarity, but she soon learnt to fend off their passes with skill and tact.

She knew, however, that the disturbing stranger smiling down at her at this very moment was not the sort of man to be fended off easily.

'I was admiring your hair,' he said quite openly. 'Don't ever get it cut.'

Such a personal comment instinctively made her bristle. 'Really? I was thinking of doing just that, in fact,' she lied.

'Don't,' he reproached. 'To do so would be a crime.'

Another smile accompanied his words, once again sending her pulse-rate into an agitated syncopation.

She glanced around in nervous defence, searching for an escape from the distress he was causing. Her veins seemed charged with electric currents, the nerve-endings along her arm prickling her skin into goose-bumps. 'I'm sorry, but the bride will be arriving shortly,' she excused herself hastily. 'I must get ready to play.'

'Of course,' came the silken reply. 'And I must find a seat.'

He flashed her a parting smile, undaunted, it seemed, by her apparent lack of response. Would he come back to try again after the ceremony?

The thought unnerved Rhea considerably, and it was with apprehension that she watched the tall, elegant figure wander down the aisle. When he stopped and slid into an empty row on the right she held her breath in anticipation of his glancing back at her, but he didn't.

Instead he settled himself comfortably in the corner, sitting half side on, one arm curved lazily over the back of the ancient pew, his long fingers tapping idly on the wood.

Her eyes were compulsively drawn to the unforgettable lines of his profile, so distinctive with its strong, almost sharp nose, its squared jawline and prominent chin. As she studied him his chin tilted up slightly so that the glossy black waves lapped over the startlingly white collar. He looked incredibly handsome and totally self-possessed.

Not so herself. Rhea was a jumble of nerves. A mess!

The intensity of her agitation now brought frustration and anger—but more at herself than at the man. Why should this particular male make her feel like this? So churned up, so upset . . . Why?

It wasn't as though he meant anything to her. He was a stranger, for heaven's sake. Oh, yes, she had seen him before. *Twice*! Which she supposed was astonishing in itself. But he hadn't seen *her* on those occasions, let alone spoken to her. She didn't know his name. She didn't know where he worked or where he lived. She really didn't know anything about him, except what she'd been able to deduce. That he was successful in whatever he did for a living—and with women.

Of course the status quo had changed now. He *had* seen her this third time, and he *had* spoken to her. In fact, he had shown quite clearly that he found her attractive. Nevertheless, why let that unnerve her so? Wasn't she used to deflecting that type of male interest?

Rhea forced herself to keep looking at him, his face, his hands, his body, his mouth . . . forced herself to finally face the feelings that even now were welling up inside her again, feelings which she could no longer pretend she didn't recognise, despite their newness.

It's because I want him too, came the slow admission. And it took her breath away.

Yes, that was it, she confessed to herself, slowly, dazedly, hardly daring to face this incredible truth. His name, his position, his background, didn't seem to matter. She just wanted him.

She shuddered, her eyes falling to the keyboard. She was appalled by her desires. Appalled! She had never wanted a man like that before. Never. Ever!

And the unfamiliar feelings terrified the life out of her.

'Mum!'

Rhea blinked. She heard Emily's voice dimly, but her mind was still in turmoil.

'Mum, the bride's waiting for you to start,' Emily whispered urgently.

Rhea finally registered her attention on her daughter's worried frown, pulling herself together sufficiently to flash her a reassuring smile. Yet her fingers felt wooden as they plopped on to the keyboard, amazing their owner by finding the right notes out of sheer habit.

The whole congregation rose for the bridal chorus, watching the bride's entrance with rapt attention. Rhea neither saw nor heard a thing for the entire time it took to complete the piece, staring blinding down at the keys till her fingers finally came to a halt.

She lifted nerveless hands and sagged into the stool before slanting an anxious glance over at Emily, afraid her daughter might have noticed her odd behaviour. But no, Emily's gaze was fixed in childlike wonder on the ceremony.

Rhea closed her eyes, hoping perhaps to wash her mind clear of any more disturbing thoughts. But it was the worst thing she could have done, for it catapulted her memory right back to the very day . . . the very moment . . . when she had first set eyes on the man.

It had been nearly six months previously—a cool windy day in August. Rhea had travelled by train into Sydney to keep an appointment at an exclusive boutique in the Centrepoint shopping complex. Her objective had been to sell some of her original handmade garments, lovingly crafted from the mohair she spun and dyed herself, a hobby which she hoped to turn into a steady source of income. Being a widow with a mortgage and a ten-year-old daughter to support was a constant battle of balancing the budget.

She had come out of the boutique on cloud nine. She had sold everything and had a contract for more! The job behind the check-out counter was already a bad memory. Of course, she would continue playing the organ at weekend weddings, for that would provide extra savings for Emily's future education.

Pleased and excited, Rhea had decided to treat herself to a cup of coffee and a sandwich at one of the exclusive coffee lounges high up in the Tower. And it had been while she sat there sipping her *cappuccino* that she had first seen the man.

He had been a couple of tables away. With a woman—a lovely young woman with soft brown eyes and stylishly cut short blonde hair. But of course it had been *he* who had first drawn her eyes, with his striking colouring and sheer male beauty. The rich black hair and deeply tanned complexion seemed spotlighted by the paleness of his light grey business suit and crisp white shirt. He was the most elegantly groomed man Rhea had ever seen—not to mention the handsomest.

She had stared and stared and stared, so much so that at one point she had had to look down quickly when he had glanced her way.

There had been no mistaking the intimacy between the couple. The smiles, the low laughter, the touches, all bespoke a relationship beyond mere friendship. And of course there had been the present he had given her —a bracelet, or a watch. Rhea could not quite see which. The girl had thrown her arms around her lover's neck and kissed him. Rhea had finally got up and left, almost running away from the most peculiarly distressing feelings that had invaded her while watching them.

The second time she had seen him had been less than two months later, in early October. Her mother and stepfather had been going on a package tour of New Zealand with some other members of their bowling club, and, since Rhea hadn't been back home to Kiama to visit for quite a while, she had offered to drive in to Mascot airport and see them off.

The plane was slightly delayed and during the unfortunate wait conversation soon dried up, as it did whenever Rhea and Bill were forced to endure each other's company for longer than a few minutes.

Their relationship had always been strained, Bill having married her mother when Rhea was at the vulnerable age of twelve, and only a year after her father had been killed in an industrial accident. Rhea had been shocked by the way her mother seemed to like Bill's physical attentions. They were always touching and kissing, embarrassing her so much so that she had kept to her room most of the time.

She had struggled through years of resentment and the feeling that she had become the outsider in her own home. It was one of the reasons she had fought so hard to maintain a secure and loving home life for her daughter after Milan's death, with as few changes as possible. She had vowed never to bring a stranger into her home by marrying again; she didn't want Emily ever to feel as she had done.

So Rhea had been glancing around the busy airport terminal in agitated silence when her eyes landed on the very same man she had seen in the coffee lounge.

He had been coming out of the VIP lounge, looking executive-suave in a navy pin-striped suit, one arm wrapped possessively around the waist of a statuesque blonde. Not the same one he'd been with before, Rhea had noted with surprise, then cynicism. So, she'd thought, he was one of those . . .

This woman had been older, around thirty, with startlingly made-up eyes in a vibrant face, a sexy mouth and a spectacular figure. He had seemed to be reassuring her about something, holding her close, talking softly in one ear.

Rhea had stiffened as she watched the man lift a hand to gently touch his companion's cheek. And when his mouth had bent to the woman's in a long, lingering kiss, she had spun away, feeling both embarrassment and a sharp stab of distress. She had determinedly not looked back, surprising her stepfather with a sudden spurt of animated conversation. Of course, when she had finally glanced over her shoulder the man and woman had disappeared.

At the time, Rhea had not recognised the emotion that had twisted inside herself. But now, as her eyes opened to scrutinise the man in the pew once more, she realised what it was she had felt. She had been jealous! She—Rhea—had wanted to be the woman in his arms, having him touch *her* cheek, kiss *her* mouth . . .

Suddenly he looked back over his shoulder towards the back of the church, and penetrating grey eyes clashed with wide blue ones. Rhea blinked, knowing she should tear her gaze away, fearing what he was already seeing in her expression. But she could not. Instead, she kept looking at him, and when he smiled at her the temptation to smile back invitingly was almost overpowering.

She stopped herself just in time, dropping her eyes to stare fixedly down at her hands in her lap, several seconds passing before she realised that her hands were shaking, literally shaking.

Oh, God . . . What on earth was happening to her?

Yet being appalled at herself did seem rather silly, Rhea decided with a flash of frank reality. So she was attracted to the man—wildly attracted. Was that so wrong, so bad? She was twenty-nine, for pity's sake. And six years a widow!

She knew full well what other widows in her position would do. They certainly wouldn't be having any qualms. They would lift their faces, smile, and give the man the message, pronto!

But you're not other widows, her conscience inserted fiercely. Not at all. Don't pretend this is just a normal, healthy frustration that you're responding to. My God, woman, be honest! You've never even *liked* sex! So why are you lusting after this man?

'I now pronounce you man and wife.'

Rhea came back to reality with a jolt, fumbling to start up the organ again to play the requested piece. The guests chattered quietly amongst themselves, and as the strains of Gounod's 'Ave Maria' wafted over them, each haunting chord clear and precise, none would have envisaged the fragile state of their player. Once again Rhea found the notes with an automatic skill, her smooth performance belying the fact that her inner composure was totally obliterated.

When the signal came to change the music to 'Here comes the Bride' her heart began pounding along with the beat of the music, but not from gaiety. The thought that at any moment the object of this unexpected and obsessive desire would stop to talk to her again was throwing her completely. Just go away, she willed wildly as she played. Go away!

The happy couple walked past and everyone else began pouring into the aisle behind them. Don't look up, she kept telling herself frantically. Just keep playing. Keep playing. Maybe he'll walk on by.

But out of the corner of her eye she saw a pair of black trouser legs stop beside her, and instantly her entire body moved into a disturbingly breathless state.

Her response bothered her terribly. She didn't *want* to want this man. Not at all. She was happy and content with her life as it was. And while she might be inexperienced—her husband had been her only lover—she was not so naïve as to believe a woman could tangle with the likes of *this* Romeo and get away scot-free.

Rhea dragged in a steadying breath, set her teeth firmly in her jaw, and with dogged determination kept playing. She kept playing till the church had emptied, stopping only because it was both stupid and futile to go on. For he was still there, one elbow leaning against the top of the organ, watching and waiting for her to finish.

'You play quite beautifully,' he remarked as she bent to switch off the electricity. 'Where did you learn?'

She closed the lid and stood up. 'A nun taught me,' she said, giving him the benefit of only the briefest glance before she began shuffling the various sheets of music into a neat pile. Without any encouragement he was sure to depart, she reasoned. Most men did.

'Ah, yes, the good sisters. They always have an ear for music. And talent.'

Rhea's chin snapped round. If there was one thing that really aggravated her it was flattery. Her organ playing was competent, and that was all. If this man thought he could . . .

He smiled at her and any retort died in her throat.

'I . . . I'm not that good,' she murmured.

'Mum, the bride's leaving,' Emily called out from where she was standing in the doorway. 'Aren't you going to come and see?'

It all happened so quickly. The man glanced first at Emily, then down at the third finger of Rhea's left hand. She had never taken off her wedding-ring, the gold band having protected her sometimes from unwanted advances. It had never occurred to her that one day it would protect her from a wanted one.

He glanced back at Emily and his face changed, from an engaging smile to a frown. He made some excuse about having to get home and left before Rhea had a chance to correct his natural assumption that she was a married woman.

Which was just as well, she reasoned a split second later, an ironic grimace twisting her mouth. One miserable smile from him and she'd been about to make a complete fool of herself!

She snatched up the envelope still lying on the organ and stuffed it into her large bag, along with the sheets of music. 'Come on, Emily.' Her tone was brusque. 'We might as well go home too.'

And with a swish of her black pleated skirt she grabbed Emily's elbow and left, totally ignoring the groups of guests lingering in the churchyard. She turned her head neither to left nor right, propelling her daughter over towards her small van.

'Are we in a hurry or something?' Emily asked as they both climbed into the hot, stuffy cabin.

'I have a lot to do before school starts again on Wednesday,' Rhea explained, winding her window down noisily. 'One of these days,' she added irritably, 'I'll be able to afford a car with air-conditioning.'

The engine fired on the third try, then lurched through the churchyard towards the narrow exit. A sleek silver sports car had the same idea at the same time.

Rhea braked, as did the sports car. She knew before she looked directly at the driver who it was. The car fitted the man.

Once their eyes actually met he gestured gallantly for her to go in front of him. But she declined, sending him ahead with an insistent wave. He nodded appreciation and accelerated quickly away, his preoccupied expression showing her that he had already forgotten her. With hands clenched around the steering-wheel Rhea watched till the powerful vehicle disappeared over the crest of the hill.

'Mum? You can go now—he's gone.'

Rhea congratulated herself on the way she proceeded smoothly out of the bumpy driveway. There was not even a hint of the emotional chaos her daughter's words had evoked.

Gone . . .

She would never know his name, never see him again . . .

I should be grateful, she told herself. Relieved. Ecstatic. Out of sight was out of mind, wasn't it?

A rueful smile touched her mouth as she turned the van towards home. What point was there in fooling herself? Rhea knew she would not forget him, or the needs he had evoked in her, in a hurry.

CHAPTER TWO

RHEA swung the van into their driveway, carefully negotiating the planks of wood that served as a bridge across the culvert. The dogs were barking and jumping up and down in their wire run as she came to a halt under the carport attached to her fibro cottage.

'I'll let Bobby and Dolly out,' Emily said eagerly.

'Make sure the chooks are away first,' Rhea warned. Emily hated locking the dogs up, but Rhea knew that it was a case of 'better to be cruel to be kind.' Their two dogs were Australian terriers who just adored chasing little things that moved. And Rhea's biggest and best hen had just hatched a dozen chickens.

Rhea was busily opening the doors and windows in the stuffy house when she was drawn outside by a commotion. Once free, the dogs had raced up the back yard and into the goat paddock and were making a real racket, barking madly and racing in circles round the old shed where Rhea kept the hay and oats.

A snake, came the immediate thought. There'd been one in there last year and Rhea had nearly had a heart attack. Dolly, who was a fearless little creature, had killed it.

'I'll go and see what's bothering them,' she said. 'Emily, you stay inside!' Without thinking of her own safety she picked up a spade and ran.

'Get away from there, Dolly,' she shouted as she scrambled through the strand-wire fence. 'Oh, you crazy fool, get away!'

19

Bobby, who was by far the bigger dog, but inclined to be timid, clustered around Rhea's feet, almost making her trip over. 'Stop being so brave, Bobby,' she growled, then laughed. 'Oh, good grief! One killer dog and one coward!'

But she loved the dogs dearly. Gran had bought them for Emily a couple of Christmases earlier, and, despite their shortcomings, they were part of the family.

Not only that, Dolly was a good money-spinner, having produced a couple of pure-bred litters to Bobby, and at this very moment was looking pregnant again. Rhea hadn't told Emily, but she intended to use the money from this litter to buy the pony that had been her daughter's dearest wish for some time.

She finally extricated Bobby from her ankles, raised the spade in readiness and crept around the side of the shed. Her heart was thudding madly, for snakes terrified the life out of her.

With her arrival, Dolly had quietened, which didn't exactly help Rhea's nerves. The silence was ominous. She took the final petrified step that brought the inside of the stable into view, surprise making her nearly drop the spade on her foot.

A little girl of maybe seven or eight was sitting on the sack of oats, staring at her and looking even more terrified than Rhea. That she had been crying was obvious.

'For goodness' sake!' exclaimed Rhea, then recovered sufficiently to lean the threatening spade against the side wall. 'What have we here?'

Bobby had joined them now, curiosity getting the better of his fear. When he sniffed the little girl's feet, she drew them up quickly and whimpered.

'It's all right,' Rhea soothed, coming forward to squat down in front of the child. 'They won't bite. They just want to meet you.'

She looked into the tear-stained eyes and saw sheer misery. Her heart turned over. 'What's wrong, sweetie? Can I help? Are you lost?'

Rhea knew all the local children and this little girl was not one of them. Of course, she could have recently moved into the area; there had been a lot of buying and selling since the Government had decided to build the new international airport only a few miles away.

'Do you live near here?' she asked. 'Would you like me to ring your parents?'

Silence. But the child had flinched at the mention of her parents and the tears were rolling again.

Rhea battled to control a growing fury. What sort of people would upset a child this way? And what sort of treatment exactly had she been subjected to?

She did not let the child see her anger. Instead she asked gently, 'How about coming down to the house with me for a cool drink? It's terribly hot in here and you look as if you've walked a long way.'

And that was the understatement of the year! The child's arms and legs were scratched—no doubt from climbing through barbed-wire fences—and her dress was dirty and torn.

Rhea's observant eyes went over the dress again and she frowned. It was an expensive garment, made from fine material with expert craftsmanship—not the clothing of a poor, underprivileged child.

'Coming?' she suggested, and held out her hand.

The child hesitated, then slipped down from the sack, curling grubby fingers into Rhea's slender palm. The trusting gesture squeezed at her heart.

Immediately the two dogs rushed up to the child, jumping up and down on their short sturdy legs, begging for a pat, but the little girl cringed away. Not used to dogs, Rhea thought. Certainly not country born and bred. 'If you give them a pat,' she explained quietly, 'they won't keep on bothering you.'

The little girl did so, tentatively.

'My name's Rhea, by the way,' she told the child as she took the small hand again and began heading back to the house. 'And what should I call you?'

Two big grey eyes blinked up at her. 'Laura. Laura Hatfield.'

'A pretty name for a pretty girl.' And she was too. Like a doll, with delicate features, a porcelain skin and jet-black curls.

Emily was waiting at the back door, looking anxious and puzzled.

'We have a visitor, Emily,' Rhea said. 'Her name's Laura. Laura, this is my daughter Emily.'

'Hello,' Emily tried, but Laura said nothing.

'Come on,' Rhea went on brightly, 'let's go inside and have a Coke.'

Emily beamed. It wasn't often Rhea allowed her to have soft drinks. 'I'll get us some glasses,' she offered eagerly.

Laura drank the Coke, but that was the extent of her co-operation. She sat at the kitchen table, the empty glass in front of her, not saying another word. All the prompting in the world hadn't got any extra information out of her. But at least she'd stopped crying.

Rhea decided to try a different tack. 'Would you like to change your dress, Laura? That one needs a wash, don't you think? Your mother wouldn't be too happy to see such a beautiful dress ruined, would she?'

That did it. Though Laura's reaction was not exactly what Rhea had in mind. The child burst into tears again, this time sobbing her heart out. Appalled that she had upset the little girl, Rhea did her best to comfort her, cuddling her close and stroking the glossy black curls. 'Oh, Laura, Laura my dear, I'm so sorry! Whatever did I say?'

'I haven't got a mother any more,' came the choked reply between sobs. 'She . . . she died last year . . . and . . . and *he's* going to send me to boarding school. My mother said she'd never do that . . . never ever! But *he* doesn't love me . . . He hates me . . . and I hate him too now!'

'There, there, my dear, I'm sure he doesn't hate you, whoever he is. Are we talking about your father?'

'Yes . . . Mr Chase.'

Rhea pulled back and frowned down at Laura's crumpled face. 'Mr Chase? But surely your father's name would be Hatfield?'

'No.' Laura blinked and sniffled. 'He . . . he never married my mother.'

Rhea gritted her teeth. 'Didn't he now?' she said tightly. 'And where does your father live, Laura? Around here somewhere?'

The little girl nodded.

'Do you know the address?'

'Lot four, Mountain View Road. It's a new house,

two-storeyed.'

'That's the place above the old dairy, Mum,' Emily joined in. 'You remember the one. We talked about how quickly it went up.'

Rhea certainly did remember. A rich man's house. A rich man who hadn't bothered to marry his daughter's mother, and who was now packing the unwanted offspring off to boarding school because she might get in the way of his lifestyle.

A storm was brewing inside her. There was nothing that enraged her more than injustice and unfairness and cruelty, particularly to children!

She stood up and strode across the kitchen, snatching up the pencil and notepad she kept near the phone. But before she returned to the table she scooped in a steadying breath. Keep the anger for the father, she told herself. No point in upsetting the child further.

'Could you write your phone number down, Laura?' she asked calmly enough. 'I'll have to ring your father—you must realise that.'

The child's eyes rounded in alarm. Dear God, Rhea fumed inside, she was terrified of the man! 'Don't worry, Laura, I'll smooth everything over and see what can be done about your going to the local school with Emily. Would you like that?'

It was heart-rending to see those grey eyes light up so. 'Could you? I mean . . . Oh, that would be wonderful! I like living out here better than in the city. And I did so hate the thought of leaving Mimi.'

'Mimi?'

'My pony. I only got her last month and I haven't even learnt to ride her yet.'

A pony . . . Something twisted inside Rhea. It annoyed her that this so-called father would probably have bought his daughter a pony without giving it a second thought. Anything to keep the kid busy, she imagined him saying. While her own Emily had wanted a pony for years . . .

'Do you really have a pony?' Emily asked, without a trace of envy in her voice, only interest. 'What colour is it?'

'Sort of grey.'

'Why don't you take Laura to your room, Emily, and have a chat while I ring her father, OK?'

The girls were gone in a flash and, despite her inner anger, Rhea felt nervous. She did so hate personal confrontations, hated the way they left her feeling sick inside. But she felt she had to do something positive for Laura, not just hand her back to this unfeeling man.

She dialled, her fingers trembling slightly. The phone began ringing at the other end. Ringing and ringing and ringing. Five, six, seven, eight times. Answer the damned thing, you . . . you . . . Simon Legree!

'Stephen Chase here.'

A lump filled Rhea's throat now that he actually answered.

'Hello? Is anyone there? Speak up, for God's sake,' the voice snapped, 'or damned well hang up!'

The impatient, harsh tone was exactly what Rhea needed to fortify herself. She coughed and straightened. 'Would I be speaking to Laura's father?'

There was a moment's hesitation before the voice said stiffly, 'You would.'

'Then you might like to know,' she went on archly,

'that at this moment your Laura is here in my home crying her eyes out, utterly distraught and miserable.' Which was only a slight twisting of the truth, she justified to herself.

'Don't be ridiculous, woman! My Laura is upstairs asleep in her room. You must have some other Laura.'

'Oh, really? Are you quite sure about that?'

She heard the sharp intake of breath down the line. 'Hold on . . .' The sound of running upstairs was clear as a bell, as was the sound of his angry return. 'Let me get this clear,' he roared down into her ear. 'Is this some sort of ransom demand? Have you kidnapped my daughter?'

Rhea was floored. And speechless.

'Speak up, woman! Are you or are you not making some sort of criminal demand?'

'Of . . . of course not!' she blurted back.

'Then why have you got her? If you hurt one hair of my daughter's head you'll wish you'd never been born!'

Rhea felt her face burning with indignation and embarrassment. 'Mr Chase! I didn't take your daughter— she ran away and I found her! And if you th——'

'Would you kindly tell me exactly who and where you are?' he cut in harshly.

'I will if you'll let me finish a sentence,' she snapped. 'My name is Rhea Petrovic, *Mrs* Rhea Petrovic, and I repeat, I didn't have anything to do with your daughter's running away from home, but from what I can see you have a very unhappy girl here, Mr Chase, and one whom I'm loath to return to you, in the circumstances!'

She could feel his fury across the air-waves. 'I'll give

you just ten seconds, Mrs Povlovic or whatever your name is, to tell me where you live, or I'll ring the police.'

'Petrovic,' she repeated with a desperate return to calm. She had sudden visions of squad cars descending on the house, an event which would keep the neighbours in gossip for years. 'There's no need to get in a flap, Mr Chase. Your daughter is quite safe with me.'

'I have only your word for that, madam, and, since I don't know you from a bar of soap, I'm hardly mollified!'

Rhea dragged in a deep breath and counted to ten. Mollified, indeed! How pompous could you get? 'Then I suggest you come here and judge for yourself. Go all the way to the bottom of your hill,' she informed him stiffly, 'then turn left. Take the first turning on your right—Creekbed Close. My place is at the far end of the road, number sixteen. The number is plainly painted on the post-box.'

'I'll be there in five minutes,' he rapped out.

'You do that,' she snapped, only to find that the phone was already dead in her hand.

'Of all the . . .' Rhea's hand was shaking as she dropped the receiver back into its cradle. Who did he think he was, accusing her of being a kidnapper? And who did he think he was that his daughter would be kidnapped? Some darned multi-millionaire or something?

She felt a queasy pang in her stomach. She conceded the possibility that Mr Chase might be quite wealthy, but so what? She gave a brave and defiant toss of her head. Did that give him special rights? Did that excuse his high-handed rudeness? No! Definitely not!

She began to pace up and down the kitchen, her mind racing with both apprehension and indignation. She kept reminding herself that she had never been nor ever would be impressed by the very wealthy of this world. They seemed to believe that they could step outside the rules of society and get away scot-free. This man had fathered a child without marrying the mother, and now expected some boarding school to do the parenting for him. What kind of man was that?

Her lips curled up in contempt as she pictured the type. Ruthless and egotistical, self-centred and arrogant, a man who gave no quarter and took what he wanted, a man who demanded and expected to be obeyed, a man who was undoubtedly used to people grovelling at his feet, saying 'Yes, sir, no, sir, three bags full, sir.'

Rhea's nicely shaped mouth set into a stubborn expression as she ground to a halt. He needn't think he could push her around. She had learnt to stand up for herself since being widowed, something that continually surprised people who had known her as Milan's quiet, slightly nervy wife. Not that she had been frightened of Milan, Rhea reassured herself. Though now that she thought about it, he had sometimes displayed a quality of suppressed violence about him.

She recalled one night early on in their marriage. They had gone to a local function where she had had a couple of glasses of punch. The hidden alcohol in it had made her more outgoing and vivacious than was her usual way, and several men had paid quite a bit of attention to her. Milan had been furious with her when they'd got home, accusing her of making a spectacle of herself. He had reduced her to fearful tears, then taken her with uncharacteristic roughness. In the morning he had apologised but the incident had lingered in her mind, and she had been so very careful after that when in company not to do or say anything that would provoke his jealousy.

'Was my father at home?' a tiny voice asked.

Rhea whirled round to see Laura and Emily standing in the far doorway. Laura was clutching Emily's Cabbage Patch doll.

'Yes, sweetie, he was.'

'Oh . . .' she frowned '. . . it doesn't matter, then. I meant to tell you he might still be out. Mrs King was minding me till he got home. I was supposed to go with him this afternoon, to the wedding, but I got sick at the last minute . . . I mean, I *said* I was . . .'

All the breath had been punched out of Rhea's body. 'Wedding?' she repeated weakly. 'Did you say wedding?'

'Yes, the man who does our garden was getting married today. It was at the old church down the road. I guess my father didn't go on to the reception. I guess he came home to check on me . . .'

'It was probably the wedding you played at, Mum,' Emily said quite naturally. 'Laura's father must have been one of the guests. Fancy that!'

No . . . Rhea clenched her fists for control. No, it wasn't possible . . . It couldn't be . . .

With an awful feeling of fate closing in, she stared into Laura's eyes. They were the same shape, the same grey. Then her scrutiny shifted to Laura's hair. It had the same blue-black luminescence, the same thick texture.

A shiver raced up and down Rhea's spine. Oh, hell!

'When's he coming?' Emily asked ingenuously.

Rhea found her voice with difficulty. 'Soon . . .' She gulped. 'Very soon.'

CHAPTER THREE

RHEA tried not to think of what lay ahead. 'Girls, I think it would be best if I went outside and spoke to Laura's father alone. You can watch TV, OK?'

Laura was only too pleased not to have to face her father and Emily seemed delighted to have company. They raced off together, leaving Rhea standing nervously alone in the kitchen.

She smoothed the pleats of her black skirt down with clammy palms, checked all the buttons on the plain white blouse, then was attempting to pat her hair into some sort of order when she heard the low rumble of a car coming down the road. Coming fast.

Her stomach turned over. She knew, no matter what the odds, that Laura's father was the same disturbing man. There was a weird sense of inevitability about the situation. Nothing she could say or do would change it. And nothing she could say or do would change how he made her feel. She would have to deal with him—and herself—as best she could.

She moved through the side door just as the silver car swerved from the road into her driveway. It careered across the culvert, missing her post-box by mere millimetres, clouds of dust billowing out behind as the wide wheels ground to a halt in the dirt.

The two dogs went hysterical, sensing the threatening nature of this arrival. Bobby put on his fiercest façade, actually baring his teeth.

Rhea tried to resurrect her earlier indignant anger,

thinking that would be her most effective weapon, but she went numb when she saw the now familiar figure climbing out from behind the wheel. He was still dressed in that immaculate dinner suit. *All* of him was immaculate, from the crisp bow-tie right down to the shiny black shoes.

It struck Rhea forcibly as she watched him stride boldly towards her that if she had to be victim to an uncontrollable, unreasoning passion she could not have picked a more dangerous subject to long for. Here was a man who had women coming out of his ears! Rhea doubted that the young lady in the coffee lounge was old enough to have been Laura's mother. And as for the blonde at the airport? Somehow she couldn't see such a vibrant-looking individual as having been the mother of someone as shy as Laura.

No . . . This Mr Chase was undeniably a man who loved variety. Not for him a settled, committed relationship. If he ever sensed that there was a pretty little widow down the road yearning for him, he would gobble her up and spit her out for breakfast.

Yet he was looking anything but a devil-may-care womaniser as he drew near. His expression was grim and formidable, and an increasingly nervous Rhea realised that this confrontation wasn't going to be easy.

He totally ignored the barking dogs at his heels, so much so that they eventually fell by the wayside, probably as stunned as she was every time she set eyes on the man. A host of feelings warred inside her, not the least an alarming loss of confidence.

But at least she was not letting it show. She stood straight and tall, arms folded, chin up, eyes steady.

He drew to within an arm's length of her, his frown giving way to an astonished recognition. 'Good God! *You're* Mrs Petrovic?'

Rhea schooled her face into a no-nonsense expression, determined not to let her undermining feelings distract her from her resolve. 'I'm afraid so,' she said crisply. 'And you're Mr Chase, I presume.'

The frown resettled on his face. 'I didn't recognise your voice,' he said, his tone suggesting that this surprised him. Rhea found this lack of recognition perfectly reasonable, since their conversation on the phone had hardly been a calm one.

'I didn't recognise your voice either,' she countered archly.

He frowned at her brusque manner before shaking his head, then sighing. 'Sorry if I was rude on the phone. My only excuse is shock. Laura has been . . .' his lips pulled back into a sardonic grimace '. . . dare I say . . . difficult?'

Rhea bristled at his lack of sensitivity for the child. 'Children are often difficult, Mr Chase,' she pointed out. 'But packing them off to boarding school won't really fix anything. You might solve an immediate problem, but you'll eventually gain a lot more.'

She saw the flash of annoyance in his face, but to give him credit he controlled it well. 'I really think, Mrs Petrovic,' he said coolly, 'that where I send my daughter to school is hardly your business. Neither should Laura have confided family matters to a stranger. Now if you'll get her, please . . .'

He fixed steely eyes upon her, but Rhea stood her ground. Later she would marvel at her audacity. 'No,

Mr Chase, I will not.' Her chin rose, her expression matching his for fierce dignity. 'Not until I've had my say. I promised Laura I'd speak to you on her behalf.'

The grey eyes widened, then narrowed. 'That was presumptuous of you.' His voice would have frozen an entire boardroom of directors.

But it only hardened Rhea's resolution. 'I'm sorry if you're offended, but my main concern is Laura's happiness.'

'Really?' His tone and expression were coldly dry. 'That surprises me. How long have you known my daughter? An hour at most. Mrs King assures me Laura was in her room at four. And yet you tell me you're concerned for her happiness. Forgive me if I'm somewhat sceptical.'

'All right.'

'All right what?' he snapped.

'All right, I'll forgive you,' she returned with a poker face.

He was totally taken aback by her attitude. Clearly he was not used to being mocked—or challenged. Rhea realised with a measure of surprise that she was enjoying doing both. Somehow it soothed that part of her that still wanted him, despite knowing now what sort of man he was.

'It's callous of you,' she went on boldly, 'to send Laura to boarding school so soon after her mother's death, particularly when her mother promised her she would never do such a thing.'

'Good God, how on earth did you pry these private and personal details from my daughter in such a small space of time? She's been living with me now for four months and I've hardly been able to get two words out of her!'

Rhea digested this information with astonishment. She'd assumed that he had been living with Laura's mother in a *de facto* relationship. Clearly they hadn't been living together at all! 'Well, I'm hardly to blame for that, am I?' she retorted with a degree of fluster. 'Perhaps if you spent some time really listening to her . . .'

'How can I listen when she never says anything?' he argued in obvious frustration. 'God knows I've tried to gain her confidence!'

Rhea recalled how frustrated Laura had made her feel with her mutinous silence, but she blocked out any inclination to feel sympathy for the man. If he was in a difficult situation then it was his fault, wasn't it? Where had he been all his daughter's life, anyway?

'When exactly did Laura's mother pass away?' she asked.

'Last September,' he sighed.

It had been early October when Rhea had seen him kissing the blonde at the airport. 'I see,' she muttered, giving him a look of disgust.

'I doubt you do see, dear lady,' he bit out. 'Neither would you appreciate how difficult it is for a bachelor to suddenly have a child thrust upon him. I've done my best, believe me. Laura just won't co-operate!'

'All the more reason why she should stay with you now,' she advised strongly. 'You obviously need more time together. I know how my daughter would feel if I sent her away. Laura clearly thinks you want to get rid of her, that she's in the way.'

'Not true!' he denied hotly. 'I love the child. I didn't realise how much till I thought something had happened to her today . . .'

Rhea felt a reluctant empathy with him, recalling the fear and panic she had felt when Emily's school bus had been horribly late one afternoon.

'But Laura has to go to school somewhere,' he was saying. 'Have you seen that atrocity they call a school up the road? It's a relic of the last century!'

Rhea saw red. '*My* daughter goes to that relic, Mr Chase. And I'll have you know it's an excellent establishment! *Teachers* make a school, not the building, and Bangaloo Creek Primary has the best staff of teachers in the world!'

He had the grace to look apologetic. 'I didn't mean to give offence . . .'

'No? Maybe you didn't, but you didn't stop to think whether you would either. Your sort never does.'

The grey eyes dilated dangerously and he drew himself up stiff and straight. 'And what do you mean by that remark?'

Rhea's cheeks grew hot. She had gone too far and she knew it.

'Nothing, I . . . I . . .'

He grabbed her elbow and she froze.

'Tell me what you mean by *my* sort?' he demanded harshly.

She stared down at the fingers gripping her flesh and added 'violent' to his already long list of faults. Wrenching her arm away, she lifted flashing eyes.

'The sort,' she burst out, 'who wants all the pleasures of the bedroom and none of the responsibilities!'

He was staring at her as though she were mad.

And she was. Mad that she had not been able to make things right for Laura. Mad for letting the situation get totally out of hand. Mad that even a passing touch from this man could send an electric thrill charging through her body. Mad, mad, mad!

And now that her outburst was over Rhea was overwhelmed by a deep shame. How could she be so outspoken, so disgustingly rude? She groaned. 'Oh, Mr Chase, I . . . I'm so sorry. What I said . . . I didn't mean it. I . . . I don't even know you. I'm so terribly sorry.'

He remained silent, but he was looking at her closely, his expression disturbingly intense. When a small smile tugged at the corners of his mouth Rhea rocked back with astonishment. 'All right,' he said with a hint of dry amusement.

'All right?' she repeated blankly.

'All right, I forgive you,' he said, the amusement definite now in his eyes. Rhea could only stare at him as she tried desperately to get a grip on the situation. And herself.

'I must say you make a good avenging angel, Mrs Petrovic. And there may be a grain of truth in what you said.' His eyes danced wickedly. 'But only a grain. I *do* try not to deliberately hurt anyone, particularly beautiful women.'

Warmth and charisma rolled form him in waves, threatening to engulf her in their tidal force. She reacted instinctively with a cool look, but it was more a survival tactic than any form of rebuke.

He frowned, pressing his well-shaped lips into a thin

line, reminding Rhea that most women would respond
eagerly to his compliments. But this knowledge only
made her all the more determined not to. After all, he
believed she was a married woman and so he should not
be flirting with her.

Or didn't he care if she were married?

Rhea was distressed that she didn't find that thought
as off-putting as she should have.

'So . . .' he breathed in deeply, then exhaled '. . .the
local school has your recommendation?' His whole
manner was now totally detached, almost cold.

'It does,' she murmured.

'How do I go about enrolment?' he asked brusquely.

'You just . . . just show up on Wednesday morning
with Laura and see the school secretary. She'll be able
to help you with everything.'

'Uniforms too?'

Rhea resisted the urge to offer him a couple of the
ones Emily had outgrown. People like Stephen Chase
didn't dress their daughters in hand-me-down uniforms.
'You can buy them at the Grace Brothers store in
Liverpool.'

'And how old is your daughter, Mrs Petrovic?'

'Ten. She'll be eleven in April.'

'Then she'll be in the same class as Laura. She turns
eleven in May.'

'Laura's *ten*?' Rhea could not hide her astonishment.

'I know—she's small for her age. Her mother was
only tiny, five feet one at the most . . .'

Rhea's mind clicked over. The young woman she had
seen him with in the coffee lounge could hardly qualify
as tiny.

'But she's shy. For the last two years she hasn't gone to school. She travelled a lot with her mother and had a private tutor. I'm told she's bright, though.'

'How exactly did Laura's mother die?' Rhea couldn't resist asking.

'A type of food poisoning. Botulism.'

She watched his face as he spoke. It was grim, but there was no pain. Definitely no pain. Whatever his relationship had been with Laura's mother, he had not loved her. 'I gather you weren't living together at the time,' she remarked, an edge of reproach in the words.

His look carried a weary exasperation. 'No, I wasn't living with Naomi when she died. Or at any other time. *Her* choice, not mine, I can assure you. There was a time when I would have married her like a shot if she'd wanted me to.'

Rhea found that hard to swallow. She couldn't imagine that a woman who had had this man's child would pass up the chance of marrying him. Unless, of course, he had already proved himself a faithless lover . . .

'What about grandparents?' Rhea went on. 'If you're finding Laura such a problem, wouldn't she better off with them?'

His jaw clenched visibly, then relaxed. 'Naomi's parents are dead,' he explained patiently. 'As far as mine are concerned, they have offered to have Laura sometimes. But they're elderly and have already raised a large family. Besides which they would be appalled with me—as I would be with myself—if I didn't accept the responsibility of my daughter. Look, Mrs Petrovic, I realise that my bachelor status doesn't find favour with you, and that you believe I'm somehow unfit to raise a child, but I hardly think you can judge the situation on such a short acquaintance, do you?'

Against her will Rhea was impressed by the sentiments expressed in his speech. He sounded as if he genuinely wanted to do his best for Laura. And at least he came from a solid family background. Not only that, he was right: she was being judgemental.

'I'm sorry,' she said with genuine apology. 'I didn't mean to imply that you were in any way a bad parent. Laura is better off with her father than anyone else—that's why I felt so strongly about you sending her away. She needs you with her, Mr Chase. She needs your emotional support, your company, your love. She——'

She broke off when she became aware that she was speaking quite passionately, and that those penetrating grey eyes were riveted to the movements of her mouth.

His eyes lifted to lock on to hers. 'Go on,' he said.

Rhea gave a nervous laugh. 'I think I was getting a bit carried away!'

'Not at all. You're a woman of rare conviction. And to be truthful I probably needed a lecture about Laura. I've been listening to too many other people's opinions on what I should be doing with her.'

He smiled at Rhea, swamping her once again with the full force of his charm. It caught her off guard and she reacted instinctively, her mouth tightening with disapproval. And fear.

A slight sigh revealed that he had noticed her reaction. He looked away, his right hand lifting to run distractedly through his hair, disrupting its 'not a wave out of place' order. When a lock fell across his forehead it evoked a vulnerability at odds with the mature strength of his features. For the first time Rhea wondered how old he was. In his thirties, she guessed. Possibly thirty-five or -six.

'So . . .' his eyes swung back to face her '. . . a small school should suit Laura very well, then, shouldn't it?'

'Yes,' she agreed, her face less tense now. Ridiculous to think his smile had been a deliberately seductive gesture, that he was going to make a serious play for her. This man would throw smiles at women like the sower threw seeds, hoping that some fell on fertile ground. Little did he know that with Rhea the seed had already germinated.

'Not to mention a ready-made friend in class,' he added, smiling at her again. But it wasn't the same sort of smile this time. There was no accompanying flash from deep within his eyes. 'You'll have to bring your daughter around sometimes so she and Laura can play together.'

Not on your nelly! Rhea decided. To see Laura's father on a regular basis—even as a neighbour—was out of the question. Talk about asking for trouble . . . 'We'll see,' she said non-committally. 'Don't you think we should go and tell Laura the good news?'

Rhea turned and walked briskly towards the house, Stephen Chase falling into step at her shoulder.

'You have a nice neat little place here, Mrs Petrovic,' he said, eyes sweeping around.

Rhea glanced first at the simple but pretty garden beds, then over at the home-made kennel, the cheaply fenced paddocks, the small cottage, remembering quite clearly the first time Milan had shown her the place. He had been so proud. A European migrant whose whole family had been killed in a civil uprising, he had arrived in Australia without a cent, and no qualifications. He had been an intelligent man, but times had been hard, unemployment high. The only work he had been able to find was as a contract cleaner, working long hours to save the deposit for his dream property.

Of course he would have preferred a real farm—hundreds of acres, not just five—but he had needed to live close enough to Sydney for work. He had used to promise that one day he would build a bigger, better home for them.

But that day had never come. He had been drowned in a rough sea off Kiama, trying to save a fisherman who had been swept off the rocks by a freak wave.

A wretched guilt claimed Rhea as she thought of her dead husband. He had loved her so much. And she had loved him, loved his quiet strength, his devoted sense of duty, his total commitment to his family. And yet she had not been able to give him what most men would expect from their wives.

The memory of her honeymoon came back to haunt her. At first there had been pain, too much pain. But then later, when things should have improved, there had been nothing. Milan had told her not to worry about it, that some women were just made that way. Rhea had often wondered if he minded. Certainly her lack of response had not deterred him from taking his conjugal rights, though she had often wondered why he bothered when she lay beneath him so unmoved.

It upset her to think that the man walking next to her

stirred her more with a smile than Milan had with the entire act of love.

'Do you and your husband only have the one child?'

They had reached the side door, with Stephen Chase at Rhea's shoulder. Her hand had been moving forward to grasp the knob when he threw the question at her. She froze, knowing the moment had come to enlighten him about Milan's death.

Her hand dropped back to her side and, biting her lip in agitation, she began to turn.

But she had not realised he was so close to her. As she turned she brushed against his chest, and, while he stepped back, he was still overpoweringly near. His superior male height loomed over her own five feet six, bringing a hot awareness to her body. Her cheeks pinked. Her skin prickled.

She grew even more disturbed when his left hand slid up the door-frame, the action pulling his jacket apart so that she was confronted by an impressively wide chest. He was leaning slightly forward as well, so that it would have been so easy for her to slide her hands up over that pristine shirt, to wind her arms around his muscular neck, to gently pull the gorgeous mouth down to . . .

Her eyes widened for a moment as she fought to squash her rampant fantasies, making her look unmistakably alarmed. His hand dropped from the door-frame as though stung by an electric shock. He drew himself up straight and took a further step backwards.

Shame swamped Rhea as she realised he had thought her frightened of his nearness. Her eyes dropped disconcertingly to the ground. Dear God, if only he knew!

The ensuing silence crackled with tension till Rhea pulled herself together enough to answer his question. 'Yes,' she said, lifting still panicky eyes, 'there's only Emily.' Then she wrenched open the screen door and fled inside, followed by her unwanted visitor.

'Please . . . sit down,' she offered briskly, standing well away from him, her backside hard against the sink, her hands clutching the counter on either side.

He pulled out one of the chairs that surrounded the round laminex table and sat down. Rhea thought he looked like a fish out of water in the old-fashioned kitchen, with its chipped blue cupboards and cheap vinyl floor, and while she wasn't ashamed of her home she couldn't help an inexplicable wave of depression—and an accompanying dismay.

She noticed that he was watching her closely, and her stomach churned.

'Is your husband away?' he asked unexpectedly.

Rhea grew even more flustered. 'Why . . . why do you ask that?'

He shrugged. 'You seem agitated. It occurred to me that he might not like a strange man being in the house when he's away.'

Rhea's head whirled. Now was the time to tell him quite clearly that she was a widow, to rectify his assumptions. Yet panic at what this announcement could produce made her hesitate. She was afraid she wouldn't be able to resist him if he did make a play for her. And he certainly might, once he was told the truth. He had already shown that he found her attractive.

'Yes . . . yes, he's away,' she said hurriedly, then gave

a nervous laugh. 'And you're hardly a stranger any more, Mr Chase. You're Laura's father, as well as a neighbour.'

She hoped that if his communication with Laura was as bad as he said, he might never find out the truth. After all, Stephen Chase was not the sort of father to go to school functions, or gossip down at the local club.

'I'll get your daughter for you,' she added, and hurried from the room.

Rhea's patience was tried to the limit when Laura refused at first to come with her. It was only after the girl had been assured several times of not being sent to boarding school that she made a reluctant appearance in the kitchen. Even so, the child was still nervous in her father's presence, shrinking into Rhea's skirt at his, 'Come along now, Laura. I think we've taken up enough of Mrs Petrovic's time and hospitality, don't you?'

It wasn't until Emily said, 'I'll see you on Wednesday,' that the girl let go Rhea's hand and did as her father asked.

Both Rhea and Emily walked with them to the car, but not a word passed between any of them. Even the dogs were unusually quiet. Rhea grew conscious of a tightness in her chest as she watched Stephen Chase see his daughter seated and the safety belt properly adjusted. She couldn't seem to take her eyes off his unconscious grace of movement and found she was holding her breath, as if counting the seconds till he would be safely out of sight.

He closed the passenger door and strode round to the driver's side near where Emily and Rhea were standing. He hesitated in front of her and for a ghastly moment she thought he was going to bend forward and kiss her on the cheek. Instead he murmured, 'Thank you,' and held out his hand.

'Glad to be of help,' she said with a stiff smile, and slowly lifted her own hand from her side. His fingers closed, strong and warm around hers, sending a tremor up her arm and right down to her toes. She froze, terrified that he might be aware of her reaction. But he appeared unperturbed, already dropping her hand and turning away.

Once settled behind the wheel he glanced up at her through the windscreen. It was an odd look, both hard and long, but it still affected her deeply. A timely warning for keeping to her deception, she thought ruefully.

When he finally reversed out and drove away, she was flooded with relief, dragging in a deep ragged breath.

Emily gave her a curious look. 'Did you have a fight with Laura's father?' she asked.

'Not really,' came Rhea's careful reply. 'He was open to reason once he realised how unhappy his daughter was.'

'He sure is good-looking, isn't he, Mum?'

Rhea's heart skipped a beat. 'Do you think so?' she managed with superb indifference. 'I didn't really notice.'

CHAPTER FOUR

RHEA kept herself even busier from that day on. Every morning she would rise early and have all her housework done before eight, then retire to the living-room, which served as her workshop. There she would put some music on her portable cassette—mostly soundtracks from her favourite musicals—and hum along while she worked.

Her coming autumn range was far more extensive than anything she had attempted before, for reasons of finance more than creative compulsion. The annual rates had come in, and there'd been a hefty rise. So, as well as the matching jumpers, scarves and berets, she was attempting some glamorous evening tops and shawls.

Most were made of mohair from her own fleeces, carefully spun and dyed the way she liked, with natural pigments, but sometimes she added shop-bought fibres, such as cotton or silk, if she wanted a special effect. All were handmade, either knitted or crocheted, depending on the pattern. And all were one-off articles, Rhea never repeating a style and colour combination.

With less than a month to go before delivery date, she was working every spare moment. And if that had the added benefit of keeping her mind off a certain person, she wasn't about to complain.

Emily returned to school on the Wednesday— blessedly catching the bus to and fro—and, while she did rave on every afternoon about what good friends she

47

and Laura were becoming, no mention was made of the
'good-looking' father.

Which was just as well, Rhea thought as she rose on
the following Saturday morning after a particularly
restless night. Though she suspected it was only a matter
of time before Emily started begging to go over to
Laura's place to see the pony. In fact, her daughter had
already dropped a couple of hints the previous evening.

Peeping through the curtains, Rhea was relieved to
see that it was beginning to drizzle. It meant fresh grass
for the goats as well as the perfect excuse to veto any
suggestion of 'visiting'. She had a sinking feeling,
however, that she was only delaying the inevitable. One
day she would have to face Stephen Chase again. And
one day he would probably find out she had misled him
about her married state.

But not today, she decided as she dragged on her
favourite old robe and padded out to the kitchen to make
herself a cup of coffee. She yawned and reached for the
kettle. Thank the Lord she wasn't playing the organ at
any function that afternoon! Terrible day for a wedding
anyway, she thought, yawning again.

'Is it time to get up, Mum?' came a sleepy voice from
behind her.

Rhea turned. 'Not yet, love. It's Saturday,
remember?'

'Oh . . . I forgot.' Whereupon Emily turned and went
back to bed.

An hour later Rhea was hard at work. One garment,
a scarlet evening sweater with dolman sleeves and a
scooped neckline, was giving her trouble. One side
wasn't quite matching the other, and, even though

Rhea's eye for shape and size was usually faultless, something had gone wrong this time.

Her hand reached down beside her chair to where she always dropped her tape-measure, but her fingers encountered a bare mat. She frowned and peered over the large arm of the chair. No tape-measure. She glanced around, knowing that it was somewhere not far away — she had used it yesterday—but still no tape-measure. She stood up and walked around, searching, picking up things.

In the end she gave up, deciding that Emily's ruler would do for the time being. She strode out into the kitchen and over to the corner behind the door, where her daughter always dropped her school-bag. It had a large zipper running across the top with a koala-shaped key-ring attached for easy undoing. When she bent over and slid the key-ring across, the two sides fell open, exposing the contents.

Rhea stared, then bent further to pick up three brown paper bags. Puzzled, she opened them. Yes . . . just as she'd thought. Emily's school lunches, untouched and uneaten.

Frowning, she put them on the kitchen table and moved slowly towards her daughter's bedroom. For a moment she hesitated in the hallway, not sure how to handle the problem. She wasn't exactly angry, but she wasn't calm either. And she knew she couldn't wait till Emily got up before tackling her about the lunches.

She opened the bedroom door and walked over to shake her daughter's shoulder. 'Emily, I need to talk to you.'

Emily blinked and yawned, then pulled herself

upright, frowning. 'What's up?'

Rhea sat down on the edge of the bed, a no-nonsense expression on her face. She had decided on the direct approach. 'Why didn't you eat your lunches at school this week?' she asked abruptly. 'I went to your bag to borrow your ruler and I found all three of them, untouched.'

There was no doubt about it—Emily looked guilty.

'You weren't sick, were you?' Rhea persisted.

'No . . .'

'Then what did you eat? Did someone else share their lunch with you?'

'Sort of . . .' faltered Emily.

'What do you mean—sort of?'

'Well, Laura had money left over and . . . well . . .'

Rhea stiffened. 'And well what?'

'Well, she orders her lunch every day from the school canteen and she sort of bought me stuff from there too.'

'Such as what?' asked Rhea through gritted teeth.

Emily was looking very uncomfortable. 'You know . . . crisps and lollies and stuff.'

'And what, pray tell, did you intend doing with your lunches? Were they to stay in your bag till they grew penicillin?' Rhea's voice had risen to a shriek.

Emily bit her bottom lip. 'I was going to give them to the goats today,' she whispered.

'Were you, now?' Rhea glared at her daughter.

'Yes . . .' The whisper was barely a squeak.

The frightened quality in her daughter's voice suddenly got through to Rhea and she felt terrible. Emily had been wrong in what she had done, but as a mother, she wasn't behaving so well either, ranting and raving like a fishwife.

'I'm sorry, Mum,' Emily sobbed, tears spilling over.

Rhea pulled her daughter into a fierce hug. 'I'm sorry too, love,' she soothed, stroking Emily's long hair. 'I shouldn't have shouted at you. You're not entirely to blame—not many people can resist having goodies bought for them. I understand, really I do.'

She drew back from the embrace and gave Emily an understanding look. 'But you must know that I try to pack you a sensible lunch, with proper nutrition. Crisps and lollies are all very well as an occasional treat, but not as a substitute for lunch. Do you understand?'

'I suppose so.' Emily didn't look entirely convinced.

'I give you two dollars a week,' Rhea reminded her. 'You can spend that on crisps and the like, *after* you've eaten your lunch.'

'Laura gets five dollars a day,' Emily said resentfully.

'Oh, surely not!'

'Yes, she does. And that's just for her lunch. She's got other money as well.'

Rhea stood up. She was aware of a growing anger deep inside her, an anger directed at one person in particular. Damned Stephen Chase! Did he have to ruin everything? Even her relationship with her daughter?

'You must realise, Emily,' she said strongly, 'that such a sum is a ridiculous amount of money to give a child. Her father's a fool!'

Emily pouted. 'Laura says he's real nice now. She likes him a lot.'

How typical of the man! Rhea fumed. Using his money to buy love!

She glared at her daughter's rebellious expression

and decided she was speaking to the wrong person. If she was to stop this situation from continuing she would have to deal with the source of the problem.

Heat raced into her cheeks at the prospect of another face-to-face confrontation with Stephen Chase till she remembered the phone. Anything she had to say to him could be handled quite well that way. There was no need to put up with his disturbing physical presence.

She stopped in the doorway and glanced back at her daughter. 'I want your promise, Emily, that you will always eat the lunch I give you. Unless you're sick, of course. If I find you disobey me in this, you won't even get your two dollars. Do I make myself clear?'

'Yes, Mum.' Emily sank back under the covers.

'Good!'

Rhea marched down the hallway, back into the kitchen and over to the counter. She flicked open her notebook to the page where the number was, then dialled before she could think better of it.

A woman answered on the second ring. 'Mr Chase's residence. Mrs King speaking.'

'I would like to speak to Mr Chase, please,' Rhea said nervously. Her heart was going at fifty to the dozen, fuelled she believed by her indignation.

'Oh, I think he's just left . . . Wait . . . No, I might be able to catch him . . .'

Rhea was left dangling for some minutes. It did nothing to improve her state of nerves—or her temper. Suddenly she heard Mrs King saying in the background, 'I don't know who it is, Mr Chase. A lady . . . She didn't give her name.'

'Did it sound like Madeline?'

'Oh no, Mr Chase, not at all.'

Rhea bristled. No doubt Madeline was his current lady-love, all glamour and polish, complete with a posh accent, not like Rhea's good old Australian drawl. Probably the sophisticated blonde at the airport. Or maybe a new one. He seemed to go for blondes!

There was a rustling sound and then the voice she was dreading. 'Stephen Chase speaking.'

Rhea took a deep breath. 'Mr Chase, I'm sorry to bother you, but I have this problem with Emily and I——'

'Mrs Petrovic?' he interrupted in sharp puzzlement. 'That is you, isn't it?'

Rhea almost died of mortification. Oh God, here she was trying to play the firm negotiator and she had forgotten to tell him who was calling.

'Yes, it's me.' Her voice sounded as deflated as her pride.

'You have a problem with your daughter? Something I can help you with?'

'No, I . . . I mean yes . . .' Rhea was hopelessly rattled. 'I was hoping you could,' she finished lamely.

'I'll do what I can. But I think perhaps you're the expert with children, not me. The change in Laura since going to that little school of yours is remarkable. I never used to be able to get her to talk. Now my only problem seems to be shutting her up,' he chuckled. 'But I'm getting off the point here, aren't I? What's Emily been up to?'

'It concerns Laura as well,' Rhea choked out.

'Oh?' There was a frown in the word.

Rhea swallowed.

'You sound upset, Mrs Petrovic,' he went on, his tone now one of sincere concern. It totally squashed any anger in her. 'I hope it's nothing serious. Would you like me to come over?'

'No!' Panic—absolute panic.

'Then can you tell me what it is? Has Laura said something . . . done something to upset Emily? I thought they'd become great mates. Laura talks of no one else.'

'It isn't really Laura's fault, Mr Chase,' Rhea blurted out.

'You certainly have me puzzled. Could you be more specific?'

'It . . . it's the lunch money you give her, you see,' she said haltingly. 'She's been . . . buying Emily sweets from the school canteen and Emily hasn't been eating her lunch.'

He laughed. 'Is that all? My goodness, you had me going there for a while! I was imagining all sorts of things.'

His amusement revitalised a surge of indignation. 'It's not a laughing matter, Mr Chase. I happen to take my daughter's eating habits very seriously. A child her age needs proper nutrition. I thought you would be similarly concerned about Laura's diet. Of course, I may have been mistaken about your intentions the other day. I got the impression you wanted to be a good father, despite your late start!'

She heard him sigh. 'I do want to be a good father, Mrs Petrovic. And I'm sure I can rely upon you to set me right whenever I stray from the straight and narrow of correct parenting.' There was no denying the weary frustration in his words.

Rhea felt guilty now. Every time she talked to the man she seemed to run off at the mouth. Nerves, she realised. But that was no real excuse. 'I'm sorry, I don't mean to be critical,' she tried to back-pedal.

'Of course not.'

'I . . . I only have the children's best interests at heart.'

'Naturally.'

'I mean . . . You couldn't be expected to know about the prices at the school canteen. You probably haven't got a list.'

'I'm so glad you're beginning to understand.' His words held a heavy-handed patience.

Rhea fell silent. She felt terribly small. 'I'm sorry to have bothered you,' she managed at last.

'Don't hang up!' he ordered.

'W—what?'

'I'll be in terrible trouble if I let you get away now that I have you on the phone. Laura's been asking me to ring you to invite Emily over. However, I wasn't sure if such an invitation would be welcome. I'm aware you don't exactly approve of me . . .'

He stopped then, obviously waiting for Rhea to make some retaliatory comment, but she could think of nothing to say. Besides, she wasn't sure her voice would work even if she could.

There was another deep sigh. 'Look, Mrs Petrovic, I know I got off on the wrong foot with you, accusing you of being a kidnapper. And I gather you aren't too impressed that Laura's mother and I were never married, but believe me, that was not my fault. Would it make any difference if I explained what happened there?'

'Oh, no, you don't have to,' Rhea blustered, through secretly dying to know.

'I realise that, but I want to. Believe it or not, your good opinion is important to me. We're members of the same small community, and our daughters seem intent on being firm friends. I would hate for you to refuse permission for Emily to come over sometimes because you think her father is some sort of rotter.'

'Oh, but I don't think——'

'Oh, but you do, dear lady. You definitely do.'

Embarrassment held her silent.

'I appreciate how it must look to outsiders,' he went on. 'The truth is that Naomi—Laura's mother—never told me that she was pregnant. She was a good deal older than the twenty-one I was at the time . . .'

Rhea frowned. Twenty-*one*? But that would mean he was only thirty-one or two at the most now. And yet he looked older. Hard living, perhaps?

'It was the typical case of the young man infatuated with an older woman. As I said before, I would have married her despite our age difference, but that was not Naomi's plan. She wanted only one thing, it seems—a baby. You know the situation. A career woman finds herself in her thirties, wants a child, but not a husband. I happened to be the bunny she chose to be the father . . .'

Rhea could visualise why. At twenty-one Stephen must have been the most gorgeous, virile . . .

'. . . but I knew nothing of Laura till after Naomi died last year in Paris. There was a letter addressed to me in her papers. You can imagine my surprise to find I had a ten-year-old daughter. I——' He broke off, irritated perhaps that he was justifying his actions to her, a mere neighbour. 'Hell, give me some credit, Mrs Petrovic, it hasn't been easy, and I am doing my best!'

'You've acted very responsibly, Mr Chase,' Rhea admitted. 'Considering. I mean . . . oh, dear, I've done it again, haven't I?'

His chuckle was low and warm. 'What say we wipe the slate clean and start again, eh? At least for the sake of the children,' he added, wry humour to the fore.

It brought a reluctant smile to Rhea's lips. 'All right,' she murmured. To say anything else would have been the height of intolerance.

'And what shall I call you? Mrs Petrovic is a bit of a mouthful, isn't it?'

'My name is Rhea. Spelt R-H-E-A.'

'Rhea . . . Unusual. And I answer to Stephen. Now, let me make a suggestion, Rhea . . .'

How marvellous her name sounded on his tongue. Like a softly played arpeggio.

'Why don't you drop over later today with Emily? I know Laura's dying to show off her pony. You could bring me one of those canteen price lists and tell me what I should order for Laura, and what a suitable amount of pocket-money is. What do you say?'

Rhea hesitated. It all sounded harmless enough. Though not even the shortest visit would be harmless, considering the feelings and thoughts he always evoked in her. 'But weren't you just leaving to go somewhere?' she floundered.

'Only to the local shop to buy the papers.'

'Oh . . .' There was no reasonable excuse she could think of not to go.

And she wanted to see him. Just see him. There! She had admitted it. Even if the mere thought made her pulse go wild. Even if she didn't get a wink's sleep for a month. 'I . . . I can't make it till after lunch,' she said, her hesitancy belying what she considered an incredibly bold move.

'Fine.'

'Will two . . . two o'clock be all right?'

'Any time.'

She firmed her jaw to keep her voice steady. 'Two it will be, then, Mr Chase.'

'*Stephen*, remember?'

'Stephen.'

She hung up, his name quivering on her lips.

CHAPTER FIVE

'IT'S stopped raining!' Emily exclaimed excitedly as they drove up the road shortly before two. 'Look, the sun's coming out. Laura and I will be able to have a ride on her pony. Oh, I can't wait to get there!' She grinned at her mother. 'Are they new jeans you're wearing?'

'No.'

'I don't remember seeing them before. But I like them—they make you look young. And that yellow top is my favourite.'

Rhea gave her daughter a wry smile. 'You wouldn't be buttering me up for something, would you?'

'Gosh, no!'

'Well, before you go all gaga over Laura's pony, I want to tell you that if Dolly has more than two pups I'm going to use the money from selling them to buy you a pony of your own.'

Rhea's heart turned over at the look on Emily's face.

'Oh, Mum, do you mean it? Do you really?'

'I do indeed,' smiled Rhea.

'Oh, thank you, thank you! And I'm sure Dolly's having at least six pups. She's as big as the side of a bus!'

Rhea laughed. 'She certainly is.'

Her laughter died once she turned the van into Mountain View Road, tension invading as she battled to keep her apprehension down and her resolve up.

Rhea had decided to tell Stephen she was a widow—not because she wanted him to know she was free, but because it was stupid to keep the deception going. He was sure to find out now that he and Laura were communicating.

But it wouldn't be easy to bring the subject up, she conceded nervously. What was she to say? By the way, Stephen, I was only joking the other day when I said my husband was away. Actually he's dead . . .

Oh, God, what a mess I've got myself into! Rhea groaned silently. In more ways than one.

She lifted a hand to see if her hair was still up. She had twisted it into what she had thought was a sensible knot, but as she glanced in the rear-vision mirror she began to worry that the continuously escaping strands lent a totally wrong image. Instead of her hair looking sleek and controlled, it seemed to project an impression of enforced imprisonment, like a wild thing caged for its own protection, just waiting to spring free and wreak havoc.

Like me, came the insidious thought.

Emily didn't appear to notice her mother's distracted state. She chattered away, exclaiming over the size and grandeur of Laura's house as the van slowly chugged up the steep hill towards it.

In truth, it wasn't a mansion. But by Emily's youthful standards it probably seemed to be. 'Isn't it fantastic, Mum? Wouldn't you like to live in a house like that?'

Rhea's tense glare flicked over the two-storeyed, Tudor-style dwelling, her thoughts taking a rueful twist at her daughter's words. Yes, she conceded with a shaming truth, she would like to live in this particular house . . . for a night or two.

But she turned a gentle glance towards her daughter. 'Money isn't everything, love.'

'No, I guess not.'

Even so, Rhea had to admit that the house and its surroundings were imposing, perched as they were on top of a hill. It was hard not to compare the 'no expense spared' quality with their own simple lifestyle.

Proper cement bridges spanned the entrance and exit to a wide, semi-circular approach that was bordered in stained logs and filled with tiny river pebbles. A brick wall extended for several metres on either side of the house and blocked any view of the back yard, but Rhea had no doubt that there would be the obligatory swimming-pool and tennis-court. Men like Stephen Chase never wanted for anything.

It was a sobering thought.

Rhea braked to a halt at the base of the front steps, the van shuddering with relief. Not so her nerves. They didn't improve either when the heavy cedar front door opened and an excited Laura spilled out, closely followed by her father.

Rhea opened the car door and virtually leapt from behind the wheel, afraid that he would do something chivalrous like help her out. Instinct told her that she was relatively safe, if she kept him at a distance.

'I do so like punctual people,' he beamed, striding down the steps towards her, looking disgustingly handsome in casual grey trousers and an open-necked blue and white striped shirt. With a kind of sick fascination, her eyes were drawn to the exposed V of chest where fine black hairs swirled into soft curls, curls that she knew would feel soft under her fingers, would . . .

Her eyes snapped up to his, appalled at how quickly her imagination ran wild whenever she was near this man.

He frowned at her, and it took Rhea some moments

to realise it was because her own features had twisted
with self-recrimination. It took a deliberate effort to
relax her mouth into a smile.

'Come on, Em,' Laura was saying in the background,
'let's go down and see Mimi. Now that it's stopped
raining we can saddle her up and go for a ride.'

Already they were beginning to run off.

'You be careful, Emily!' Rhea shouted after the
fast-disappearing girls. 'No mad galloping, and I'll pick
you up at five, OK?'

Emily turned and waved. 'OK!'

'Pick up?' Stephen repeated slowly. 'I thought you
were going to stay.'

Rhea swallowed. 'I am, but . . . but not for three hours.
I have work to do at home.'

'Has your husband returned?'

Now was the moment to tell him. There is no
husband . . . But suddenly a million unnamed fears
gripped her, and the words just wouldn't come.

'N-no—no, he hasn't. I use my home as a workshop,
making specialised knitwear.'

She felt oddly gratified by his obvious surprise.

'I have a few angora goats,' she went on, suddenly
impelled by an irrational and unnecessary need to
impress him. 'I spin and dye the mohair myself, then
fashion original garments for sale in boutiques.'

His hand had somehow found her elbow and he was
directing her towards his front door. Rhea was too
stunned to pull away. His fingertips seemed to be
burning their brand into her skin, propelling her along
a previously unknown path. So this is what it feels like
to be overwhelmed by desire, she thought dazedly.

Helpless, breathless, reckless . . .

'How fascinating,' Stephen was saying. 'When do you find the time?'

'Time?' she repeated blankly.

'You look after a husband and child, as well as dogs and goats, not to mention playing the organ. Now you tell me you make clothes as well. You must get very tired.'

'Sometimes,' she choked out, hating herself for letting the misconception continue.

'All the more reason why you should take this opportunity to put your feet up for a while. Besides, you promised to explain to me all about the canteen.'

She ground to a halt at the front door, her blush deep and instant. 'Oh dear, I forgot the price list . . .' Which wasn't surprising. Her mind had been in a whirl since the moment she had agreed to his invitation.

'Never mind. Another time will do.' His smile bestowed understanding—and potent charm. 'Would you like a cool drink, or a cup of coffee?' he asked as he ushered her inside.

It was indeed a beautiful house—though Rhea was hardly in the frame of mind for noticing details of décor. She vaguely recalled a deep-piled mint-green carpet running throughout the foyer and hall, then a very modern grey and white kitchen. Her host seated her in the room beyond the kitchen, a family room she supposed one would call it, with wide windows, a parquet floor and expensive leather furniture in a warm ochre colour.

Rhea was glad to be able to occupy her mind watching Emily and Laura in the distant paddock. Not with total success, however. Agreeing to a cup of coffee was a far cry from agreeing to an affair, but somehow it felt the same. She couldn't get out of her mind that she was the fly to Stephen's spider, and that he was just waiting patiently, playing the gentleman before making his move. And then what would happen?

'Milk and sugar?' he called from the kitchen.

'Milk, no sugar,' came her shaky reply.

She turned her head when she heard him come into the room, her gaze travelling over his well-proportioned body as he walked towards her, two coffee mugs in his hand. Rhea was shocked at the intense charge she received just watching him move—shocked and ashamed. She tore her eyes away, wishing with all her heart that she hadn't been so weak as to come.

'I forgot to ask you if you preferred decaffeinated,' he said as he placed the mugs on the coffee table in front of her chair. 'Most people don't, but I have the feeling you might be one of those health-food addicts . . .'

Her eyes flew to his, a ready retort coming to her lips. But he was smiling so charmingly at her that she found herself smiling back. 'You shouldn't tease, you know,' came her soft rebuke.

'Would I do that?' Stephen laughed as he sat down in the chair opposite, and Rhea thought how laughter changed his face from handsome to devastating. Their eyes met momentarily, his grey ones sweeping over her face and body with an unexpectedly frank appreciation. I find you desirable, they seemed to be saying. I'd like to make love to you . . .

Her heart stopped. She looked away, then back. His expression now was quite closed and she wondered if she had imagined that brief message. Her imagination was certainly working overtime lately!

She stared grimly down into the coffee mug.

When he leant forward and lightly touched her fingers, her hand froze, her head jerking up to look at him. 'Why the frown, Rhea? Have I said something to offend you? I was only joking about the health foods, you know.'

A depressing awareness that her inner panic was escalating brought Rhea up with a jolt. Pride insisted that she get herself under control.

'Of course you were,' she said with a quick bright smile.

He gave her a look that showed he wasn't quite sure how to take her.

'You must tell me,' she went on as she picked up her coffee mug, 'why you chose to build your home way out here.' It was merely something to say, though the question had probably lurked in her subconscious for quite a while.

He shrugged. 'Convenience, I suppose.'

'Convenience?' She gave a short laugh. 'I wouldn't call Bangaloo Creek in any way convenient. We have to travel miles to even go to the doctor.'

'That wasn't what I meant,' he explained. 'As soon as I found out about Laura I decided I didn't want her to grow up in the city. Too much pollution!' He slanted Rhea a meaningful look. 'That should find favour with you. No, don't defend yourself, you and I both know you've been quite right in everything you said to me. I know nothing at all about fathering, but I'm a willing learner. Anyway, my problem was finding a house on a rural acreage which wasn't too far from my office in Sydney. I'd recently bought this land as an investment for my company and it seemed quicker to build a house here than find one suitable to buy.'

'It certainly went up quickly enough,' Rhea murmured thoughtfully. So he owned a company. What kind? she wondered.

'Amazing what a promised bonus to the building supervisor can do,' he added.

The thought slid into Rhea's mind that whatever Stephen Chase couldn't get through normal channels he would buy.

She glanced up at him over the rim of her mug to see him glaring irritably at her. 'You really let your feelings show on your face, do you know that? I said *bonus*, Rhea, not a bribe. It happens to be a very normal business practice, not some shifty, underhanded tactic!'

Rhea was taken aback by his outburst—and thoroughly embarrassed. She hadn't realised she was so transparent. She placed the mug carefully down on the glass table. 'I'm sorry . . .'

He sighed. 'You don't have to apologise, Rhea. However, I wish I knew why you're so quick to judge me.'

A wave of heat swept up her neck.

'Is it because of the way I spoke to you at the wedding?' he asked softly. 'Did you think I was trying to pick you up?'

She shook her head in wide-eyed denial.

His sad smile threw her. 'I think it is, Rhea. And do you know what? I was . . .'

Rhea's eyes grew wider.

'I wasn't to know you were married,' he elaborated. 'Not only that, I'm quite experienced at picking up signals from women. And I picked up definite signals from you that day.'

'That's not true,' she rasped. 'I . . . I hardly spoke to you. I . . .' Her voiced trailed away, the guilty heat in her face much more telling than any verbal protest. A strangled, shamed sound fluttered from her throat.

The silence in the room was electric.

'And I like you too,' said Stephen at last. 'Much too much.'

Her groan was one of total confusion and panic, her eyes swinging away, then returning to his in a type of pained pleading.

'God, woman, don't look at me like that! I'm not about to jump on you.'

Rhea forced herself up on to shaking legs.

He leapt to his feet. 'Don't you dare leave!'

'I . . . I have to . . .' She began to move towards the door, but he stopped her, curving firm hands over her slender shoulders.

'No, you don't *have* to. You're an adult, with free will, Rhea Petrovic. OK, so we're attracted to each other. Admit it! I do. But you're a married woman and I'll respect that, but that doesn't mean we can't be friends, does it? Does it?' he repeated, shaking her.

Rhea was incapable of answering. She looked up into his flushed face, increasingly aware that he was staring down at her full quivering lips with a disturbing hunger. 'What is it with that husband of yours anyway?' he growled. 'Is the man mad, that he goes away and leaves you alone all the time? The fool's asking for trouble. Doesn't he realise how beautiful you are? Beautiful and sensual and desirable . . .'

He lifted his hands to cup her face, rubbing his thumbs over her cheekbones. She groaned and closed her eyes, turning her face away from his touch, but only succeeded in pressing her lips against one of his palms. When she heard the air whoosh out of his lungs her eyes flew to his. He wanted her, came the amazing thought, perhaps almost as much as she wanted him.

She battled to keep the insidious feelings from taking over her body, reminding herself of the dangers this type of man presented. Sheer common sense screamed at her to pull back, to stop him. For if she didn't, then all would be lost.

But how could she when he was looking down at her with such passion? One hand moved from her cheek to smooth across her forehead, making her shiver. The feathery fingertips then pressed her eyelids shut before following the line of her nose down to the corner of her mouth.

Rhea took a ragged breath, hoping to get some air into her starving lungs. She had ceased breathing from the moment he touched her.

'Beautiful lips,' he murmured, his words thick with arousal as his touch traced her mouth. 'Beautiful Rhea...'

Her eyes fluttered open again to see his head slowly descending.

But then he hesitated, looking deeply into her eyes, waiting perhaps for her to resist, to protest, or shout, or do something. The future flashed into her mind with a blinding and startling clarity. Within seconds of Stephen's kissing her she would be blurting out the truth, giving him the perfect excuse to go full steam ahead. In no time she would be in his arms, then ...

Her well-ordered life would become a shambles, her hard-won independence and peace of mind a thing of the past. And it wasn't only herself who would end up being hurt. There was Emily to consider, Emily who deserved more than a mess of a mother. Rhea's only hope was hold on to whatever means she had to protect herself and her child.

She pulled back. 'No, Stephen,' she said shakily.

Stephen looked as if she had slapped him. 'But . . .'

'No . . . This is not what I want.' Was that her voice? So clear, so strong . . .

He stared at her for an eternity, clearly troubled, not at all accepting of her words. 'Rhea,' he urged, 'are you happy?'

'I'm very happy,' she said stiffly.

He shook his head. 'I find that hard to believe.' He gave her a sharp glance before shaking his head. 'And I suppose you won't even accept my friendship now, will you?'

'Stephen, I don't think that . . .'

'I promise this will never happen again,' he insisted. 'Contrary to what you think of me, I don't play around with happily married women.'

What about unhappily married ones? came the cynical thought. Rhea was not so gullible as to think he wouldn't try again, if and when he got her alone. 'I must go,' she said grimly. 'I'll come back for Emily at five.'

He sighed, closing his eyes briefly before looking at her again, his expression bleak. 'I'll see you to the door.'

Rhea made it all the way home and into her bedroom before she burst into tears. She felt shattered—totally shattered. She tried telling herself that she had done the right thing, the only thing. But somehow her heart did not agree.

Heart?

Rhea sat bolt upright. What had her heart got to do with it? It was her body she was having to fight, wasn't it? Her body and its uncharacteristic, uncontrollable desires . . .

And yet what she kept thinking about wasn't what it would feel like to have Stephen take physical possession of her. Her mind kept recalling the incredible tenderness of his touch, the gentleness. She had wanted to lose herself in his arms, not only to assuage her aching body, but to gain solace for her lonely soul. The way he had caressed her had made her feel cherished, loved . . .

Rhea jumped to her feet, angry now. It was one thing to know Stephen Chase desired her, quite another to start fantasising that he might love her. That was the stuff movies were made of. Stephen wanted her, and he wanted her unencumbered, without a husband lurking in the background. Men like him didn't change their spots. They had affairs, not relationships. They had mistresses, not wives. And she'd better never forget it!

But all the logic in the world couldn't blot out how he had made her feel in those brief, wonderful moments—far more warm, more responsive, more female than she had ever felt in her life.

Rhea shivered, admitting to herself that, if Stephen ever chose to touch her again, she could not resist a second time.

CHAPTER SIX

RHEA handed the problem of picking up Emily the only way she could bear. She asked Gavin Bicksford, the next-door neighbour's son, to do it for her, making the excuse to Mrs Bicksford about having a migraine and being unable to drive.

Needless to say she paced up and down as she awaited Emily's arrival, half expecting Stephen to ring and make some enquiry about her health. But he didn't, and for that she was grateful, though not surprised. He had sensibly decided not to pursue her further.

She had not, however, anticipated her daughter querying her behaviour.

'But you never get migraines,' Emily puzzled as soon as she got home.

Rhea didn't look up from where she had just begun peeling the potatoes for the night's meal. 'They strike some people later in life,' she muttered.

'Then shouldn't you be in bed? I can do that.'

Emily went to take the vegetable peeler out of her mother's hand, but Rhea refused. 'I'm feeling better now,' she said. 'And it helps to keep busy.'

Emily pulled out a chair at the kitchen table and sat down. 'Mr Chase seemed put out when you didn't come to pick me up,' she said. There was a short sharp silence, then Emily asked, 'Don't you like Mr Chase, Mum?'

Rhea glanced up. 'Why do you say that?'

Her daughter shrugged. 'Oh, you know . . . I can just tell.'

Rhea resumed peeling, her hand actions stiff and clumsy. 'I don't dislike him really,' she said tautly. 'But he's not my type of man.'

'Oh . . . Laura and I were hoping . . .'

Rhea's hands stilled. 'Hoping what, for heaven's sake?'

Emily looked uncomfortable. 'Nothing . . . It was Laura's idea. I mean . . .' She gave her mother a worried look, then burst out, 'Well, she was telling me how her father's just broken up with this actress he's being going out with for ages—Madeline something or other. They had an argument after he told her Laura wasn't going away to boarding school. It was her idea, it seems . . .'

So she had happened into Stephen Chase's life between bedmates, had she? It made his pursuit of someone like her more understandable.

'Anyway, Laura reckons her father didn't really love this Madeline. But she told me if he married her she would have run away again. But she said she wouldn't mind if he married you, even though she knew it could never happen because you were already married. But then I told her that no, you weren't, that my dad was dead, and she said wouldn't it be fantastic if you and her father got together!'

Emily was as breathless as Rhea by the time she finished. All Rhea could think of was that it wouldn't be long before Laura blurted out the truth about Emily's father's being dead. And then there would be hell to pay!

Emily sighed at her mother's shocked silence. 'I know you're always saying you don't want to get married again. But, Mum, that's silly! You're real pretty, and you can't be sad about Dad dying forever. I know you probably loved him a lot, but Mr Chase is real nice. He played games with us this afternoon when it started raining again. And I miss not having a dad of my own. Mum . . .?'

Tears raced into Rhea's eyes. Tears for all the lies she'd been living with for years. For as she had listened to Emily talk of her father, Rhea realised with a crippling burst of honesty that she had never loved Milan, not as a woman should love a man. She had married him as an escape from what she considered an intolerable life at home. He had been the typical father-figure, older and totally dominating, taking her young life into his hands and moulding her into what he considered a dutiful spouse should be.

Oh, yes, she had cared for him, but as an obedient daughter more than a wife, a grateful girl more than a mature woman. It was a pitiful tribute to her marriage that she much preferred her life since being widowed. That was why she had resolved never to marry again. Not so much as a noble sacrifice for Emily's sake. It was quite clear her daughter would welcome the right stepfather. No . . . she had not wanted to have to lie there in a marital bed, night after night, enduring . . . enduring . . .

But that was not the case any more, was it? She was well and truly awakened. But it wrenched at her insides to think that, having finally achieved this long-awaited womanhood, she would choose a man such as Stephen Chase. Emily was just a child. She couldn't understand that Laura's father would never marry her, would never offer anything more than a passing sexual relationship, an affair.

More tears flowed as another more devastating realisation set in. She was in danger of falling in love with this man. Crazily, madly, irrevocably . . .

'Please don't cry, Mum,' Emily sobbed, racing

around to wrap fierce arms around her mother's waist. 'I'm sorry, I shouldn't have talked about Dad dying. I'm really sorry. Please . . . I'll tell Laura never to mention it again. And I'll make sure she doesn't say anything embarrassing to her father.'

'It's all right, love,' Rhea managed on seeing her daughter's distress. 'It's not what you said, really . . . It's just this headache.'

'You should lie down for a while, Mum. Let me finish the potatoes.'

Suddenly all the energy drained out of Rhea. Her shoulders slumped and the idea of lying down was very appealing.

'I can cook the dinner,' her daughter offered. 'You go and rest.'

Rhea gave Emily a grateful smile through misty eyes and walked slowly from the kitchen. She made her way along the narrow hallway and into her tiny bedroom. A sleep would do her good, she decided as she sank down on to the edge of the crocheted quilt. You couldn't think while you were asleep. Then later, after dinner, she would get up and work.

Yes, work was always a good antidote for problems. Rhea kicked off her shoes and lay back. But sleep was slow in coming. Slow . . . And not as soothing as she had hoped.

By the following Tuesday evening Rhea was still having difficulty with the scarlet evening top. Three times she had unravelled and redone the neckline, but not to her satisfaction. She hurried back to the living-room after an early dinner, intent on giving it one final try, knowing she would not be happy to offer it for sale as it was.

She had been hard at work for over an hour when Emily popped her head into the room. 'Hey, Mum, aren't we going to the meeting up at the school? It's almost seven-thirty!'

Rhea jumped to her feet, the things in her lap scattering on to the floor. 'Oh, my goodness, I forgot!' She scooped up the mess and tossed it all on to the armchair, then hurried from the room. 'There's no time to change,' she muttered as she stuffed the minutes book into her large carryall. 'They'll just have to take me as I am, ponytail, old clothes and all. Come on, Emily, let's go.

Rhea glanced in the rear-vision mirror as she reversed out of the drive and sped up the road. 'Goodness, I look a mess!' she groaned. It was just as well that her old blue jeans and black granny top had been fresh on that morning.

'I think you look very young and pretty,' Emily insisted.

'You're a dear,' smiled Rhea, but as she swung the van into the paddock that served as a school yard, the smile died on her lips.

One of the cars already parked there was sleek and low and silver.

Her first thought was to reverse out and go straight back home. But there was a limit to how many migraines she could claim in one week. And she was the secretary of the Parents' and Citizens' Association, after all. How could they conduct the first and most important meeting of the year without her?

Of course all that wonderful reasoning didn't stop the sick nerves crowding into her stomach as she locked up the van. Who would have dreamt that Stephen would turn up at a parents' meeting?

Rhea's eyes lifted to the school, and she remembered how he had disparaged it as an old relic. Which no doubt it was . . . structurally. The barnlike building with its high-pitched iron roof and wide wooden verandas would not have won any architectural prizes, and its three classrooms weren't sufficient for the school's needs any longer, which was why there were four portable classrooms under the trees behind it.

But it was still a good school, as Rhea had defended. A happy school. And Rhea had been happy in her position of secretary of the P & C. It had brought her out of her shell, given her confidence. At least it had, up till now . . .

Her legs felt heavy as they mounted the steps on to the veranda where she stopped to give Emily a goodbye peck on the cheek. 'You behave yourself for Mrs Fraser now,' she warned. 'And keep the noise down.'

Emily hurried into the fourth-class room where Mrs Fraser, an old-age pensioner, kindly minded any children on meeting nights.

With marked reluctance Rhea walked along to the far end of the veranda, and the sixth-class room which served as their meeting place. She paused before the door and gathered every resource of inner strength she had, yet her hand still trembled as she turned the doorknob and went in.

'Sorry I'm late,' she said perfunctorily, and made her way to where she always sat, at the front, to the right of the teacher's desk. All eyes followed her, and it bothered Rhea considerably that tonight of all nights she looked as she did, but she kept her chin up and her own eyes rigidly forward.

'Don,' she murmured, nodding to the headmaster who was standing behind the teacher's desk. She sat down, extracting the minutes book and a Biro before propping her bag against the legs of her chair. Having put them on the desk she looked up, her expression admirably bland.

Several familiar faces smiled at her. She smiled back.

One face, however, was definitely not smiling.

He was sitting at a desk to the right of her, three rows back, but still close enough for her to see the unmistakable message that was glaring from those steely grey eyes.

He *knew*!

Who had told him? her mind raced. Laura? Some local? Had he perhaps started asking questions about her errant husband, only to find he didn't exist any more?

'Since we're running late,' boomed Don Gregson, 'I think we'll dispense with the reading of the minutes of the last meeting.'

He had one of those typical schoolteacher voices that carried, and tonight it seemed to cut right through Rhea's head.

'As you know, the last president of the P & C, Mrs Doreen Stonewell, has left the district, so we'll have to find ourselves a new victim—I mean volunteer . . .' He chuckled, as did several others. 'Any nominations?'

There was an ominous silence.

Rhea fiddled with the Biro and stared blankly at the floor.

'Perhaps Mr Chase will take on the job,' he suggested at last.

Rhea's eyes snapped up.

'What about it, Steve?' Don went on, a wide smile on his ruddy face.

Rhea was stunned as much by the familiarity of the headmaster's manner as the suggestion itself. It seemed to intimate that Stephen Chase was already a tried and true friend in the community, something that usually took much longer than the few short weeks he'd been living in the area. The people of Bangaloo Creek were a reserved bunch, cautious in the giving of friendship.

Her eyes shot to the object of her thoughts. He looked totally unperturbed, his long legs stretched out beside the desk, ankles crossed. He dwarfed the furniture but still didn't look awkward.

'Let's put it this way,' Stephen said with a dry laugh. 'I haven't got a clue what a Parents' Association does yet, let alone its president. Perhaps it would be better to nominate someone more familiar with the task.'

'There's nothing to it,' he was assured. 'A simple matter of chairing meetings, plus the occasional speech—child's play to the managing director of a company. Rhea here could show you the ropes, couldn't you Rhea?'

She swallowed as those assessing grey eyes swung her way. The way he arched a single dark eyebrow was decidedly cynical.

'Oh ... er ... yes, I suppose so.' She had difficulty getting the words out, so much so that her strangled tone sounded most unenthusiastic.

Out of the corner of her eye she saw a flicker of cold anger pass across Stephen's face. 'I don't think Mrs Petrovic looks too keen on the idea.'

'Ridiculous,' the headmaster vetoed forcefully. 'She'd be delighted, wouldn't you, Rhea?'

'Er ...' Rhea felt cornered for a few seconds, then annoyed. With herself, as usual. 'We can always do with some fresh blood,' she pronounced firmly, then topped it off with a dazzling smile.

It brought an immediate frown to Stephen's face—and a measure of satisfaction to her bruised self-esteem. Till he smiled back. There was something vaguely threatening hidden in that smile.

'Great!' the headmaster exclaimed heartily. 'Then I officially nominate Mr Stephen Chase for the position of President of the Bangaloo Creek P & C. Rhea? Will someone second the nomination? Good! Better note that down for the minutes. Secretary and treasurer to remain the same. That *is* all right with you, Betty, isn't it?'

Betty Waymouth, a young local mother, nodded vigorously, then slid a blatantly admiring glance over at Stephen. Rhea sighed, thinking it was just as well Betty's husband wasn't present, but took some comfort from seeing that Stephen affected all women the same way. She herself was not the exception but the rule!

'That's all settled, then,' Don continued happily. 'Steve, why don't you come up and take this seat and you can chair the meeting?'

Rhea would have had sympathy for most people being thrown in at the deep end like that, but Stephen stood up and came forward with such supreme confidence that she only felt irritation. Why couldn't he be like other people? Unsure ... hesitant ... *human*!

But no! He wasn't like other people. He certainly wasn't like any of the other men in this room, dressed as he was in an elegant business suit, the sheen on the dark grey material advertising an expensive silk blend.

Not that any of the others would look so well in it. This man had the body, the bearing to make the most of whatever he wore, be it Pierre Cardin or Levis.

Rhea realised before it became embarrassing that she was staring at him, and quickly turned her head, returning it only when he was safely standing beside her. Though that in itself had its disturbing aspects. He was so close she could now actually smell his aftershave. It tantalised her nose, drawing all her senses into an appalling awareness. Her skin prickled beneath her clothing; her palms grew moist and clammy.

She turned her nose away, but it was a useless gesture. The scent was all around her, invading, infiltrating. Somehow it made her doubly conscious of her own drab appearance, and particularly resentful that no attractive fragrance was wafting from her skin to disturb him!

Not that it would, she thought mutinously. Men like Stephen Chase didn't spend their lives lusting uncontrollably after women like herself. They might find an inexperienced little widow suitable as a temporary bedmate, but on the whole the rich men of this world had their appetites catered for by glamorous exotic creatures with names like Madeline who undoubtedly always had ultra-feminine perfume lingering around their pulse-points.

And what did Rhea have at home to make her smell like a desirable woman? Nothing except baby powder and cheap deodorant! Her one bottle of perfume, given to her by Milan the Christmas before his death had long since run out.

Guilt consumed her at this sudden thinking of her dead husband. She had never worried about perfume when Milan had been alive, had never had her mind filled with romantic fantasies then. Even now, all she could think of was Stephen bending down and pressing his lips to hers . . .

She shuddered and shut her eyes, miserable in her awareness of the hot shaft of yearning pulsating along her veins. The depth of her arousal sickened her, and she wondered whether Stephen Chase had sold his soul to the devil to give him such wicked powers over women.

'I gather the purpose of this organisation is chiefly to raise funds for the school,' he began, then waited.

Everyone assented by nods or murmurs of agreement.

'In that case, I think I would like to hear the treasurer's report. And then I would appreciate it if our Madame Secretary here would read the minutes of the corresponding meeting last year. If she has them . . .'

She could feel his eyes boring down at her, but had no intention of raising her own. 'They're here somewhere,' she muttered. 'It will take me a few moments to locate them.' She began flipping through the book.

His sigh showed impatience and Rhea felt a surge of returned anger. What did he think this was, a fancy board meeting with her cast as his super-secretary?

'We'll use the time to hear from our treasurer,' he went on efficiently. 'Betty, wasn't it?'

Rhea looked up in time to see him throw Betty a heart-stopping smile. The silly woman preened, batting her lashes at him like a coy schoolgirl.

Rhea squirmed inside when Betty virtually simpered her way through the report. Everyone else, however, seemed more embarrassed by the contents rather than the treasurer's gushing manner.

The upshot was that the Association's bank balance stood at the pathetic amount of eighty-seven dollars and ten cents. The previous year had not been a good one, what with a break-in at the school and a disastrous fire in the store-room that had destroyed all the sports equipment.

'I see,' Stephen said slowly as the final tally was announced.

Rhea felt irritated that everyone was looking somewhat uncomfortable, as such a reaction was not warranted. Yet it was only human, she conceded, to want to look prosperous in the eyes of such an obvious success story as the man standing before them. But, to give Stephen his due, he came to their rescue.

'I must say it's damned good to find an organisation that's not in the red these days,' he praised. 'I can see I shan't mind this job at all. Now if you'd asked me to take on the railways . . .' He wiped his brow in mock distress.

Everyone laughed, including Rhea.

He slanted her a look. 'Careful, Mrs Petrovic,' he muttered under his breath. 'You might give the impression that you actually approve of me!'

Oddly enough, his aside did not intimidate or unnerve her any more than she already was. Instead, she was suddenly charged by the crazy urge to spar with him. 'Oh, but I do, Mr Chase,' she countered sweetly, 'in the position of president.'

The corner of his mouth lifted in a mockery of a smile. 'But not as anything else, it seems.'

'I don't know what you mean,' she answered in a brilliant parody of Betty's put-on breathless voice.

A shiver of alarm ran up and down her spine when he

leant down close to whisper, 'I hope you've got a damned good reason for the ridiculous games you've been playing with me. If you think you——'

'I've found the minutes you wanted, Mr Chase,' she said loudly, cutting him off. 'Shall I begin?'

If looks could kill ...

'By all means.' He sat down with a thump.

When she hesitated he drummed up a wide smile, patted her hand and said with exaggerated condescension, 'Now don't be nervous, my dear. We're all friends here, aren't we?'

Rhea wanted to hit him. Her hand actually itched with the effort of keeping it down. Instead, she smiled sweetly, then began to read.

She was a good reader, with an expressive musical voice, but it was rather hard to perform well with such a storm of emotions warring inside her. Still, she did her best, for it was important to her not to let Stephen undermine what she knew she could do well. She certainly didn't want to look a fool, as Betty had done.

At the end, she made sure she dropped her voice, not falling into the trap of finishing with a rising inflexion as so many women did, then calmly closed the book.

'Excellent,' murmured Stephen, and when she looked up she could see he was not mocking her in any way. The flush of pleasure she felt at his approval unnerved her more than anything had that evening.

With slow deliberation he rose to his feet once more. 'Hmm . . . I think the first thing we have to do is get the community working more solidly together in our fund-raising efforts. We have sixteen people here tonight and yet the school has approximately one hundred and thirty pupils, I'm told. Clearly involvement on a parental level is not overly high.'

Betty cleared her voice.

'You wish to say something, Betty?' Stephen offered. She shifted in her seat, smiling coyly. 'Well . . .'

'Please.' He waved her to her feet and reseated himself.

'I think, Mr Chase,' Betty ventured, a smug expression on her quite pretty face, 'that we do have a problem with most of the parents not knowing each other. I mean, we all live on acreages out here and it sometimes takes *years* even before you get to know your neighbour.' She hesitated, making certain Stephen knew she didn't want it to take that long to get to know him! 'And there are so many new folk moving in all the time now . . .' She stopped suggestively, and Rhea could have sworn she fluttered her eyelashes again. She wanted to crawl into a hole and die of embarrassment for the whole female race.

'So what do you suggest? Some more social gatherings to get to know each other?'

'That would be marvellous!' gushed Betty. 'We had a bush dance one year——'

'And when it rained,' Rhea inserted bluntly, 'only a few people turned up and we lost money.'

'Did you sell the tickets beforehand?' Stephen asked, disarming Rhea with his businesslike manner.

'No,' she conceded reluctantly. 'It was pay at the door.'

'Always a mistake. People are fickle creatures. They're more likely to turn up if they've already paid, regardless of the weather. But a bush dance sounds just the thing, Betty. How about you all throw some ideas at me and we'll discuss it?'

It was a lively talk, and a very productive one. Everyone seemed in agreement that a bush dance would be a good start, and each person was allotted a specific task, from booking the band to providing bales of straw as decoration for the local community hall.

Stephen himself took on the job of having proper tickets printed, which would be sent home with each pupil and distributed through all local retail outlets. There was to be a barbecue and a fantastic raffle, prize to be supplied—again by Stephen.

It seemed he meant to be a generous president, although Rhea reserved judgement on this aspect of his character. It was easy to throw money around when one had oodles.

The clock on the wall chimed nine-thirty.

'I think we'd better wrap this meeting up,' Stephen decided. 'Nothing worse than meetings that go on too long on a work night.'

'My wife's prepared supper in the staffroom for anyone who wants it,' the headmaster announced.

Rhea hung back as everyone began filing out for the short walk to the tiny staffroom next door. Her plan was to sneak out, grab Emily and head for home before anyone noticed. Meanwhile, she stayed where she was, seated at the desk, pretending to be organising her records.

The trouser legs were grey this time, but they belonged to the same man.

Her chin lifted as though it were connected to a puppet string. He was glaring down at her, his face like granite.

'Come along, Mrs Petrovic,' he said brusquely.

'You're dragging the chain again. And there I was before tonight thinking you were perfect!'

Her heart sank, all her earlier bravado dissolving into mush. 'Stephen, I . . . I . . .' She fell silent, her mind and tongue no longer connected.

'What? Nothing to say? No advice to offer? No criticism to make? No more *lies* to tell? Good God, I'll have to mark this day down on my calendar!'

Rhea flinched at his anger. 'I meant to tell you,' she managed haltingly. 'But . . . but the time was never right.'

The anger in his face faded, replaced by a confused exasperation. 'Now that I can't fathom at all. Why on *earth* couldn't you just have said right from the beginning that your husband was dead? The whole thing is beyond comprehension. If you only knew what I——' He broke off, clearly at the end of his tether with her. 'What stuns me is how you thought you'd get away with it. You must have known I would find out. So why, Rhea, why?'

There was no excuse she could possibly make, except the truth. And that was far too humiliating—and revealing. She turned away from his probing glare to put the minutes book into her bag.

His sharp intake of breath had her whirling to face him. She was taken aback to see his eyes blinking wide with realised horror.

'It was because of *me*, wasn't it?' he accused. 'You don't want to get involved with someone like *me*!'

There was little use denying it when a betraying heat was already claiming her cheeks.

'What in God's name do you think I am?' he gasped. 'Some sort of ogre?' He was clearly bewildered to the point of real distress.

'Hey, Steve! Rhea!' Don called from the doorway. 'Leave that chit-chat and come and have a cup of coffee. The wife wants to wash up and get home before midnight!'

'Coming,' Stephen returned with a quick smile.

He sighed as he turned back to face her. 'Common sense tells me to walk away from you, Rhea—you're a very mixed-up lady. But I've never been large on common sense where women are concerned. I want you, Rhea. And I mean to have you, make no mistake about that. You can lie and play games till the cows come home, but one day, madam, you are going to be in my bed, ready and willing.'

Rhea listened to these incredible words with an ever-increasing pulse-rate, all the time telling herself that this wasn't happening. No man said things like that to a woman. Not out loud. Not here, in a lighted classroom. It was shocking!

But oh, so exciting . . .

The heat that had earlier invaded her face leapt to boiling-point.

'And now,' Stephen went on, a coldly satisfied smile coming to his face as he surveyed her telling blush, 'you and I are going to have a cup of coffee. Together!'

CHAPTER SEVEN

RHEA'S thoughts were tumbling every which way as Stephen propelled her from the classroom. What he had just said to her seemed even more incredible with every passing second. If he did mean it, then it made a mockery of his outrage at discovering why she might have lied to him. He had virtually just corroborated her opinion of his attitude to women—which had the unexpected bonus of putting a halt to any feelings of love she might have imagined she was harbouring for the man. *Love* Stephen Chase? Impossible! She made up her mind then and there that, no matter what her body felt about him, no matter what he said or did, she was not going to have an affair with him!

Nevertheless, she was relieved to reach the safety of the crowded staffroom, believing he wouldn't dare to say or do anything embarrassing in front of the others.

Don descended on them immediately with a cup of coffee each, then proceeded to regale Stephen with words of praise and gratitude at his taking on the presidency.

Everyone else wanted to speak to Stephen personally as well, keeping Rhea's fears of being somehow cornered by him at bay. Even so, he managed to keep her at his side, exuding a proprietorial manner towards her that she found perversely flattering.

Betty looked pea-green with envy, while the others were merely curious to find out exactly what relationship their normally man-shy Rhea had with their new president.

It seemed that Stephen's being a single father was no secret, neither was the surprising news that he was a tourist resort developer of some fame. Rhea was not a magazine or newspaper reader, so she wasn't familiar with the rich and famous of Sydney. When several people made allusions to his many property deals and his company—Chase Investments—she was left feeling stunned and ignorant. She found herself looking at him with even more wariness, this added knowledge reaffirming her belief that all he would ever want from her was sex.

Rhea knew she should excuse herself from his company, perhaps even go home, but she didn't. She stayed with him, looking and listening, watching and waiting, intrigued by the magnetism of the man. She was flirting with danger and she knew it.

As supper drew to a close, several couples having already departed, Rhea was to wish she had been more aloof. Without warning, Stephen slipped an arm around her waist, drawing her to his side, an intimate hand remaining on her hip. Her whole body stiffened, her eyes flying to him in outrage.

But his attention was focused on the couple they were talking to.

'I know they had to put the new airport somewhere,' Don's wife was saying, 'and it's far enough away not to be too noisy, but still . . . I don't think I like progress.'

'It's useless to fight against what's inevitable,' Stephen advised. 'Isn't it, Rhea?' He gave her a little squeeze and a quick smile.

Perhaps his only intention was to bring her into the

conversation, but Rhea didn't think so. His words clearly held a double meaning. The thought that he could be so boldly presumptuous of her capitulation gave Rhea the courage to move away from his touch, even though it only looked as if she was replacing her empty teacup in the sink against the wall.

'I don't think people should ever be apathetic,' she said coolly over her shoulder. 'They should stand up for what they believe in, and not allow minorities or governments to push them around.' She turned and fixed Stephen with a steady eye. 'I've often thought *progress* was a word coined by the greedy money-makers of this world. It often has little to do with the common good.'

He held her eyes, cocking his head slightly to one side. He would have to be stupid, Rhea decided, not to be getting her underlying messages.

'There again, I'm old-fashioned, I guess,' she went on. 'I still believe in things like marriage, which probably makes me an anachronism these days. People seem to drift in and out of relationships with all the thought some folk give to their purchases at the supermarket.' Rhea looked Stephen square in the eye. 'Most choices there are based on what's packaged best or what's closest at hand, which is hardly the way to find quality.'

An uncomfortable silence had descended on the group with Rhea's speech. Stephen continued to stare at her in puzzlement till finally Don cleared his throat and announced that poor Mrs Fraser would be wondering what was happening tonight and it was high time they all went home.

Leaving was fractionally easier than arriving. Once Laura and Emily joined them Stephen had no more opportunity to make any hair-raising comments, though he did give Rhea another penetrating look when she hurriedly said goodnight. Then as she walked over and unlocked the van he said quite loudly, 'I'll give you a call tomorrow night.'

She spun round, her face bristling with indignation.

'About the arrangements for the bush dance,' he added, a sardonic smile coming to his lips.

'Can't we go and visit instead, Dad?' Laura implored. 'I'm dying to see Emily's dogs. She says one of them's going to have puppies soon.'

'Not on a week night, sweetie,' Stephen returned gently. 'You'll have to see the dogs some other time.'

'Oh . . .'

Rhea was moved by the little girl's disappointment, but how could she invite her around without including the father?

'Couldn't Laura come home from school with me on the bus tomorrow, Mum?' Emily suggested. 'Then we could drop her at home when you go up the road to buy the oats and hay. We've run out, remember?'

Rhea sighed. Yes, she remembered—now that she'd been reminded. Just lately she would have forgotten her head if it wasn't screwed on. And the reason for her absent-mindedness was standing right before her.

'Would that be all right, Stephen?' she asked tautly.

His returning look carried surprise. 'If it's all right with you .'

She nodded wearily, having accepted that once again she was in a corner.

'I won't be home till six at least,' he added, walking over closer. 'Would that be too late?'

'No.'

'Perhaps you and Emily would like to come for dinner? It would be easy enough to tell Mrs King——'

'No, thank you,' Rhea cut in chillingly before the girls could jump on the bandwagon. 'I really can't spare the time—I have some urgent work I have to finish tomorrow night. But thank you for inviting us. Some other time, perhaps.'

Stephen gave her a tight, dry little smile. 'You will, however, stay long enough for coffee this time, won't you?'

'Of course,' she returned stiffly. 'We have to talk about the dance.'

That smile was hovering again. 'Ah, yes, the dance. . . '

'Goodnight, Mr . . . Stephen,' she amended, though curtly.

'Goodnight . . . Rhea.'

Before she could object he strode over and opened the van door for her. She had no option in front of the children but to get in, and, while she kept her eyes glued to the steering-wheel, she was sure he was looking at her legs, and the way the jeans pulled tight around her thighs as she climbed in.

Her cheeks felt hot and she was grateful when he swung the door shut, plunging the cabin into darkness. She shouldn't have unwound the window and glanced up to thank him, but she did and, whatever he read on her face, it took all the tension out of his.

'My pleasure,' he drawled, leaning his hands on the

window and bending towards her. 'See you at six tomorrow,' he said, grey eyes narrowing till they were nothing more than slits of wicked intent.

Rhea stared up into them, captivated, enthralled this time by *his* physical desire, not her own. He was staring at her mouth, staring as though he wanted to drink it dry, wanted to take it, to possess and seduce it with a mastery learnt from many years of experience . . .

Her lips parted with a soft moan.

'Mum? Have you lost your key or something?'

Rhea's eyes fell to the floor at Emily's voice and she fumbled with the ignition. God give me strength, she prayed.

But her hands were quivering as she fired the engine, her heart pounding madly. And, despite her earlier resolves of virtuous resistance, she knew—in that place reserved for the bitterest of truths—that she was already on the slippery slide to hell.

CHAPTER EIGHT

'BLUE suits you,' were the first words Stephen said to Rhea the following evening. He had been coming out of the double garage as she arrived, looking startlingly handsome in a charcoal-grey suit. On seeing her, he deposited his briefcase in the boot of the car and strode forward, opening her door and simultaneously giving forth with the smooth compliment about the colour of her silk dress.

Rhea gave him a cool look in reply.

'I hope Laura was no trouble,' he went on, taking her arm as she alighted from the van, his eyes running appreciatively over her figure.

She pulled away from his touch as swiftly as good manners would allow. 'No trouble at all.'

'Laura's got to go down and feed Mimi, Mum,' Emily told her as the girls scrambled from the passenger side. 'Can I go with her?'

'Oh . . .' Rhea had planned on keeping the children close by. 'All right, but don't be too long. I have to be home by seven at the latest.'

Stephen looked at his watch. 'It's already ten past six. That doesn't give us very long to talk.'

She lifted sharp eyes. 'It won't take all that long to finalise plans for the dance.'

He held her with a long uncompromising look. 'It wasn't only the dance I wanted to talk to you about, Rhea, as you very well know.'

Her stomach somersaulted. Surely he wasn't going to

94

start saying the same sort of thing today as he had last night?

'Do you have to look so damned scared?' Stephen flung at her in reproach. 'Look, Rhea, I . . . Oh, what the hell, I'm wasting my time making an apology, aren't I?' He muttered something more under his breath, then, taking her arm again, shepherded her into the plush-carpeted hallway.

'Mr Chase?' called a female voice. 'Is that you?'

'Yes, Mrs King.'

A portly woman in her fifties bustled into the hall, wiping her hands on a brightly flowered apron. 'Your dinner's all ready in the oven and—— Oh, sorry,' she broke off, noticing Rhea. 'I didn't realise you were going to have a visitor. Dear me, there's only enough food for ——'

'It's all right, Mrs King,' Stephen soothed. 'Mrs Petrovic's not staying.' These last few words had an edge to them, making Rhea feel guilty.

'Mrs Petr . . . goodness me! Then you're Emily's mother. Laura talks of no one else but Emily and you, isn't that so, Mr Chase?'

'Indubitably,' he said drily.

'It was so kind of you to look after her the day she ran off, Mrs Pet . . . Mrs P . . .' the woman laughed. 'I don't seem to be able to get my tongue around your name! Anyway, you look too young to be a Mrs with a ten-year-old daughter.'

Rhea blushed. 'That's very kind of you to say so. Call me Rhea, please . . .'

'Then you must call me Maisie. I don't fancy Mrs King much.' She cast a sheepish look at her boss at this announcement.

Stephen sighed. 'For pity's sake, then why haven't

you said so, Mrs K . . . Maisie?'

Maisie shrugged. 'It didn't seem proper, I suppose, you being my employer and all.'

Stephen made a disgruntled sound.

'Now now, Mr Chase, don't go getting all uptight over a silly name! You must be very tired. He was up at five this morning, love,' Maisie directed at Rhea, 'to catch an early flight to Brisbane, then he rushed home to be here for Laura. You know what happens to these people who burn the candle at both ends . . .' She wagged a motherly finger at Stephen. 'Now why don't you two pop along to the living-room and I'll bring you both a nice cup of coffee, eh? Or shall I get you something stronger?'

Stephen sighed again and Rhea could see he did look tired. 'Coffee will do fine. If I had a Scotch I don't think I'd stop at one. As for Mrs Petrovic . . .' he shot her a cynical look '. . . I doubt she would even dream of sullying her body with anything as poisonous as alcohol, would you, Rhea?'

Rhea could feel the heat zooming back into her cheeks, but she met him, eye for eye, not noticing the housekeeper's surprised expression. 'I've been known to try a drop or two occasionally,' she said defiantly, thinking of the sherry she had downed one sleepless night, all to forget this infuriatingly aggravating man. 'But coffee will do for now.'

Stephen shrugged indifferently before turning to stride down the hall. Rhea had no option but to follow or be left standing there like an idiot.

She stopped in the doorway of the large living area, watching as her ungracious host flicked open his suit jacket and slumped down into one of the deep leather armchairs. He looked up at her with an exasperated expression and indicated the chair next to him. 'Come over and sit down.' He yanked his tie loose, then undid the top button of his shirt. 'You make me nervous, hovering in the doorway.'

Rhea was taken aback. 'Nervous?' she queried.

'Yes! Nervous!'

'I'm sure you never feel nervous, Stephen Chase,' she stated primly, walking stiffly across the room and sitting down, totally unrelaxed with a straight back and clenched knees.

He sighed irritably. 'OK, so I'm behaving abominably. But you always make me feel so bloody inadequate!'

Her eyes snapped up in astonishment.

'That surprises you?' Stephen grated out. 'Don't worry, it surprises me too. I don't usually let women get under my skin.'

The oddest feelings claimed her stomach, a mixture of satisfaction and anger. Satisfaction that she was at least affecting him in some way. Anger at his easy dismissal of any vital female role in his life.

Knowing how tell-tale her face could be, Rhea dropped her eyes, staring down at the floor in acute discomfort as the silence between them lengthened.

'Rhea?' he said at last.

'Yes?' She looked up when he didn't go on, only to find his gaze raking hers with disturbing penetration.

'Was I right?' he asked tautly. 'About why you lied to me?'

Rhea stared at him, searching her mind frantically for some way out. She hadn't seriously expected him to bring the subject up again today. But then she hadn't expected Emily to run off with Laura. She had planned to keep her daughter close—as protection.

She turned her face away, then stared back down at the floor, twisting her hands together in a nervous knot.

Stephen leant forward in his chair, bringing his face disturbingly close. She flinched back.

'For God's sake, woman, what are you frightened of?' he demanded, suddenly enclosing her hands in his. When she tried to snatch them away he held them fast. 'Do you think I'd hurt you?' he whispered thickly.

Rhea looked up at him with anguished eyes, knowing that she couldn't just sit there with his flesh around hers for much longer or her body would burst into flames. 'Please, Stephen, let me go,' she gasped. 'I . . . I'm not frightened of you. Please . . . I just don't like being touched . . . I came here today to discuss the dance, that's all.' She pulled back from his grasp, jerking back in the chair when he suddenly released her.

'Do you expect me to ignore how I feel about you?' he charged. 'Or how *you* feel about *me*?'

For an electric moment his words hung in mid-air. Rhea could feel her heart pounding in her chest, her whole being straining towards him. But she held firm and strong, believing that if she could get past this one trial she would be safe. 'And what is that,' she countered, 'except a passing attraction? I'm sorry, Stephen, but I'm not interested in casual sex, or one-night stands.'

'Neither am I,' he snapped impatiently.

'Oh? What are you offering, then—an affair?' Her voice was beginning to shake with emotion. 'Sorry, but that's not on either, Stephen. I *don't* want to become involved with you. And my reasons are my own.'

'What reasons?' Is it something to do with your husband, is that it? Do you think you're being disloyal to his memory? My God, Rhea, the man's been dead for six years!'

She flushed. So he *had* been making enquiries about her. 'That's not it,' she said truthfully.

'Then what, for pity's sake? Don't go pretending you're not attracted to me!'

His arrogance fired a resentful anger. 'Oh? Would that be so unlikely? Or do *all* women fall at your feet when you choose to turn your eye their way?'

An answering fury swept across Stephen's handsome face. 'Don't be ridiculous! I've never thought of myself as God's gift to women! Not only that, I work too damned hard to be worrying about sex every minute of the day. It isn't the be-all and end-all of my life.'

'That's not the impression you gave me last night when you virtually threatened to get me into your bed, by fair means or foul. I was shocked by that, Stephen. Truly shocked.'

His features took on a ravaged regret. 'I know . . . Dear God, don't you think I know? I was angry and frustrated. I made a mistake . . .'

'A mistake, Stephen? Or merely an error in tactics? Your aim is still the same. You want me in your bed.'

He gave her the oddest look. It was half grim, half exasperated. 'I can't deny that.'

'At least you're honest about it, I suppose. But let me be equally honest. I do find you attractive. You're an exceptionally attractive man, as you well know, but I have no intention of going to bed with you. Do I make myself clear?'

'Very clear,' he sighed, though he continued to glare at her for several seconds. No doubt he found her behaviour both annoying and incomprehensible. Despite what he'd said Rhea knew that women probably rarely rejected him.

Finally he leant back in his chair. 'There's not much point pursuing this subject, then, is there? About the catering . . .' And with a manner briskly efficient and businesslike he began tying up all the loose ends pertaining to the dance.

It was perverse of Rhea to be hurt by his sudden coldness towards her. She had asked for it, had rejected all his persistent and flattering attempts to seduce her. But hurt she was. Perhaps in the corner of her female mind she had wanted him to pursue her with a passion that brooked no opposition, literally sweep her off her feet and carry her up to bed, thereby taking all responsibility for her actions away from her.

'What are you going to have as the raffle prize?' she asked in a flat little voice. 'I'd like to be able to say what it is in the school bulletin.'

'How about a saddle?' Stephen suggested. 'Or an open order at the nearest saddlery for five hundred dollars. Everyone around here seems horse-mad.'

'Five hundred dollars!' She frowned. 'That's an awful lot, isn't it?'

He shrugged. 'I can afford it. Ah, here's the coffee.'

'Sorry I took so long,' chirped Maisie as she waddled into the room with a tray. 'I thought I'd put the kettle on, but it was turned off at the power-point.' She placed the tray on the coffee-table and began taking off her apron, totally oblivious of the tension in the room. 'I have to fly, Mr Chase. Bingo starts down at the club at seven-thirty and I have to change.'

Stephen reached into the breast pocket of his suit and drew out his wallet. He extracted a selection of notes. 'A little extra, Mrs K . . . Maisie . . . for all your overtime.'

'Oh, Mr Chase, you needn't!' she protested.

'You deserve it. Now off you go and have a good time. Breakfast at six tomorrow, OK?'

'You really are a kind man, Mr Chase.' Maisie beamed her approval at him, then smiled at Rhea. 'Nice to have met you, love.'

As Maisie hurried from the room Stephen looked at Rhea. 'Don't worry,' he drawled coldly once they were alone, 'you don't have to think well of me for any of my supposedly generous gestures. I donate money to a hundred different charities, mostly for tax reasons, and I always bribe my house staff. Then I don't have to feel guilty about asking a little extra of them.'

'It's none of my business what you do, Stephen,' she said unhappily, 'though I'm sure everyone at the P & C will be very grateful for your donation to the raffle.'

'But not you.'

The uncomfortable moment was saved by Emily and Laura running up to the back porch and opening the sliding doors. 'It's raining again,' Laura announced as they both skipped inside.

Stephen scowled. 'Damn it! I hate flying in bad weather.'

'Where are you going to tomorrow, Dad?' Laura asked, sitting on the arm of his chair and winding her small arm around his neck.

He flipped her curls. 'Back to Brisbane, poppet.'

'But you were up there today!'

'That's life,' he sighed. 'Problems with a bank manager—not to mention the local council. They seem determined to block a road I need.'

'I wish I could come too,' she complained.

'You have to go to school. Now, how about taking Emily into the kitchen for a lemonade while her mother and I have this coffee? It's getting cold.'

Both girls gave them a curious look before racing from the room, giggling as they went.

'I hate the sound of girls giggling,' Stephen muttered after them before picking up the coffee-pot to pour. 'Milk and no sugar, isn't it?' he said, flicking Rhea a swift glance.

She nodded, feeling depressed that he seemed to be avoiding looking at her now. 'You have a good memory,' she remarked.

One corner of his mouth lifted in a wry smile. 'I'm good at most things,' he said, and handed her the cup.

Rhea took the cup with slightly shaking fingers, trying desperately to ignore the way her thoughts had taken flight at his comment. She was relieved when the phone rang, requiring Stephen to stand up and move away.

He strode quickly across the room to swoop up the receiver from the table in a corner. 'Yes?' he asked in a brisk tone. A brief silence ensued, then she heard him sigh, deeply. 'Madeline, I thought we had this out before . . .' His back was to Rhea, but in the silent room even his low tones carried well. 'I see . . . all right . . . I suppose I can manage that . . .'

Rhea's mouth went dry as she listened unhappily to the one-sided conversation. Undoubtedly Madeline was trying to patch up their relationship. Which wasn't surprising; Rhea couldn't imagine a woman getting over Stephen in a hurry. Somehow she could hear the unhappy woman's desperation, begging her ex-lover to see her again, asking for one more chance, settling for some lukewarm acceptance of her invitation. It was totally humiliating, and only served to remind Rhea what lay in store for her if she fell victim to this man's charms. Not that she hadn't already . . .

'. . . Very well, I'll meet you in front of the theatre . . . around seven . . . Don't worry if I'm a bit late . . . That's perfectly all right . . . I understand . . . What was that . . . ? You could be right . . .'

Unexpectedly he laughed. It had a soft sensual sound to it that curled through Rhea's stomach, stabbing her with a fierce jealousy. A wild urgent voice clamoured in her brain to go to him, to tell him he didn't need Madeline, that she, Rhea, would give him what he wanted, anywhere, any time!

Rhea drained the coffee-cup and got unsteadily to her feet. It was definitely time for her to go.

'You always were persuasive, Maddie dear,' he was saying teasingly. He gave another low laugh. 'But don't push your luck! See you Friday. Bye.'

He hung up and turned, a weary resignation sweeping across his face when he saw Rhea ready to leave. 'I'll see you out,' he said in clipped tones.

Rhea held herself proud and tall. 'There's no need.'

'Nevertheless . . .' He turned sharply on his heel and preceded her to the door, calling to the girls on the way.

Rhea made it all the way home and into the bathroom before the tears came.

CHAPTER NINE

THE DAY of the bush dance arrived without producing in Rhea the nerves that had preceded her other meetings with Stephen. Her feelings for him had reached a crisis point on the Friday night two weeks previously, the night of his date with Madeline.

Rhea had been watching the late-night news on television when there was a brief spot covering the première of a new musical that night at the Capitol Theatre. As the camera swung over the crowd tumbling out after the performance Rhea glimpsed both Stephen and the blonde from the airport, confirming in Rhea's mind exactly which blonde Madeline was. Neither appeared to mind the way the crowd were crushing them up against each other.

Upset, Rhea had paced her bedroom for hours, torturing herself with visions of their making love together later. At the crack of dawn she had literally hauled Emily out of bed, packed up the small van, fed and watered the animals, then driven down to Kiama.

Her mother had been astonished though delighted to see them, although she soon noticed her daughter's agitation. Rhea had never been a good confider, however, and after a few tentative attempts at probing at the problem her mother didn't press. She and Bill took Emily down to the beach and left Rhea to cry out her misery in private.

Rhea was surprised how nice Bill was to her during her weekend stay, fussing over her and buying her a bottle of white wine because he knew she disliked the beer he normally stocked. She had been touched, going so far as to join him in a mild drinking session that Saturday night. It was the first time in her life that she had felt comfortable in his company, and she really appreciated his genuine attempts at cheering her up.

She found herself looking at her stepfather with different eyes. He seemed genuinely moved by her warmer manner towards him, all of which made her feel more than a fraction guilty. What had she ever done to deserve his affection? Not much.

It was good, too, to be able to watch him touch her mother without cringing inside. Rhea's new understanding gave her an insight into their relationship that the teenage Rhea had not had a hope of appreciating. They clearly loved each other, with a deep and passionate love, a love which could not always confine itself to the bedroom.

Rhea could see now that her upbringing prior to her father's death had set her on a path to physical shyness which she was only now getting over. Her father had never been one to hug and kiss, not even in the privacy of home. He had been a silent, reserved man, a man not given to sentiment or emotional love, or the physical demonstrations of them. Milan had been much the same, Rhea realised with another burst of enlightenment. He had confined his attentions to her till the lights were out at night, not liking to even hold hands in public.

By the time she began the drive home on the Sunday, Rhea had achieved a satisfying mental peace regarding Bill and her mother. Not so regarding Stephen. She could see no solution to her problem, particularly now Madeline was back on the scene, not forgetting the young woman in the coffee lounge. Who was to say Stephen wasn't still sleeping with her as well?

Rhea might have succumbed to the temptation of an affair with Stephen if she'd been the only woman in his life, but she could not commit herself to such intimacy with a man who the very next night could be doing the same thing with another woman. That would tear her apart.

By the time she reached Banagloo Creek she had resolved to cut him out of her mind and heart, totally, irrevocably. She wasn't in love with him yet, of that she was almost sure. The balance of her feelings was still on the physical side. It was a case of mind over matter, she believed.

Oddly enough, she almost succeeded, but as she did so a depression descended, heavy and sluggish, so that everything she did was an enormous effort. She felt tired all the time. Not agitated as she had been before, just bone-weary.

By sheer force of will she finished her autumn range of knitwear, the last garment being pressed and delivered the day before the bush dance. The troublesome red top had never made the grade, however. It had finally been discarded, thrown into the bottom of a drawer with a few other rejects, most of which she eventually resurrected for wearing herself

One of them, a crocheted top of natural mohair and raw silk—suffering from a slight stain— was Rhea's selection for the bush dance. A couple of weeks back she might have gone out and splurged on a new outfit, pretending it was not to impress Stephen but underneath knowing it was.

Now, she didn't seem to care. A pair of her old jeans would do, along with her high-heeled ankle-boots, bought when they were in fashion years before.

Rhea pulled on the stone-washed jeans she had chosen and struggled to do up the zipper. Damn, she thought irritably, why did cheap clothes always have to shrink when you washed them? She turned side-on and looked at herself in the mirror, a grimace curling her lips at the way the stretch denim hugged her figure. Thank goodness the top came down over her hips, hiding most of the displayed curves.

Rhea sighed and turned her attention to her hair. It was being its usual stubborn self, refusing to be easily tamed. She brushed it vigorously before corralling the mass high on her head with a tight elastic band. She was just about to secure it with pins when Emily came into the room.

'Oh, Mum, don't!' she exclaimed. 'It looks great! The pins will only come out when you dance anyway and then it'll look messier.'

'I have no intention of dancing,' Rhea pronounced, suddenly worried that Stephen might ask her if he saw her on the floor. She might have discarded him from her day-to-day thoughts, but that didn't mean she would survive being imprisoned in his arms.

'But what if someone asks you to?' asked Emily with a little giggle. 'You can't be rude and say no. That's what you told me.' Her face was split with a mischievous grin.

Rhea gave her daughter a sharp look. What was she up to? Had she and Laura inveigled Stephen into asking her to dance? She prayed not. 'I . . . I'll be too busy with the supper to dance,' she said, almost defensively.

Emily said nothing, but as she left the room she was still smiling.

'My, my, don't you look sexy!' was the first thing Betty Waymouth said to her that evening.

Rhea glanced up in astonishment from where she was preparing salad in the small servery attached to the community hall. 'Sexy?' She glanced down incredulously at her old jeans and crocheted top.

'You haven't got a bra on, have you?' Betty said slyly.

Rhea blinked. 'Of course I have.' She stared down at her front, noting for the first time that her flesh-coloured underwear did blend in with the natural colours of the raw silk and mohair top.

'Have you seen Stephen yet?' Betty went on. 'He's out helping set up the barbecue. God, he looks gorgeous! I thought he might be one of those suit men—you know, the kind that need to be dressed formally to look good —but what that man can do for a pair of tight jeans is wicked!'

'I'm sure Mr Chase would be thrilled with your observation,' muttered Rhea. Talking about the man seemed to be reviving all those old breathless feelings. It was very annoying.

Betty laughed mockingly. 'And I'm sure you don't call him Mr Chase when you're having one of your cosy little meetings, do you? Come on, do tell!' She came up to Rhea and leant close. 'What's he like in bed? Fantastic, I'll bet!'

Rhea recovered from her initial shock at such impertinence to give Betty a withering look. 'I really wouldn't know.'

The other woman merely shrugged. 'Not telling, eh?'

'There's *nothing* to tell! Look, Betty, why don't you make yourself useful and start helping me cut up this salad?'

'Sorry, I've already promised Stephen I'll help on the barbecue,' Betty said airily as she swept from the hall.

Rhea shook her head and set to work, determinedly ignoring the apprehensive gnawing in her stomach.

She managed to avoid seeing Stephen during the preparations for the dance. Not consciously. It just happened. Though it did cross her mind once that perhaps he was deliberately avoiding her. The thought hurt much more than it should have, she realised uneasily, if she were truly over him.

By eight o'clock the dance was in full swing, with the barbecue sizzling, the band booming, feet tapping, people dancing and drinking, eating and laughing. The supper was all perfectly prepared and laid out, leaving Rhea no further excuse to hide in the servery. But she felt too strung up to go and join in the dancing, deciding instead to step outside the hall for a breath of fresh air.

She squeezed past the group of people standing smoking around the entrance and walked slowly down the wide front steps, stopping on the last one to look back up at the coloured lights hanging along the guttering. They lent a real party atmosphere, and the music pounding out from the windows had a marvellously invigorating sound.

'I think we could call it an unqualified success, don't you?'

Stephen's voice emerging from nowhere spun Rhea

around. She stared at the emptiness of the surroundings in bewilderment till he suddenly stepped out from the shadow of a nearby tree.

'You nearly scared me to death!' she reproached, a defensive hand fluttering to her throat.

He didn't make any attempt to cross the few paces between them. 'I appear to have that effect on you all the time,' he drawled.

She gave a nervous laugh. 'Don't be silly!'

He took one step towards her, bringing him into better light. Rhea swallowed. Betty had not been exaggerating. What he did to jeans was wicked!

'You were certainly right about selling the tickets beforehand,' she chattered away. 'We've got a big roll-up. Though it's just as well we organised a separate dance for the kids up in the classrooms. This hall couldn't have coped with the children as well.'

She was well aware that she was babbling on, but Stephen was standing far too close, watching her far too intently.

'I still make you nervous, don't I?' he said slowly.

She lifted panicky eyes. 'Please don't start anything, Stephen. I thought we'd come to an understanding.'

He gave a dry laugh. 'You might have come to an understanding, Rhea, but I certainly haven't.'

Her hand reached up to rub the base of her throat. It was a nervous habit of hers, but it drew his gaze. When her hand moved lower, to rest half frozen in the valley between her breasts, his eyes followed. Hot lights blazed deep in their grey depths, telling her he still wanted her. She tried to control the mad response of her heart by reminding herself that he didn't keep his virility exclusively for her. But somehow that thought didn't work this time. Her breasts were swelling under his searing glare, the rock-hard tips pressing painfully against her bra.

'Come inside and dance with me,' he invited huskily.

Rhea stood frozen, watching with wide eyes as he reached out his hand towards her.

'Don't say no,' he almost pleaded.

Rhea realised dazedly that it was this soft tactic he often employed that was so appealing. There was no grabbing, pushing, forcing. He got what he wanted with a seductive persuasiveness that was more tempting than the most macho approach.

Without her making a conscious decision, her hand seemed to find his. She was unnerved by the smile on his face when it did so. Perhaps she might have understood triumph. But this was relief, a gut-wrenching relief combined with such joy that all Rhea's preconceptions about this man were shaken. Could it be possible that he really cared about her? came the astonishing thought.

Her lips moved back in a tentative smile. 'I . . . I'm not familiar with square dancing,' she murmured. 'I won't know what to do.'

'That's all right,' Stephen reassured her in a low, gentle voice. 'Just follow me.'

He led her up the steps, carefully making a path for her through the crowd, protecting her from any jostling. A rigorous reel was in progress, the movements looking complicated. They joined the group nearest, Rhea's attention swinging away from Stephen as she concentrated on picking up the steps.

It was easy really, after the first time. At the beginning
of the round partners faced each other in two parallel
lines. With hands behind their own backs they surged
forward, retreating before they actually touched. Then
the couple at the head of the lines held hands and
skipped sideways down the aisle till they reached the
end, while the other clapped, at which point the pairs
surged forward again, this time linking arms and going
into a vigorous spin. Then the whole procedure was
repeated, with a different couple this time at the head of
the lines.

No dance could have been more simple, or less erotic.
So Rhea mistakenly thought in the beginning.

It was the eye contact, of course. From his
vantage-point opposite Stephen stared at her the whole
time, his half-lidded gaze incredibly sensuous. When he
surged towards her, she felt as if she were literally
burning under the heat of his scrutiny. She found herself
holding her breath, waiting for the brief moments when
he dropped his eyes to her breasts, which were too well
rounded to be sedately still while dancing.

Even when he spun her round his head twisted to one
side to keep her eyes locked to his, making her
continually conscious of what he wanted of her.

It was agony. And ecstasy.

Heaven. And hell.

She was sure people were watching them, sure they
could see the interplay between them. But with each
passing round, each nerve-shattering contact, she
gradually ceased to care.

In the end the crowd and the other dancers receded
totally from her conscious mind. It was all Stephen,

Stephen, Stephen. Rhea knew she was looking back at him with an equally hungry gaze, but she didn't care, she didn't care. She was too aroused, too besotted with those tempting grey eyes, that tantalisingly virile male body, to appreciate the disastrous depth of her susceptibility.

Even before the music died, he was sweeping her outside the hall, drawing her into the shadows of the trees, pressing the heated length of her against a tree-trunk, holding her shoulders captive, bending his lips to hers.

Why she turned her face away at the last moment, she didn't know. It wasn't because she was resisting him—she was past that. It was just one of those instinctive gestures.

His lips landed on her neck. He groaned, then sucked at her flesh with a primitive, almost ravenous ferocity. A sob of naked desire caught in Rhea's throat.

His hands were already moving over her body, tracing the lush curves, making her shiver uncontrollably. 'I thought you didn't like to be touched,' he growled deep in his throat. And with slow deliberation he leant against her, moulding his aroused body to hers, rubbing himself against her. Her breathing grew more ragged. Her skin felt seared.

'You're a witch, do you know that?' he breathed huskily. 'A teasing, tormenting witch.'

His fingers intertwined with hers and he slowly wound her hands back, back, till they were pressed against the bark behind her, with no leverage to escape his physical domination of her.

Not that she wanted to. Her whole body was like a

furnace, burning for him.

'Kiss me, Rhea. Kiss me . . .'

Why did he ask? He took her mouth without waiting, expecting no further opposition. So he was taken aback to find her lips pressed sedately shut.

'Don't play any more games with me, for God's sake.' His voice was thick with passion. 'Open your mouth!'

Rhea blinked up at him, for she had never ever kissed with her mouth open before. She had asked Milan about it once, having read about it several times in books. But he had told her that was the way sluts kissed, and men didn't want their wives kissing like that.

Stephen released one of her hands, bringing his own up to run a finger over her mouth, at first encircling the shape, then rubbing along the line between her lips. Quite involuntarily her tongue tip moved to meet it.

'Yes,' he groaned. 'Like that . . . That's what I want . . .'

This time when his head bent Rhea was more than ready to give him exactly what he wanted. And more . . .

Her lips parted willingly, hungrily, the invasion of his tongue kindling a passion in her which till now she had only suspected lay inside her. Somehow her hands found their way around his neck, her fingers twisting into the thick black curls as she pulled him down to her, wanting him closer and closer, his tongue deeper and deeper.

A more experienced woman would have realised how far she was inviting him to go. His legs pushed between her thighs, his hands sliding down to cup her buttocks. In the deep state of her arousal she welcomed the feel of his hardness against her and without thinking she began to move wantonly against him. She was in another world, a world of heated flesh, and pulsating places.

The sound of nearby laughter catapulted her back to reality. 'Some people just can't wait, eh?' came the hideously truthful comment.

Rhea jerked upright, her action bringing a gasp of pain from Stephen.

'What the . . .?' Then he too heard the laughter. He swore softly under his breath before dragging in and expelling a single shuddering breath. 'They can't see us properly, you know,' he muttered, and drew her deeper into the shadows.

Rhea made a sound which must have shown how distressed she was, for he gathered her quickly into the deep haven of his arms, rocking her gently. 'Hush, darling, hush!' he whispered.

She was not crying, but she was trembling, so much so that her teeth were rattling.

'There, there,' he soothed with his incredible gentleness. 'Don't let those oafs bother you. So we got a little carried away . . .'

Rhea groaned.

'Hey!' He gave her a little shake. 'It's nothing to be ashamed of, you know.'

'Isn't it?' There was a wealth of misery in the words. For with the cooling of passion had come shame. She had vowed not to become involved with this man, but a clever smile, a sexy dance, and she'd been his for the taking. She was disgusted with herself!

Stephen pulled back and held her at arm's length,

gazing at her in the dim light with darkly troubled eyes. 'No, definitely not! Embarrassing perhaps to be interrupted publicly, but not shameful.'

'Maybe not for you,' she threw at him, face flushed, eyes tormented. 'You're probably used to doing things anywhere with anyone, but I . . . I'm . . . Oh, God!' She wrenched away from him, cradling her heated cheeks with shaking hands.

'Rhea . . .'

He went to take her in his arms again, but she fought him off in a panic. To have him touch her again would be inviting disaster. She closed her eyes and shuddered.

'You're acting like a little goose,' Stephen reproved, impatience in his voice. 'I agree that this is hardly the most appropriate place to attempt to assuage our mutual passion, but we didn't go through with it, so it's not the end of the world!'

Rhea's eyes flew open to stare at him, her mind awash with the implications of his coldly insensitive speech. And she had thought he might care for her! 'My God, but you are a bastard!' she rasped.

His hands shot out to close around her arms and he yanked her against his chest, grey eyes lancing her with the icy steel of anger. 'If I were the bastard you've always thought me, I would have had you long ago!'

'Why, you . . . you——'

'Don't bother with the insults,' he interrupted savagely. 'You know and I know that this . . . *attraction* . . . has been between us from the start, even when you were playing your little games. Though why you bothered, I don't know. Your having a husband wouldn't have kept a bastard at bay, would it?'

She groaned and tried to escape, but he held her fast, pushing her back up against the tree. 'I want you, Rhea,' he muttered thickly. He cradled her face in his hands, taking her mouth in a hard, hungry kiss. 'Hate me all you like, but you're going to let me make love to you one day. It's as inevitable as the day dawning!'

She opened her mouth to deny it, to argue, but he took her lips again, this time using every masterful technique of erotic persuasion his experience possessed.

It was hardly fair, with Rhea already in an advanced state of arousal. She tried to fight him, tried to resist, but it was useless and he sensed it. 'Rhea, Rhea, don't fight me . . . Just kiss me! Kiss me . . .'

And she did—madly, resignedly, desperately.

'Oh, darling, darling,' Stephen murmured against her swollen mouth. 'You want me too, don't you?'

A tiny tortured sound fluttered from her lips. Why did he need words from her when every vestige of her body was showing him her complete vulnerability? It was there in the way she was clinging to him, the way her body was afire for his touch.

A shiver raced up her spine.

'Don't be afraid of me, Rhea,' he whispered huskily. 'I won't hurt you, I promise . . . We'll take everything very slowly. All I want for now is to make love to you. All you have to do is let me . . .'

Rhea closed her eyes against his chest. She could hear his heart beating, as crazily and as loudly as her own. Perhaps she could have fought her own desire, but not his as well. It was like the ultimate drug, knowing that he wanted her with such intensity.

'Come out with me tomorrow night,' he urged.

'I can't!' she gasped, unable to cope with such immediacy.

'Why not?'

Why not? Why not? Her mind blurred till it grasped the first excuse she could think of. 'Emily . . .'

'. . . can sleep over with Laura,' he finished persuasively. 'Maisie will look after them.'

He tipped up her chin and looked her straight in the eye. 'I can't go on like this, Rhea,' he said fiercely. 'I want you so badly I ache all over. Say you'll be with me.'

'I . . . I . . .'

'Say it!'

'All right,' she gasped.

A light gleamed in his eyes and he drew her to him, his hands stroking her back. 'You won't regret it, darling,' he whispered, his lips in her hair. 'Never. Ever. It's going to be wonderful between us. Wonderful.'

Wonderful . . .

Full of wonder . . .

Rhea laid her dazed head against Stephen's chest, her brain indeed full of wonder. Was this all real? Was it happening to her? Had she really just said yes?

One part of her mind implored her to think again, to find a way to back out. The other had more insidious thoughts.

You want this man, Rhea. Want him in a way you have never known before. Why shouldn't you have him? Why shouldn't you experience, at least once, the pleasure, the satisfaction, he can give you? What harm could come of it?

It was a reasonable and very tempting line of

thinking, and one which she yearned to embrace. But somewhere at the back of her mind she knew that there was harm in it. For her.

'What is it?' Stephen murmured. 'You keep shivering. Are you cold?'

She shook her head with a deep shudder, hating herself for her weakness, but when he pulled back and stroked her cheek with a gentle hand any idea of potential danger went from her mind. It felt right when he touched her—more than right. It felt incredible.

He bent to kiss her again, softly this time, but even more seductively. 'I don't know how I'll be able to wait,' came his husky whisper when they finally drew apart. 'Tell me again you want me. Give me something to remember, to make the next twenty-four hours bearable.'

'I want you, Stephen,' she said shakily, nestling her face under his chin.

'I want you,' she repeated as her lips grazed his neck. 'Oh, how I want you!'

CHAPTER TEN

RHEA was awakened the next morning by her telephone ringing. She dragged herself out of bed, making it all the way down the hall before she remembered what had transpired at the dance.

She stopped dead in her tracks, at once appalled and incredulous as the vivid memories of her behaviour hit her. How could she have been so . . . so . . .? She must have been mad!

Visions of people staring at them when Stephen took her back into the hall made her cringe. She had been sure they all knew what they'd been doing. Sure!

Yet Stephen had carried himself off with such panache, smiling at everyone, drawing the raffle with a laugh, even flirting with a speechless Betty when she came up to accept the prize. *He* didn't feel embarrassed in the slightest. Oh, no, why should he? He was on familiar territory, seducing females probably being second nature to him.

What had he said to her in the shadows? All he wanted to do was make love to her . . . No mention of anything else, such as, 'You're special, Rhea, I like you, I could fall in love with you.' Heck, no! Just, 'All I want for now is to make love to you.' No promises, no commitment. Nothing more than a brief encounter!

And what had *she* done?

Wrapped herself around him like a clinging vine, confessing how much she wanted him, without pride or shame or the slightest reservation.

The sound of the phone's insistent ringing brought her self-reproach to a swift end. With a groan Rhea raced into the kitchen. It would be her mother ringing to check up on her. If only she knew!

Her hand hovered about the receiver as she pulled herself together, resolving with a quiet desperation not to let her panic show through in her voice. She was a grown woman now and had to stand on her own two feet, not let someone else bear the burden of her follies.

'Hi,' she breezed into the receiver.

'You sound happy this morning,' Stephen answered.

'Oh . . .' Her chest tightened, her thoughts instantly jumbled.

'I gather it wasn't me you were expecting,' he said, dry amusement in his voice.

'No, I . . . er . . . I . . .' Irritation at her bumbling firmed her voice. 'I thought you were my mother,' she stated with gritted jaw.

He laughed. 'Sorry. Lover here, not mother.'

Rhea almost curled up with embarrassment at the ease of his flirtatious banter. But she was determined to extricate herself from this unthinkable situation. It staggered her that she had put herself into it in the first place.

'Stephen, I'm glad you rang,' she began, nerves making her sound aggressive.

'No!'

She swallowed. 'No what?'

'No backing out. No cold feet. No! I want you, Rhea, more than I've ever wanted any woman. Now either you lied to me again last night or you want me just as much. Which is it?' he snarled.

Oh, God! Her head was pounding, whirling.

Stop fooling yourself! an inner voice dictated. Sooner or later you'll see him again, and this mad desire will take possession once more. Wanting him won't go away. It's like a sickness, an obsession. Say yes, Rhea, the crazy voice urged. Go to bed with him! Maybe it will burn itself out and you'll be able to get your life on an even keel once more.

'I won't let you, you know,' Stephen went on in a low, dangerous voice.

'Won't let me?' she gasped.

'Do this to yourself as well as me. You're coming out with me tonight if I have to come over there and drag you out by the hair!'

Rhea took a startled breath, the implacable force of Stephen's intent sweeping away all her wafflings, replacing them with an insidious excitement. She felt like a butterfly caught in a net after its last struggles for freedom had died. She was waiting, breathless with anticipation, for her fate.

'Rhea?'

'Yes?'

'I trust I won't have to do that.'

'No . . .'

There was a brief silence between them, the passing seconds charged with a crackling tension.

'Where . . . where are you taking me?' she asked at last.

'I have a place in town.'

So . . . There was to be no pretence of anything else. No romantic dinner first. Just straight down to business. The thought should have chilled Rhea. Instead, it aroused her — horribly so.

'I thought we'd have a couple of drinks there first,' Stephen went on briskly, 'then catch a taxi to a restaurant for dinner. Is that OK with you?'

A niggling thought insinuated that she had jumped to the wrong conclusion about him. Again. 'Yes . . . yes, that's all right.'

'You don't sound so sure.'

She could hardly tell him she didn't know what she thought or wanted any more. Except him.

She heard him sigh. 'I'll pick you up at six,' he pronounced, and hung up.

'Gosh, you look fantastic, Mum!' Emily exclaimed.

Rhea smiled tightly at her daughter, her nerves at breaking-point as the clock struck six. 'I'm glad you think so, love.'

'Laura's father is going to flip!'

Rhea had to admit she did look good, the troublesome red top suiting her, the slightly irregular neckline not even noticeable on her full-breasted figure. Though thank heaven Betty wasn't around to comment on the amount of cleavage on display, this time definitely with no bra!

'The black trousers turned out great, didn't they?' Emily complimented. 'Just as well you didn't have to play at a wedding today!'

Rhea agreed, having spent all afternoon making the trousers from a piece of black silk she owned. She had given the simple pull-on style a more elegant line by tapering the legs at the ankles.

'I'm glad you didn't put your hair up,' Emily went on gaily. 'You look ten years younger with it out like that.'

'Oh, thank you very much,' laughed Rhea, clutching

at any distraction. 'How old do I normally look?'

Emily grinned. 'About twenty-five.'

'And now I look fifteen?'

Emily giggled. 'Heavens, no! Oh, listen, I think I can hear Mr Chase's car coming. Gosh, I just can't wait! This is so exciting, my sleeping over and your going out with Laura's father. Maybe you and he will——'

'Go and get your bag, Emily,' Rhea cut in firmly. 'We don't want to keep Mr Chase waiting, do we?'

'Gosh, no!'

She raced off and Rhea closed her eyes. Her stomach was churning dreadfully, her heart galloping.

One of the dogs started barking as a car definitely turned into her drive.

'Oh, by the way, Mum,' said Emily on her return, 'I couldn't find Bobby and Dolly earlier when I went to feed them, so I put food into their kennel, is that OK?'

'What? Oh, yes, that's fine.'

'The chooks are away, so it doesn't matter if the dogs aren't locked up,' Emily went on.

Rhea frowned at her daughter, not really hearing anything. She was listening for Stephen's footsteps, yet when his knock came she almost jumped out of her skin.

Gathering herself, she walked across and opened the door.

There was only one way to describe how he looked to her. Breathtaking! Dressed in tailored black trousers, a smoke-grey silk shirt and a black leather jacket, he looked like every woman's dream come true.

'Hello,' she breathed, her eyes lifting to his face, tracing over the classically chiselled features, marvelling again at the way Mother Nature had fashioned each perfect bone.

She stood there staring at him for some moments before realising that *he* was metaphorically devouring *her*. Rhea's pulse-rate soared as she saw his admiration. 'You look ... fantastic,' he murmured. 'And smell divine.'

A wave of pleasure flooded her at his having noticed her perfume, recklessly bought with money she had put aside for a special emergency. Ironic, she conceded nervously, that her first affair was considered an emergency!

Stephen grinned at Emily over Rhea's shoulder. 'Got your night things, gorgeous Gussie?'

'Sure have!'

'Come on, then. Laura will murder me if I don't have you back there pronto. She gave me five minutes.'

They made it in record time, Rhea waiting in the car while Stephen deposited Emily and her things in the house with Laura and Mrs King. *His* idea, not hers.

'I know what mothers like you are like,' he had laughingly told her as he got out of the car. 'You spend half an hour with a whole list of dos and don'ts and spoil the kids' fun. Maisie will keep them in line, never fear. I have three strict rules for Laura when I go out of an evening. No going outside, no cheek and to bed by ten-thirty, OK?'

Rhea had nodded, aware that for once her thoughts were not for her daughter or anyone else. Selfish it might be of her, she acknowledged, but tonight was hers!

But as she waited in the car, her apprehension over the evening ahead grew. Would it turn out as she had fantasised, as Stephen had promised? Would he find her gauche and unsophisticated? Would she make an utter fool of herself?

But, more to the point, where would it all end? She had not forgotten his other women. Not by a long shot.

By the time Stephen finally reappeared on the front porch, stopping briefly to lock up, her throat was dry, her hands twisting agitatedly in her lap. With a sickening churning in her stomach she watched him practically skip down the steps, whistling as he opened the door and slid in behind the wheel.

He darted her a quick glance and stopped whistling. 'You look petrified!' he pronounced, but before she could say anything he leant across and kissed her, with shocking intimacy. 'See?' He smiled into her stunned face. 'Nothing to be frightened of. I won't eat you. Well . . .' a wicked glint flashed into those beautiful grey eyes '. . . not literally'.

Rhea's blush was automatic.

Suddenly his face was serious, with a tender yearning lighting his eyes. 'I love it when you do that,' he murmured thickly, reaching out to smooth a cool hand down her heated cheek. 'You are one special lady, Rhea Petrovic, do you know that?'

She couldn't say a word, her whole being concentrating on the way his fingers were now sliding down her throat. His eyes dropped to the rapid rise and fall of her breasts before lifting to caress her face once more. Her lips had parted slightly in an effort to gain more breath for her burning lungs, her own eyes plummeting the depths of his with an insatiable yearning.

'Hell,' he muttered, snatching his hand away from where it had almost reached her breast. He sat up straight, a returning glance half reproaching her. 'If you keep looking at me like that, woman, we won't make it out of the driveway, let alone all the way into the city!'

'Oh!' Her hands automatically flew up to cover her face.

'Hey,' Stephen drew them down, forcing her to look at him again, 'none of that, now! I was only joking. I really like the way you look at me.'

'Oh, God . . .' Rhea was all afluster, her mind revolving with a mixture of embarrassment and insecurity.

'I'm well aware, Rhea,' he said gently, 'that you don't make a habit of doing this. But please . . .' his hand returned to touch her face, tracing down her cheek and around her lips '. . . do me a favour. No more guilt, eh? It's hardly flattering to me, you know. And it's not necessary. The way you feel is perfectly natural, perfectly normal, and not in any way shameful!'

With one last reproachful glance, he fired the engine and accelerated away, leaving Rhea to stare dazedly out of the passenger window, her nerves only slightly soothed.

They had reached the freeway and been driving for quite some time before Stephen spoke again. 'Tell me about your marriage,' he asked carefully.

She glanced over at him. 'What . . . what about it?'

'Where you happy?'

Rhea was never comfortable with a deliberate lie. 'I thought so . . . at the time.'

He darted a frowning look her away. 'And now you don't?'

She frowned. 'It could have been happier.'

'In what way?'

Rhea bit her bottom lip. She really didn't want to talk about her marriage. Or Milan. She still felt upset by her recent discoveries, still felt guilty that she had married

Milan for all the wrong reasons. He had not been a bad man, and had probably deserved better than his child bride.

'I was very young when I married,' she hedged. 'Just turned eighteen and barely out of school. My husband was a good deal older . . .'

'How much older?'

'Thirty-one.'

'And your parents were happy to let you marry him at such a tender age?'

Of course they hadn't been happy—Rhea could see that now. But she had insisted, like the stubborn adolescent she was.

'My father was dead by then,' she said, 'and Mum had married again. I think she was reasonably pleased to see me settled. I . . . wasn't getting along too well with my stepfather at the time.'

'Hmm. Always a tricky situation, that, a stepfather and daughter. Needs a lot of patience and understanding, I would think.'

Rhea sighed. 'Yes. And I wasn't an easy child to live with, I'm afraid. Bill was really very good to me. I've only just realised how much . . .' Her voice trailed away, tears of regret pricking her eyes as the thought of all the times her stepfather had tried to reach her. In the end he had resorted to buying her things. A stereo, then the organ—and lessons—not to mention piles of books and clothes. If only she could go back and undo some of things she had said . . .

'Hey, they aren't tears, are they?'

They had stopped at the lights at the end of the freeway and Stephen reached over to tip her face towards him. 'I'm sorry, Rhea, I didn't mean to make you cry. Was it that bad? Your childhood?'

'No,' she whispered, his fleeting touch sending her mind back to why she was here, in this car, at this moment.

'Let me kiss you better,' he murmured, leaning over to brush his lips lightly against hers.

Her hand came up tremblingly to touch the side of his jaw, to keep him there. But he drew back, taking the hand with him and pressing her fingertips to his mouth, all the while holding her with darkly hooded eyes. 'You must put them behind you, Rhea,' he said softly. 'Your childhood, your marriage. You're a woman now, a beautiful, desirable woman . . . Live your life as you see it, without fear, without any shackles from the past.'

The blaring of horns told them the lights had gone green, but Stephen did not hurry. He gave her a last, lingering look before dropping her dazed hand and turning his attention to the road ahead.

Neither of them said another word till they reached the inner city and he turned the car sharply to drop into an underground car park.

Rhea glanced around in confusion. 'But aren't we right in the middle of the city? Isn't this an office block?'

'It surely is,' Stephen smiled as he drew to a halt in a reserved parking space. 'Mine . . . I had the top floor converted into an apartment. Come on.'

He gallantly helped her out of the low-slung car and led her over to a bank of lifts. He inserted a key into a lock under a sign that said 'Penthouse Suite' and the doors whooshed open, shutting silently behind them after they entered.

Rhea was too uptight to make any comment,

especially as it was obvious that it was a private lift, reserved for the owner of the building. She threw Stephen a troubled glance. She knew he was wealthy, but somehow being confronted by such overwhelming evidence was undermining. He was way out of her league in so many ways.

'Problems?' he asked, startling her with the way he seemed in tune with her feelings.

'I . . . I . . . No . . .'

He was frowning now. 'Sure?'

Rhea dragged up a smile. 'Sure.'

The lift whisked to a halt, the doors shooting back to reveal another door. Again Stephen inserted a key. He threw open this door and ushered her inside. Rhea put her bag down on a hall table before letting Stephen take her hand and lead her down some marble steps into a sunken lounge-room. He deposited her on a black leather sofa before moving across to the bar.

'I think we could both use a drink,' he tossed over his shoulder. 'I'll mix up something potent.'

Rhea looked around the living area in a type of chilled awe. It was breathtakingly spacious, with white shag carpet, deep sofas, subtly piped music, dusky lighting and a spectacular view, not to mention the lavishly stocked bar. She wondered how many women had been bowled over with the sheer luxury of the place.

'I can see why you don't live here with Laura,' she remarked, unable to disguise her distaste at the visual scenes her mind was evoking.

Stephen looked up sharply from where he was mixing a couple of cocktails behind the bar. 'She stayed here for a month till we moved into the house.'

Rhea flinched. Surely he hadn't . . . Not while Laura was here . . .

'No, I didn't,' he grated out, walking towards her with the two drinks in his hands. 'My God, Rhea, must you always believe the worst of me?' He shoved her glass in her hand. 'I have never taken a woman to bed in front of Laura. Never!'

She stared up at him, shaken by his repeated readings of her mind. And his anger. 'I'm sorry,' she muttered. 'It's just that . . . well, this place is rather . . .'

'What?' His gaze swept around. 'Plush? Expensive? Why not? I've worked damned hard for what I've got. But it's no orgy palace. Maybe it's your narrow, prejudiced mind that sees it that way.'

A prickle ran up Rhea's spine as she saw him drain his drink in a single swallow. Everything seemed to be going wrong. 'Stephen, I'm sorry I——'

'If my lifestyle is so reprehensible,' he cut in in clipped tones, 'then why are you here with me, Rhea?' Why not find someone supposedly respectable to sleep with? Or does the idea of going to bed with a bad boy give you an extra kick?'

She clenched her glass defensively, the blunt thrust of his words cutting her to the quick. 'That's a rotten thing to say!' she rasped.

'Why? It's the truth, isn't it?' His laughter was bitter, his eyes angry. 'You can dish it out, Rhea, but can you take it? Go on, admit that all you want is for me to——'

She slapped him, hard, drowning out the crude words. 'I wish I didn't,' she choked out, hating herself and him.

Stephen rubbed his cheek and got to his feet. 'That's

becoming painfully obvious, my dear.'

He swung away, striding over to the bar to refill his glass, downing the drink with one gulp.

Rhea put her glass down and stood up. 'I . . . I want to go home.' Her voice sounded small, lost.

He turned slowly to face her. 'No.'

Her eyes rounded at him.

'Being a bastard, I couldn't possibly let you leave, Rhea.' He began walking leisurely towards her, his face chillingly cold. 'Certainly not without your expectations being fulfilled.'

Rhea was galvanised to the spot, apprehension and anticipation sending her mind into a chaotic whirl. She couldn't think, couldn't move. She watched him approach, somehow expecting him to grab her and kiss her, but he didn't. He stopped in front of her, his mocking gaze raking her body from top to toe before quite unexpectedly cupping her breasts with his hands.

'This *is* what you came here for, isn't it?' he derided, leisurely finding and playing with her nipples through the wool. 'Not for making love,' he went on caustically. 'Just this . . .!'

She swayed, squeezing her eyes shut against the flood of feeling that had erupted deep inside her. She knew she should knock his hands away, but she couldn't, she couldn't. It was insidious the way she wasn't able to resist. So she stood there, in her dark, erotic world, holding her breath, saying nothing, yet all the while expecting, waiting for the next barrage of insults.

But they didn't come.

When his hands dropped away her eyes fluttered open, only to find him standing there, his fists clenched tightly at his side. He looked furious. And desolate. 'I could kill you for doing this, do you know that?' he growled.

'Don't!' she choked out.

'Don't what?' he snarled.

Rhea didn't know. Her whole being was a mess. She still wanted him to take her, but she wanted something else too, something so unattainable she dared not speak of it. She looked up at him with tortured eyes. 'Don't be angry with me!'

His eyes locked harshly on to hers and suddenly, the anger drained from him, his shoulders slumping.

She moved forward, sliding her hands underneath his jacket and over his chest. 'I don't really think you're a bastard,' she said softly. This time it was *her* hand lifting to *his* mouth, *her* fingers tracing *his* lips. 'I want you, Stephen,' she urged. 'I want you now — quickly!'

He groaned, grasping her brutally by the shoulders as though he was going to push her away. Instead he dragged her against him, claiming her mouth in a kiss that was so unlike him. It was brutal and savage and wild. It punished and ravaged and obliterated till Rhea was left limp and drained.

When he pushed her back across the sofa, stripping off her black trousers with a vicious yank, she was too stunned to resist. She lay there watching dazedly as he stood over her, his hands fumbling with his belt.

Suddenly he stopped.

'What . . . what is it?' she gasped.

He groaned and turned away from her, staggering over to lean shaking against the bar. 'Get dressed,' he ordered thickly.

'Dressed?'

'Yes, dammit! Straight away!'

'But . . . don't you want to . . . to . . .?'

'For pity's sake, of course I want to!' roared Stephen. 'Now get dressed!'

Rhea did as he asked, tears coming to her eyes, tears of confusion and dismay. Why had he stopped? Why?

He must be lying about having wanted to. Lying! No man would have voluntarily stopped at that point! She must have done something wrong, something to turn him off.

'I'm dressed,' she said in a little voice.

He turned and surveyed her, anger still in his face. 'Now, Rhea Petrovic,' he announced, 'we are going to go out and have some dinner. And then . . . *then* . . . we will come back here and *make love* . . . at my leisure. *Not* quickly, and *not* at your command! Do I make myself clear?'

'Yes, Stephen,' she said meekly, though waves of a delirious joy had rocketed through her veins at his forceful words. He still wanted her. He did. He did! It had been his male ego that had stopped him.

And if some other part of her inner self thrilled to his decision not to take her in anger, she brushed the feeling aside. Of course it was only his ego, she decided logically. What other reason could there be?

An exasperated smile smoothed the frustration from his face. 'What *am* I going to do with you?' he said, shaking his head as he propelled her from the room.

CHAPTER ELEVEN

'YOU'RE not eating.'

Rhea stopped fiddling with her fork. 'I don't seem to be very hungry.'

Stephen made am impatient sound. 'I bring you to an exclusive restaurant, order you lobster and you waste it!'

'You haven't eaten much yourself,' she pointed out.

He sighed and put down his cutlery. 'True.'

There was a brief awkward silence. 'Shall we go?' he asked.

She nodded, an acute shyness descending as she waited till he settled the account.

They hardly spoke during the short taxi ride back to the unit, even their meagre conversation drying up once they were in the lift.

'You've gone quiet,' Stephen remarked as the doors opened at the penthouse.

Quiet. And nervous. And totally lacking in confidence. It was one thing to be carried away with spontaneous passion, quite another, Rhea was discovering, to deliberately plan a night of intimacy.

'Sit down,' Stephen commanded once he had shepherded her inside and closed the door.

She sank into the large black sofa, watching nervously as Stephen moved behind the bar.

'This time tell me what you like,' he said, rather ambiguously.

Rhea gulped down the lump in her throat. 'Vodka and orange.' She had never had one before.

'Easy or heavy on the vodka?'

'What do you suggest?'

He lifted one eyebrow in a dry fashion. 'Heavy, by the look of you.'

She laughed, and it eased some of her tension. 'OK . . . heavy.'

He was very adept at the mixing of her drink, and she remembered how he had once said he was good at a lot of things. She believed him.

'Aren't you having anything?' she quizzed when he came over with only the one glass.

Stephen smiled, shaking his head as he handed the drink over and sat down next to her. 'Alcohol is a good relaxant for women,' he commented quite naturally, 'but a poor aphrodisiac for men.'

Rhea coloured.

'You blush beautifully,' he murmured, one of his arms sliding along the back of the sofa to play with the hair on her shoulders. 'But I've told you that, haven't I?'

She felt even hotter but lifted a defiant chin. 'I think you like to embarrass me.'

His eyes teased her. 'You could be right. I have to pay you back somehow.'

She frowned. 'Pay me back?'

He gave her the oddest look. It was both sardonic and sad, pricking at her conscience. Though why, she didn't know. Men like Stephen Chase were invulnerable.

Rhea lifted the drink to her lips, holding his gaze over the rim of the glass, reminding herself every time her heart lurched of all the women he had used and discarded over the years.

'Sometimes I wonder what goes on in that pretty little

head of yours,' he said.

She gave another nervous laugh. 'You seem to be able to read my mind very well!'

'Only in some matters.'

'And what am I thinking now?' she challenged, taking several more sips of the potent drink.

'God only knows ... Women's minds can be the ultimate mystery. They often say one thing and mean another.'

'Is that why you've never married one?' she asked, and took a bigger swallow.

'Not at all,' Stephen answered with a laugh. 'I adore female company, but I realised quite early on that I couldn't work the hours I did and keep a family happy at the same time. It was as simple as that.'

She took another sip, trying to control a surge of irritation at the offhandedness of his reply. 'Did you come to this *simple* decision before or after you met Laura's mother?' came her caustic query. 'Maybe she didn't tell you she was pregnant because she knew your feelings on the subject of marriage and family.'

He stared at her for a moment, then leant over and lifted the glass from her hand. 'I think perhaps we'll dispense with this,' he muttered, putting it down on a side-table with a thump. 'You seem to be one of those aggressive drinkers.'

'Don't be ridic——'

'Hush!' he whispered, placing three fingers against her lips. 'Don't spoil things.' The fingers moved lightly over her lips, then down to her throat.

Rhea was instantly spellbound, any annoyance dissolving as she became caught up in the shivery feelings his feathery touch was producing. He traced the neckline of her top, making her gasp when he dipped into the valley between her breasts. The thought that he was going to touch her breasts, to stroke and fondle them, had her holding her breath in dizzy expectation, but instead that tantalising hand reached up to brush her hair back on one side.

'Lovely hair . . . Lovely ear . . .' Even now a fingertip was encircling its outer shell, breaking her skin out into goose-bumps.

'Stop it!' she shuddered, but made no attempt to strike his hand away.

'Why?' The grey eyes mocked her.

'Because . . .'

'Come now, you like it. You don't really want me to stop, do you?' Stephen leant forward to replace his fingers with his mouth. 'Do you?' he breathed into the ear.

'No,' she shivered.

He sat up straight, his face almost world-weary. 'Then close your eyes and enjoy it, Rhea. We haven't got all night.'

For a few appalled moments she could only stare at him, his attitude throwing her, but then her eyes were closing and he was tipping her back till her head rested against the soft sofa. She sensed rather than saw his face loom over hers, her whole body stiff with anticipation.

'When I kiss you,' he murmured against her lips, 'I want you to relax. Give yourself up to me—totally.'

She made some sort of sound, like the quivering cry of a frightened animal.

'Relax, Rhea . . .'

His lips were so soft on hers she didn't realise they were there for a moment. But then they moved, sensuously, rubbing across hers in a side-to-side movement till her mouth tingled with sensitivity. 'So sweet,' he whispered. 'So incredibly sweet . . .'

Then it was his tongue moving over her lips, moistening them with warm licking movements, sending hot jabs of sensation darting through her brain. She groaned when he drew back slightly, the air cooling her heated lips, making her even more aware of their pouting swollen state.

But his desertion was only brief. This time the kiss was deeper, his tongue penetrating into her mouth, sliding down beside hers into the warm depths. Rhea's body leapt in response, blood racing in heated cirles in her head. Her shoulders lifted from the sofa as she strained to be closer to him, for while their mouths were fused, no other part of their bodies were touching. She wanted—no, *needed*—more physical contact.

Unexpectedly, one of his hands slid up under her top, capturing a single breast, the weight of his possession pushing her back. She gasped with delight and shock, shivers running up and down her spine as his hand moved, stroking the tip into a taut tight bud of bursting sensation.

Her heart seemed to suspend its beat in her chest till in the end she grew light-headed from lack of air. She tried to twist her head away, but in vain, for his other hand had moved to firmly cup the back of her head, keeping her mouth captive beneath his.

The kiss went on and on, the hand on her breast arousing her still further with its sensuous explorations till a swirling blackness hovered at the edges of her mind.

Finally, terrified she might lose consciousness, she burst from his mouth. 'Stephen!' she gasped.

'Yes?'

She was shocked by the coolness in his voice, the complete control he appeared to have over his emotions.

'I . . . I . . .'

He cupped her face with steady hands. 'You what?' he murmured, his annoyingly passive gaze searching hers.

'Oh, God,' she moaned, knowing that she was definitely out of her depth here, with this man. The butterfly had been well and truly pinned.

'Let me take this off,' he suggested, plucking casually at one of the sleeves of her top.

'No!'

He reproached her silently with a look.

A surge of rebellious anger sent her sitting upright, whipping the scarlet top over her head and flinging it to the floor. 'Satisfied?' she threw at him.

Lazy grey eyes flicked over the full, rosy-tipped curves. 'Infinitely,' he drawled, and his head began to descend.

She watched, astonished, fascinated, as his mouth drew closer, holding her breath in an agony of apprehension and anticipation. When the parted lips closed over one aching point, the breath was punched from her body. Her chest heaved, grew still, then heaved again as she dragged in several gasping, life-saving breaths.

'Don't . . . Oh, don't!' she whimpered, barely able to stand the pleasure-pain of his attentions. But he went on, tugging a nipple into his mouth, nipping it gently with his teeth, licking it with his tongue, then releasing it to the sting of the air before beginning again.

Rhea's head dropped back on to the sofa, her mouth falling open, her eyes wildly dilated. Her flesh pulsated, ached, pleaded to be soothed and stroked.

Only gradually did she realise that the pleading was not silent. 'Oh, please . . . Stephen, please!' she begged in a voice she scarcely recognised.

Suddenly she was abandoned, her glazed eyes opening to find him standing up looking down at her. Still, amazingly, he seemed unaffected. 'I want you to undress me,' he said, the thick harshness of his voice betraying that perhaps his composure was a sham, that to appear calm he was actually exercising an enormous control over himself.

Trembling, Rhea pulled herself upright, then stood up, her face flaming as she remembered her semi-nakedness. 'Right here?' she rasped. 'With . . . with the light on?'

'Yes.'

An unnerving panic at her own lack of experience made her hesitate, but he waited patiently, watching her through half-closed eyes. Finally her hands lifted, shaking as she pushed the leather jacket from his shoulders, unable to catch it as it fell to the floor.

'Leave it!' he growled.

Then, with tremulous fingers, she started on the buttons of his shirt. All the time he was staring at her, holding her with that sensuous, hooded gaze.

She stopped at the last button, loath to proceed, to expose his magnificent male chest. For he *was* magnificent, a perfect specimen of masculine symmetry, broad where necessary, tapering down to a lean, tight hardness.

It had been one of her fantasies, to have him invite her touch. Yet now it was all too frighteningly real. She wasn't sure how she would react or cope once she let her hands loose on him.

'Something wrong?' he muttered.

'No . . . It's just that . . .'

'Don't you want to touch me?' Cynical eyes taunted her. 'Is this another of your little games, Rhea?'

A surge of anger exploded inside her head and she ripped the shirt asunder, paling afterwards at the shock of what she had done. But he only laughed, a low, sexy sound, shrugging off the torn garment and throwing it aside.

'I often wondered what you were hiding behind that prim exterior of yours, my lovely Rhea. Now I know,' He snatched up her hands, spreading her palms against his chest, holding her wrists. 'Touch me, Rhea . . . touch me properly,' he demanded, the fever in his eyes at last reassuring her that he was as aroused as she was.

She gazed back at him, wanting to explore him oh, so badly, but still feeling awkward, foolish.

'Like this . . .' He moved her hands over his skin, down across his ribcage, then back up through the soft curls in the centre of his chest.

His hands dropped away, but his half-closed eyes held her, their smoky sensuality inviting her, exciting her.

Her fingers moved, slowly, tentatively, tracing across his male muscles like a sculptor lovingly modelling clay. How smooth he felt, smooth and warm and strong, like corded velvet wrapped around steel.

She grew bolder, moulding the muscles as she went, feeling and kneading with a growing sense of awe at the way he was responding to her touch. His breathing had quickened into deep ragged bursts. His eyes flashed with incandescent lights whenever her palms inadvertently grazed across his male nipples.

'Enough!' he barked at last, yanking her roughly against him, rubbing her naked breasts against him with vigorous, tortured movements. Then abruptly he swept her up into his arms, striding into the bedroom, where he dropped her on a king-sized bed, yanking off her shoes, then stripping her totally naked.

'The light!' she gasped, her face turning away as he stared down at her spread-eagled nudity.

Again he laughed. 'I want to see you, Rhea. All of you!'

She lay there, riveted by his smouldering gaze, watching breathlessly as he began to undo his belt. But despite her arousal, despite her desperate longing for him, she was horribly nervous. What if it was a disaster, after all? What if they were both left disappointed?

'Stephen, I . . .' She stopped as he unzipped, then stepped out of his trousers. 'I . . .' Any protest died in her throat as he discarded his underpants.

'It's . . . been a long time,' she whispered hoarsely at last.

He joined her on the bed, leaning over her to kiss her with tender understanding. 'I know,' he murmured.

'But I have to tell you, I'm not . . .' she turned her face to one side '. . . not very good at this.'

He turned her face back with a gentle hand, making her look up at him. 'Who on earth told you that?' he soothed. 'My God, Rhea, you're the most responsive, the most sensual woman I've ever known!' He ran a fingertip lightly over one breast, making her quiver with pleasure. 'See?'

All she could see was that it was *his* skill, not hers. 'I

. . . I'm not usually like this.' She shivered. 'You make me feel things, Stephen. You . . . Oh!' she moaned as he began to lazily encircle her nipple. 'Don't . . .'

He stopped, bringing a wide-eyed pleading glance from Rhea. Of course she hadn't really meant him to stop. It was just that the intense feelings his touch produced sometimes frightened her.

There was something oddly sad in his smile. 'You really must stop doing that—saying no when you mean yes.'

'But I——'

He placed a restraining finger on her lips. 'Hush! I understand—really I do. Better than you think. It's just that . . . Oh, hell, I might as well be noble just this once . . .'

His kiss was heartbreakingly tender, tasting her lips, tempting her with the withholding of his tongue till she whimpered, opening her mouth wider, sending her own tongue forward to invite his. He complied with a hoarse moan.

Time after time, Rhea's senses were to be shocked, then soothed, excited and extended. Stephen kissed her where she had never been kissed before, touched and explored with a bold breathless intimacy that left her quivering with expectation and wonder. Nothing he did to her seemed wrong. Nothing. He gave her pleasure such as she had never experienced, or even fantasised about, gave and gave and gave till she was teetering on an unknown brink, gripped by an unbearable tension that demanded a release that till now had remained a mystery to her.

She began to tremble, to cry, to feel helpless,

hopeless, frightened.

He stopped.

Her groan carried anguish, and sheer frustration.

He stroked her face. 'Soon, darling, soon,' he murmured, holding and caressing her till her breathing steadied and she lay pliant and relaxed in his arms. Then quietly, with an incredible gentleness, he moved over her, filling her with his strong, awe-inspiring virility, taking her breath away.

'Oh, Stephen!' she sighed.

Wonderful, he had said it would be. Rhea would have chosen another word: overwhelming.

It overwhelmed her. *He* overwhelmed her, slowly at first, then surging powerfully till every nerve-ending in her body was throbbing with an unbelievable pleasure. Swiftly and silently she soared, higher and higher than before, heart beating, head whirling, on and on till with a burst of bliss everything shattered around her and she was catapulted headlong into another dimension. And while she was still being consumed by this incredible ecstasy, she heard him cry out, felt his shuddering climax.

Then she was clinging to him, holding him tight, telling him he was wonderful, confessing that she had never felt anything like that before. Never! All the while trying to stop the tears from coming.

And if, in the deepest corners of her soul, that secret wish stirred again, she tried to ignore it, steadfastly telling herself that she had gone into this with her eyes open, and not to expect more than was offered. Sex was all there would be with a man like Stephen. He would never offer more.

He sighed, lifting his head from her breasts to look at

her briefly, then he sank back down, his lips grazing a still sensitised point. She shuddered.

'Don't move,' he commanded softly. 'I need to rest for a few minutes.'

Rhea closed her eyes, willing herself not to think or worry, but to just lie there and enjoy the feeling of the moment, the way her body was floating down, down, relaxing, melting. Contentment was spreading, as was an insidious desire to sleep. Eventually she sighed, her body shifting slightly under his.

'Hush, my darling,' he murmured. 'Hush now. Go to sleep—rest. It's over.' And he pulled the quilt around them, the warmth embracing her, his hands and voice calming her till she was lying still and silent.

Rest, she told herself. Rest . . .

But she couldn't rest, couldn't sleep. She lay there, eyes wide, listening as Stephen's breathing gradually became deep and even, his arms heavy upon her. The tears had dried on her cheeks, but her soul was crying as it tried to come to terms with his last word.

Over . . . Over . . . Over . . .

She didn't want it to be over. She didn't want it *ever* to be over! She wanted Stephen now, even more than before. She wanted him in her heart as well as her body. She wanted him in her life, her thoughts, her every breath.

With a groan she turned her face into his chest, pressing her lips to his flesh. He stirred slightly, his arms instinctively moving around her, but remained asleep.

'Oh, Stephen,' she cried softly in the dark, 'I've fallen in love with you . . . I have been all along. Whatever am I going to do?'

CHAPTER TWELVE

'RHEA!'

She shot awake with a gasp to find Stephen fully dressed standing over her, shaking her shoulder.

'It's almost seven,' he explained.

Her mouth gaped. 'Almost *seven*! Oh, heavens, why didn't you . . . ?' She went to jump up, remembered her naked state and groaned, clutching the quilt defensively. Panic at the situation crowded all other thoughts from her mind.

'Don't worry,' he went on, calmly seating himself on the edge of the bed. 'I rang Maisie and explained that we'd stayed in town rather than drive all the way home through the Saturday night traffic. She said the girls were still asleep, so I told her not to say anything about my not coming home, to let them think I was already up and down the road buying the Sunday papers if they awoke. Still, I think we'd better get a move on.'

Rhea had stared at him in appalled silence during this speech. The words came out so smoothly, the excuses sounding depressingly practised.

Which of course was perfectly understandable. 'Mornings after' were an everyday occurrence for him, not a once-in-a-lifetime happening. It brought home to her even more forcibly how stupid she was to have let herself fall in love with him.

Yet despite her dismay Rhea suddenly found herself looking at his mouth, his hands, his body. A telling heat spread through her as memories flooded her mind, and she bit her lip in shy embarrassment, dropping her eyes to the floor.

Stephen sighed, and got to his feet. 'The en-suite's in there. Coffee and toast in ten minutes.'

The shower, the getting dressed, the hurried breakfast, the drive home, were all agony. Rhea couldn't bear to look at Stephen, let alone talk to him, so the time passed in a series of unbearable silences.

But she had to speak once they turned from the main highway on to the road that would lead to Bangaloo Creek.

'Please, Stephen,' she whispered in a tight, hoarse voice, 'don't roar down my street like you usually do. 'I . . . don't want . . .'

'. . . the neighbours to hear,' he finished for her, his words clipped and curt.

'Yes . . .' She hung her head, knowing he thought her an unsophisticated bore.

'I don't think they would really care, do you?' he said wearily. 'But I'll do my best not to embarrass you, Rhea. I also think it wise that we don't see each other again—at least not on a personal basis. I do realise we can hardly avoid each other completely.'

Her eyes flew to him, pain filling her face. 'But *why*?'

His sidewards glance was astonishingly bitter. 'Let's just say I don't fancy playing stud for a woman who doesn't like or respect me as a man.'

Rhea's mouth opened, then snapped shut. Playing stud? Was that how he saw last night? She struggled to see the evening from his point of view, finally conceding that it might have appeared she was using his body merely to service her needs. He wouldn't understand that she had pushed aside all her other feelings for him to focus on the sex, because she thought that was all she could have.

But she knew now that her feelings for him went far deeper than physical desire. And it wasn't true that she didn't like or respect him. She liked and admired him tremendously. She admired the way he had taken on his responsibility regarding Laura. She admired his intelligence and self-assurance. She certainly admired his capacity for being sensitive and gentle. If only she could explain that she had been overly critical about his bachelor lifestyle because she was falling in love with him, and wanted him to be different in his attitude towards women and marriage!

But how could she do that? He didn't love her back, and it would seem as if she was begging him to stay with her. He would probably accuse her of using emotional blackmail to get what she wanted from him. It reminded her of that phone call from Madeline . . .

Rhea groaned. Thinking of Madeline brought a rush of new thoughts. Perhaps Stephen's excuse for leaving his relationship with her at a one-night stand was just that—an excuse. Maybe he wanted to drop her because she'd disappointed him in bed. Maybe he liked his partners to be far more uninhibited, far more adventurous.

Rhea cringed as she thought he might have found her boring. She glanced across at him, but he wasn't looking at her. He was staring straight ahead, his jaw jutting forward with cold resolution.

A black pit yawned in her soul. It was useless, she realised. Useless . . . It *was* over.

Her eyes closed, tears hovering.

Stephen turned the car into her road very carefully, putting the gears into neutral and gliding silently down the hill, where he swung into her driveway, coming to a halt with only the barest noise. 'I'm afraid I might not be able to leave as quietly,' he muttered, 'but I'll do my best.'

Rhea turned her face away while she got the tears under control, the atmosphere one of strained silence.

'You'd better go inside,' he said at last, his tone brusque. 'I'll drop Emily off after lunch.'

'Thank you.' She went to open the door, her heart breaking, and suddenly she couldn't do it, couldn't let him go without telling him something of how she felt. 'Stephen, I——'

'For God's sake, Rhea,' he cut in brutally, 'don't make polite conversation now! Your silence this morning said more than enough, believe me.' He twisted to fully face her in the car, his expression one of controlled anger. 'Be honest, darling! You needed a man, probably have done for six years. I just happened to be the poor lad you finally chose to work out your frustrations on. Fair enough—I can accept that. Hell, I did, didn't I? But the least you could have done was look me in the eye this morning and say thank you, Stephen, I enjoyed it, Stephen, not slink out of my place as if you were a fallen woman!'

He leant across her, unsnapped her seatbelt and pushed open the door. 'Now be a good girl and run along. And next time, Rhea, find someone you actually *like* as your lover, then he won't mind coming back for seconds!'

Complete humiliation had her scrambling from the car and literally running up the path. As she fumbled with her key, she heard the car reverse out and drive off.

She stumbled inside, Stephen's crippling taunts whirling through her mind. Did he have to be so hard, so cruel? OK, so she had probably been wrong, selfishly taking the pleasure his body could give her because she knew that was all of him she would ever get. But did he have to throw her inexperience, her feelings of shame in her face?

With a sob, she slumped down in a chair at the kitchen table, her head falling into her hands as she burst into tears. 'Bastard!' she cried. 'Bastard . . .'

Bobby came into the kitchen and whimpered at her ankles till Rhea bent down and scratched his ears, the sobs slowly receding. 'Miss me?' she asked the dog.

Bobby sat and whimpered some more.

Something niggled at Rhea's memory and she sat upright, dashing the dampness from her cheeks. 'Where's Dolly?' she asked with a frown.

Another whimper.

Rhea stood up, a sickening sensation claiming her stomach. What was it Emily had said the night before? Something about the dogs not being there when she brought the food? That was not like them, particularly not like Dolly . . .

'Oh, no!' Rhea groaned, and was already up and running.

She dashed out to the kennel, fearing what she would find. But it was worse than she had imagined. Two tiny dead puppies lay in the straw, and Dolly . . . Dolly was lying with terrifying stillness in one corner.

Rhea crashed to her knees, her face white. 'Oh, please God, no, I couldn't bear it!' she gasped, trembling fingers running over the small bundle. Suddenly Dolly made a sound, opening her eyes and looking at Rhea with intolerable pain. Rhea rocked back, at once relieved yet distressed at witnessing such agony.

'It's all right, Dolly,' she soothed, stroking the now shivering animal with infinite tenderness. 'I'm here now, I'll get help—you'll be all right. Mummy's here . . .' She went to leave, but Dolly made a sound, a whimpering plea for the solace of her owner's presence. Yet Rhea knew she had to get a vet. And fast.

A decision had to be made. As slowly and as gently as she could, she scooped the dog up into her arms, carrying her into the house. There she wrapped her in a rug, holding her with one arm as she looked up the number and dialled the vet, the receiver tucked under her chin.

'Is the vet there? Oh, it's you, Margaret. It's Rhea Petrovic here . . . My dog's in trouble. She's having pups and a couple have been stillborn. She's in awful pain, and I wondered . . . He can't come? Operating . . . Bring the dog round. All right, I'm on my way.'

She hung up. It wasn't far, she reasoned, trying to keep herself calm. Only a couple of miles. It wouldn't take long . . .

She didn't bother to lock up, carrying the dog out to the old van and laying her gently on the front seat. Dolly was moaning softly, the sound cutting through Rhea's heart. She inserted the key with a trembling hand, all the while looking anxiously at the dog. She turned the ignition.

It wouldn't start. The rotten old thing wouldn't start!

Rhea could not believe it. Ancient it might be, but it usually started. This time it didn't.

She swore and thumped the wheel, trying the ignition again and again in panic until of course the battery was totally dead.

For a moment she couldn't think, her head sinking down on to the wheel. Then suddenly she grew aware that Dolly was not making any sound. She leant over and touched her, but there was no response. 'No!' she cried, sweeping the little dog up and racing inside, stumbling over a bewildered Bobby as she went. Desperate fingers found the right numbers as if by some miracle.

'Stephen Chase here.'

'Oh, Stephen,' she sobbed, her eyes awash, 'it's Dolly! She had her pups last night and she's . . . I think she's dying . . . I rang the vet, but . . . but he couldn't come . . . He's operating. He said to bring her, but the van wouldn't start . . . Oh, please come, Stephen! I need you . . .'

'I'll be right there.'

She found herself standing there, staring into the dead receiver. Only then did she realise what she had done. In her desperation and need she had automatically turned to the man she loved, the man she had just called a bastard.

And what had he done? He'd asked no questions, given no excuses, wasted no time. He was coming straight away, answering her plea without any thought of retaliation for the way he believed she had treated him.

Rhea frowned, baffled by his behaviour. Could she be terribly wrong about him? About everything?

Bobby whimpered at her feet, bringing her thoughts back to the little dog in her arms. 'Oh, Dolly,' she cried, 'you have to get well! You just have to!' And she went outside to wait for Stephen.

This time he made no attempt to arrive quietly. He roared down the road in an arrival reminiscent of his first, careering across the culvert of the driveway with no heed to life or limb.

Rhea ran up to the car. 'Don't get out.' She climbed in, throwing him a grateful look. 'It was good of you to come so quickly. In fact, it was good of you to come at all . . .'

His mouth thinned. 'You didn't think I'd let an innocent dog die, did you?' He glared at her. 'Perhaps you would,' he muttered, reversing out of the drive with a sudden burst. 'You don't have to give me directions—I know where the veterinary hospital is.'

They screeched off at a hair-raising speed, with Rhea grateful that there was little traffic early on a Sunday morning. 'Emily!' she blurted out as they swung round the first corner. 'You didn't tell her about Dolly, did you?'

'Of course not! What do you take me for? Don't answer that! Anyway, neither of the girls have surfaced yet. Look, shut up, will you, and let me concentrate on getting that dog of yours and us safely to the hospital? These roads are disgusting!'

Rhea bit her lip and glanced down at the limp little body in her arms. An overwhelming guilt swamped her and she began to cry softly, torturing herself with the thought that if she hadn't been so wrapped up in her own selfish desires the evening before she would have noticed something was wrong with Dolly. Knowing now that she loved Stephen didn't make her feel any less guilty. It was all her fault—Dolly's condition, Stephen's obvious contempt, the whole rotten mess her life was in!

Sobs, deep and wretched, racked her body.

Stephen muttered something under his breath and drove even faster.

The vet's wife, Margaret, was watching for her, coming out to meet the car as it pulled up. 'Sorry we couldn't come to you,' she apologised, opening the passenger door and taking Dolly from a teary Rhea. 'Richard's just finishing with the other op. Hmm . . . looks bad, but she's still alive. And dogs are incredibly resilient. Do you want to wait?' she asked kindly.

'Yes,' husked Rhea.

'Right—I'll be a while. Richard's nurse isn't on duty this early on a Sunday, so I have to help.'

'We'll wait out here in the car,' Stephen said.

The woman hurried off, all efficiency and business.

Rhea let out a trembling sigh, sinking back into the seat. 'If Dolly dies,' she whispered shakily, 'I'll never forgive myself. Never!'

'Rhea,' Stephen said tautly, 'this could have happened any time, while you were anywhere, not necessarily . . .'

The unspoken words hovered in the air. Not necessarily cavorting all night in bed, thinking of no one but yourself . . .

'No, it *is* my fault,' she confessed. 'There were signs, symptoms, but I failed to notice them because I was too caught up with . . .' She made a choking sound and turned her face away, guilt again overwhelming her.

'You're being too hard on yourself, Rhea,' he insisted. 'We all make mistakes.'

She groaned. 'And the biggest was last night.'

Stephen sighed and fell silent. Time dragged on.

An hour later the vet made an appearance, startling Rhea at the open passenger window. She had been sitting in the car with her eyes closed.

'Well, Rhea? You have one very sick little dog there. I've done all I can. She had a extra large pup left inside, blocking her passage in the breach position. I'm afraid I couldn't save it. But the mother's hanging on, and I believe you have reason to hope. Tough little beasts, these terriers. They cling to life just like they cling to everything else, the devils.'

He tapped Rhea on the arm. 'Now, no more tears . . .' But even as he spoke tears were swimming in his own eyes. He coughed. 'You women and your pets,' he said gruffly. 'Now off you go home . . . ring me after lunch.'

He swung away, striding back into the building, leaving Rhea feeling drained, and only mildly hopeful. Somehow she felt fate did not mean to deal her a kind hand over this. Fate wanted to punish her for her wicked selfishness.

Stephen started the car in silence, driving home slowly and without saying a word. Once they had pulled up in the drive, he alighted, helping a limp Rhea from her seat in true gentlemanly fashion. 'Do you want me to stay with you?' he asked softly.

She glanced up at him, trying to see what lay behind those inscrutable grey eyes. Was he just being kind in a neighbourly fashion? Or did he still have some feeling left for her? He had liked her once, she was sure of that. Liked and desired. She doubted if much of either remained now.

He shook his head at her failure to answer him, the gesture betraying a regret that he had even offered in the first place. 'I'll keep Emily with me for the day,' he said. 'I'll tell her I organised it with you last night, that you wanted to sleep in today.'

Rhea nodded a weary agreement, no longer amazed by his generosity of spirit. She had always known he could be kind.

'No reason to upset the girls yet,' he went on. 'Besides, you might have good news later.'

Good news . . . Rhea almost laughed. Even if Dolly lived, damage had been done, innocent people had been hurt. 'I was going to buy her a pony,' she murmured, more to herself than to Stephen. 'Emily always wanted a pony . . .'

The tears flooded back and she turned to walk away.

Stephen's hand closed over her shoulder, staying her. 'Rhea . . .' She glanced up at him through soggy lashes. 'I don't like to see you upset like this.'

'Don't you think I deserve it?' she croaked.

He didn't answer, a deep frown creasing his forehead.

Rhea shook her head, turned and walked away.

CHAPTER THIRTEEN

DOLLY lived.

It was touch and go for quite some time, but in the end she survived, perhaps even better than Bobby. The poor little dog spent the entire time of Dolly's stay in hospital in a bleak depression, moping about with a long face, not eating a scrap. He grew so thin, Rhea began to worry.

But it was a different picture when Rhea brought Dolly home on the Saturday morning two weeks later. 'Out you go,' she said, opening the door of the patched-up van for Dolly to jump down.

The two dogs were instantly all over each other like a rash, Bobby's little eyes lighting up with joy. He leapt around in delighted circles, his stumpy tail going fifty to the dozen.

'He sure missed Dolly, didn't he, Mum?' Emily said.

Rhea sighed. 'Yes, he sure did . . .'

As *she* was missing Stephen. He hadn't called, not since he had brought Emily home that Sunday night. But Rhea hadn't really expected him to.

'Grandma rang while you were getting Dolly,' Emily said. 'She wants us to come down tomorrow for the day. I said you'd ring back.'

Rhea sighed. She didn't feel up to driving all that way. She went inside, picked up the phone, and dialled.

'Mum? Yes, Emily told me . . . Dolly's fine . . . Well, it's like this, Mum. I'm feeling awfully tired and . . .' She stopped, having unexpectedly seen her reflection in the kitchen dresser. How awful she was looking, thin and drawn. She hadn't been eating much. Just like Bobby.

'Mum? I've changed my mind,' she said. 'I'd love to come. Only one thing . . . I'm bringing the dogs.'

Rhea perked up immediately, now the decision had been made. Besides, she had been wanting an opportunity to give something to Bill, just some small gift to show how much she wanted their relationship to be closer. But what? Clothes were out of the question as she wasn't sure of his sizes.

In the end she bought him a carton of his favourite beer. It put a hole in the next week's housekeeping, but what the heck? Bill was worth it!

She would always remember the look on his face when she gave it to him the next day. He had difficulty stammering out his shocked 'thank you'. Rhea had the sneaky suspicion that his bending to pat the dogs at that moment was so he could surreptitiously blink away a tear or two, for when he straightened up again his eyes were suspiciously damp.

'That was a sweet thing you did for Bill, Rhea,' her mother commented as soon as they were alone. They were sitting on the beach under the umbrella. Bill and Emily and the dogs had gone for a walk along the sand looking for shells. 'I know you don't have much money.'

Rhea shrugged. 'We manage OK.'

'Bill was surprised.' Her mother's face showed she was surprised too.

'I know,' Rhea murmured, a lump forming in her throat. 'I . . . I wanted to make it up to him for being such a bitch all these years.'

'But, Rhea, you haven't been any such thing! My dear, don't ever think that. Bill understood—we both did—how you must have felt when we got married so soon after your father's death. I particularly felt guilty because it seemed disloyal to your father's memory, but I . . . I couldn't seem to help myself, love. I fell in love with Bill and I . . . we . . . I didn't want the neighbours sniggering behind your back, so we got married. I know we should have waited longer, but . . .'

Rhea could hear the guilt in her mother's words, and it reminded her forcibly of how she had felt about feeling passion for Stephen, as though it were wrong to feel that way. But of course it wasn't wrong, and especially not wrong if one was in love!

'You did the right thing, Mum,' she said gently. 'You deserved to be happy. It couldn't have been easy living with a man like Dad.'

Her mother's face snapped up, her eyes rounding.

'I've grown up, Mum,' Rhea went on with a reassuring smile. 'I don't see things with adolescent eyes any more.'

Her mother was truly taken aback. 'Bill is so different from your father,' she explained haltingly. 'He wants me as a woman, not as a wife or mother or housekeeper. He makes me feel beautiful. I did love your father, Rhea—I did! But not in the same way I love Bill.'

Rhea's heart went out to her mother's distress, for she knew exactly what she was feeling. 'Please don't feel guilty any more, Mum,' she said, hugging her. 'The love you and Bill share is very special. And it doesn't belittle what you felt for Dad. It's just . . . different. Better.'

'Oh, Rhea, it's so good to hear you talk like this. I never thought you would understand.' Her mother drew back and dabbed at her eyes, then gave her daughter a closer look, a frown crossing her face. 'You know, Rhea, you don't look all that well.'

Rhea sighed. 'I haven't been the best,' she admitted.

'Is that why you gave up playing the organ? Emily told me you'd cancelled all your engagements.'

'I suppose so . . .' In truth she couldn't bear the thought of playing music at weddings for a while.

'Is it a virus? Have you been to the doctor?'

An odd little laugh came to her lips. She pictured herself going to the doctor and describing her virus. It was a new strain, called 'Stephenitis'.

Rhea glanced up at her mother and was taken aback at the depth of concern she saw there. With her newly enlightened eyes she realised that the woman next to her felt about her the same way she felt about Emily. Rhea had never thought about her own mother's love in that light before. But it paved the way to her being more open, more frank than had been her custom.

'It's a man, Mum,' she found herself saying.

It was her mother's turn for astonishment. 'A man?'

Rhea smiled softly. 'Is that so strange?'

'No, I . . . well, you've always been a bit . . .'

'Anti-men? Frigid?'

'Well, I wouldn't say that, exactly. But you did seem . . . withdrawn. I often wondered if Milan had been . . . well . . . kind to you.'

Rhea was amazed. 'What on earth do you mean?'

Her mother scrunched up her face in agitation. 'Don't

take me the wrong way—I don't mean he'd beaten you or anything, but to be honest, Rhea, I could never take to that man. He was far too possessive, far too rigid in his ways. Chauvinistic too. He seemed to regard you as a prized possession, not a person with feelings. He . . . he reminded me of your father.'

Rhea sighed. 'I've come to the same conclusion. But only recently. I guess till I met Stephen I didn't know any better.'

'And it's this Stephen who's opened your eyes?'

Rhea nodded.

'Tell me about him, love. Is it serious between you and him?'

Serious? Was going to bed with a man serious these days? Rhea shrugged. 'If you mean have I slept with him, then yes, I have. But it's over now. He doesn't want to see me any more.'

'But you love him?'

'Yes, I love him.'

'I see . . . Why don't you tell me about him?'

Rhea did, leaving out nothing, even to baring the unbearable words Stephen had flung at her that ghastly morning.

'So you see, Mum?' she finished. 'He doesn't want anything more to do with me. And I can understand that. The man does have his pride. Not to mention Madeline and who knows how many other women?' she finished bitterly.

'But can't you see he really liked you, Rhea? More than liked, I would say. And you don't know for sure that he's still seeing these other women, do you?'

Rhea frowned. 'No . . . No, I suppose not.'

'Oh, Rhea, don't cut off your nose to spite your face. If you really love this man then fight for him. Go to him, tell him how you feel.'

'Oh, no, I couldn't!' Rhea protested.

'Why not?'

'Because I . . . I . . . because he doesn't love me!'

'How do you know?' asked her mother.

'Well, if he did he would have told me!'

'Would he?' her mother inserted gently. 'The same way you told him, I suppose?'

Rhea gasped, a thousand tiny hopes springing into life. She tried to dampen them down, tried to stop them from sweeping aside all the facts as she knew them. How could she dismiss the girl in the coffee lounge, Madeline, Laura's mother, not to mention all the others she had never seen or heard of? Stephen was a lover of the female sex, not a lover of love.

'Rhea?' her mother cut into her thoughts. 'Do you love this man or don't you?'

She nodded again.

'Well, then? What have you got to lose?'

Rhea turned to stare at her mother, her luminescent blue eyes showing that hope had won at last.

'Yes, my darling . . . go to him! Tell him how you feel. At least give yourself a chance of happiness.'

CHAPTER FOURTEEN

RHEA glanced up at the office block, not recognising it from street level, but knowing it was the right one. 'Chase Investments' was engraved in bold black letters above the glass doors.

'Mr Chase has gone into his office,' Maisie had told Rhea when she had called at Stephen's house. 'He won't be back tonight either. He's working late and will stay the night in the penthouse.'

'Oh!' Rhea's face had fallen. She had never imagined he would be working on a Sunday afternoon.

'Why don't you drive in and see him, dear?' Maisie was no fool and she could see Rhea was dressed up to the nines, in full make-up and wearing the blue silk dress Stephen had once admired. 'I'm sure he could do with a break—he's been working non-stop for days on end. I'll mind Emily for you.'

Rhea had said thank you but that Emily was staying with her grandmother for a couple of days in Kiama. Maisie gave her Stephen's office address, assuring her that there would be someone to let her into the building. Rhea had almost backed out at that stage, but somehow found herself parking the van at the nearest railway station and catching a train into Sydney's Central Station.

Now here she was, hovering nervously on the pavement, thinking she was a fool to believe her life could be sorted out by the simple admission of, 'I love you, Stephen.' Even if Stephen did care for her, he was not a marrying man. He had already stated his views on that matter.

What would he ever offer her except a few hours here, a night there? Deep in her heart Rhea desperately wanted much more than that. She wanted to marry him, to share his life, to make a family with himself and Laura and Emily. But she knew, deep down, that was only a pipe-dream.

Anguish pressed into her heart and mind, and she almost turned away. Almost . . .

But she couldn't. She realised that now. She couldn't turn her back on trying to secure for herself even the smallest part of Stephen's life. If she didn't, she would be utterly miserable anyway. Better that Emily should have a mother who was at least happy sometimes. An hour, a day, a minute with Stephen was preferable to a lifetime without him, whether he loved her or not!

The glass doors of the building were locked, but Rhea could see a security guard sitting at the reception desk inside the foyer. She knocked and waved till she attracted his attention, inspecting her appearance in the glass during the time it took for the man to stride over.

The wrap-around silk dress suited her both in colour and style, but she was dismayed at the obvious dark shadows under her eyes. With her recent weight loss she looked all eyes and cheekbones, particularly with her hair scraped back into a tight roll. But it was the image she wanted, that of a mature, confident woman, not some silly young sex-starved widow.

'Yes?' the guard asked abruptly, once he had unlocked and swung open one of the glass doors.

Rhea swallowed. 'My name is Mrs Petrovic, Rhea

Petrovic. I'd like to see Mr Chase—I believe he's working here today.'

'Is he expecting you, Mrs Petrovic?'

'No, but I'm sure he'll see me. If you just tell me which floor he's——'

'I'll have to check,' he interrupted firmly.

'Oh . . . Yes . . . Yes, of course.'

The guard ushered her inside before leaving her to glance agitatedly around the spacious foyer while he marched over to the reception desk. Nerves crowded into Rhea's stomach as he made a brief telephone call.

'It's OK, Mrs Petrovic,' the man called over. 'Mr Chase's secretary said you could go right up. Seventeenth floor. His office is directly opposite the elevator doors.'

Rhea's heart sank. His secretary . . . She hadn't anticipated he would be working with someone. She had wanted to see him alone.

The best laid plans of mice and men, she muttered to herself as she walked over to the one lift that showed a red light above. She punched the seventeen, noting that it was the the highest floor—other than the penthouse. The doors shot back straight away. She sighed. Not even a minute's respite in which to gather her composure.

The ride up was as smooth as the building, and the man who owned it, with Rhea fortifying herself with clichés all the way. Nothing ventured, nothing gained . . . Every cloud has a silver lining . . . Anything worth having is worth fighting for . . .

When the doors slid back at the seventeenth floor she was far from confident. But she tried not to look it, walking purposefully across the bouncy green carpet and pushing through another set of swinging glass doors with 'Chase Investments' gilded on them. The luxurious reception area was empty, bringing a further rush of uncertainty.

Suddenly the heavy wooden door directly in front of her opened, and Rhea's heart turned over in her chest as a beautiful young woman walked through. Stephen's secretary. she concluded. But also the same beautiful young woman Rhea had seen him with in the coffee lounge.

Immediately, dark thoughts swamped her mind. Dark, jealous thoughts. So! He was working night and day, was he? How convenient, when his bedroom was one floor up from his office and his secretary was doing a lot more than type his letters!

Just as swiftly Rhea pulled herself up short. No! She was not going to do this any more, jump to conclusions about Stephen without proof. OK, so he might have slept with his secretary at one time. Why not? He was single, and she was . . . *married*!

Rhea gaped at the engagement and wedding rings on the girl's left hand as she reached up to push a blonde curl back from her forehead.

'Mrs Petrovic?' the secretary was saying with a warm smile. 'I'm Melanie Roberts, Stephen's secretary. Do come inside . . . Stephen wasn't here when your message came through. He'd just gone upstairs to have a shower and a shave, but he won't be long. Poor man, he was working most of last night on a presentation he's making tomorrow in Brisbane.'

She gave Rhea a surveying look as she showed her into an expansive office, but there was not a hint of the competitive bitchiness in her manner that Rhea might have expected.

'Please . . .' Melanie pulled out a comfortable chair for Rhea to sit in, then settled herself in the smaller of the two swivel-chairs behind the huge and very cluttered desk that dominated the room.

'It's a mess, isn't it?' the secretary smiled as she saw Rhea's glance. 'But Stephen knows where everything is. If I tidy it up too much, I'm in real trouble!'

Rhea nodded and swallowed. The girl was very natural. And very beautiful.

She gradually became aware that she was being stared at also. She blinked her surprise.

'Mrs Petrovic . . .' Melanie began.

'Yes?'

The secretary glanced a little nervously at the open door. 'I hope you won't take offence, but I must speak out now that I have the chance.'

'About . . . about what?'

'About you . . . and Stephen.'

Rhea stiffened. How on earth would this girl know anything about her and Stephen, unless he had confided their brief affair?

'Oh, please, don't go thinking Stephen has been talking about any personal relationship you and he might have, because he hasn't. He keeps his private life private. I'm putting two and two together here, merely because I know him so well . . .'

Rhea tried not to let her feelings show on her face.

'I've worked for Stephen for five years,' Melanie went on. 'He's like a big brother to me. He gave me away at my wedding last year because my father died some years back. See this beautiful watch? He gave that to me after I came back from my honeymoon because he missed me so much . . .'

She paused, letting her words sink in.

'I care about my boss, Mrs Petrovic,' she added sincerely. 'And I know his moods very well. I know when he's happy, or sad. I certainly know when he's deeply disturbed. You see, when he's troubled in any way, he works. Not that he doesn't work long hours normally, but when he's really upset he's like a demon. In the past, the reason for his workaholic bursts has always been some bad business deal. Believe me when I tell you this is the first time a woman has been the cause . . .'

Rhea held her breath.

'. . . and I think that woman is you, Mrs Petrovic.'

'But . . . how can you . . .?'

'Stephen has naturally talked to me about his problems with Laura, and how things have changed for the better since he followed your advice about the local school. So in that context he has spoken of you quite often, and I couldn't help but notice the way he looked every time your name was mentioned. You should have seen his face when he told me about the way you set him straight the day Laura ran away!'

Rhea groaned as she remembered.

'Please don't be embarrassed,' the girl insisted. 'He admired you for it! There haven't been many women, believe me, who've told him what to do and where to go. They're usually only too willing to fall at his feet! Then one day last month I flew with him to Brisbane on business and he had the biggest grin on his face. I asked him what coup he'd managed, but he shook his head, then burst out with, "She's a widow, Melanie! A widow!" as if all his birthdays had come at once. I knew then, Mrs Petrovic, that Stephen had finally fallen in love.' She slanted Rhea a hopeful look. 'I only hope that your coming here today means you love him just as much.'

Rhea wasn't sure what to say, her heart leaping with joy and relief. Till another, more cynical train of thought took over. Did this girl know her boss that well? Did anyone know *anyone* that well? Couldn't Stephen's pleasure have been an egotistical burst of triumph at finding out a chink in the armour of the one woman who had dared to spurn him? She would have been a challenge for him, just like a difficult business deal. And now he was in a black mood because things had not worked out his way.

The distinctive sound of lift doors swishing open punctuated the quiet air of the deserted building.

'There's Stephen now,' Melanie said as she stood up. 'Please don't mention that I said anything, Mrs Petrovic,' she whispered urgently. 'He'd be furious with me!'

The secretary fell silent as her boss breezed into his office. 'That feels better. One more hour should see us——' Stephen broke off, staring with his mouth open at Rhea.

She got slowly to her feet, unable to stop staring back at him. Somehow during their two weeks' separation she had been so engaged in realising how deeply she loved him that she had almost forgotten the intensity of the attraction between them.

Immediately, it had a tendency to blot out everything else for her. Her eyes drank him in hungrily, from the still damp black waves curving around his finely shaped head down to his impressively proportioned body, clad all too revealingly in a chest-hugging black sports shirt and white canvas shorts. He didn't even have anything on his feet.

If only his secretary was right, Rhea thought breathlessly. If only he did love her! She swayed on her feet, clutching at the arm of the chair to steady herself.

Stephen was the first to pull himself together. 'Rhea? What are you doing here?' he said sharply. 'Is there something wrong at home? Emily? The dogs?'

Rhea's heart sank. How telling that he would assume her only reason for visiting him would be some outside problem!

Tears flooded her eyes, making her look down in a fluster of embarrassment. She hadn't realised how strung up she was, how she had been holding herself together with the mad hope that he would be overjoyed to see her. Yet here he was, coldly asking her if some crisis had forced her to ask him for help once more.

The depressing realisation of dreams shattering sent the tears spilling over her eyes and down her cheeks in an unchecked flood. 'Oh, God!' she sobbed, her trembling hands moving up to hide her face.

Then somehow she *was* in his arms, though perhaps not quite as she had dreamt. He was holding her with obvious reluctance, an angry tension in the hands that were patting her head and back.

'There, there,' he muttered. 'Don't cry . . . For pity's sake, don't cry!'

'I'm sorry,' she choked, not even knowing what she was saying sorry for. 'Sorry . . .'

Stephen sighed, then gathered her more gently to him, holding her wet face against his chest. 'Hush! Don't try to talk,' he soothed. 'Be still . . . Hush!'

He must have mouthed something to his secretary, or made signals, for when at last Rhea calmed, the sobs dying away, she pulled back and glanced around to see the office was empty.

'I sent Melanie home,' he remarked quietly, leaning over to pull a handful of tissues from a box on his desk. 'Here . . .'

Rhea wiped up the tears, noting ruefully that when she did so quite a bit of mascara came too. 'I must look a mess,' she muttered, her eyes still downcast. Stephen's reluctance to hold her had not escaped her notice. He had merely been doing the gentlemanly thing in comforting her, the only thing he could do when a woman burst into tears in front of him.

Her heart was shrivelling up further by the minute. 'I'm sorry,' she repeated dully.

'For what, Rhea? came his weary words.

When she finally lifted her chin to look at him he had moved away from her to stand behind his desk, eyeing her with a grim wariness. It struck her quite forcibly that he looked like a man who was hurting as much as she was. Her stomach twisted with a last stab of desperate hope and she sought frantically for the right words.

'For . . . for a lot of things,' she said haltingly.

'Oh?' He adopted a closed expression and moved to sit down in the large black leather chair. He indicated the chair she had used earlier. 'Then perhaps you should sit down, Rhea, and explain them to me.'

Rhea swallowed and did so, lifting eyes that belied the battery of butterflies in her stomach. She hated seeing the raw pain in his face, yet clutched comfort from it. Pain usually meant that at some time there had been deep emotion involved, maybe the love her mother and his secretary had suggested. If so, Rhea hoped she wasn't too late to salvage some of it.

'I'm sorry,' she began, 'for the way I've treated you. I . . . I know I've behaved very badly. I shouldn't have lied to you about being married, and I know it looks as if I was only using you for sex. But you have to understand, Stephen, I'm not very experienced where men are concerned. A man like you . . . You frightened me, Stephen. Just look at you! Look at this place . . . You're rich and successful. You could have any woman you wanted . . .'

She sighed, not sure she was saying the right things, his increasingly strained face not giving her any indication that she was getting through to him. 'I . . . I couldn't imagine you'd really want me, certainly not for anything else except sex. I . . . I know I misjudged you . . . But it isn't true that I don't like or respect you, Stephen. I do. More than that. I . . . I . . .' She lifted a trembling hand to her temple, trying to still the throbbing in her head, feeling she was putting everything very badly.

She clung on to her mother's words—'What have you got to lose?'— and looked the darkly frowning man opposite her straight in the eye. 'I love you, Stephen. Terribly.'

He froze, then snapped forward in the chair, closing

his eyes briefly before opening them to reveal an unutterable weariness. He shook his head. 'I don't think so, Rhea.'

For a second, Rhea could not believe what she had heard. 'But . . . but I do!' she protested.

'No.' He set anguished eyes upon her. 'You're confusing sex with love. It's easily done—I did it myself once. But it doesn't last. It isn't real.'

'No, Stephen, you're wrong. Wrong!' She was on her feet and her hands gripped the side of his desk. 'I admit I thought it was just a physical attraction too—at first. My response to you really shocked me.'

He looked confused. '*Shocked* you?'

'Yes, shocked me.'

'That seems a trifle melodramatic, Rhea,' he said with undisguised scepticism.

'Oh, God . . . can't you see? Haven't you realised? Not only are you the first lover I've ever taken, Stephen, but you're the first man I've ever even wanted. You're the first man who's ever given me . . . satisfaction.'

Now he was on his feet, looking at her across the desk with total exasperation. 'For God's sake, Rhea, do you expect me to believe that? You were married for five years! You must have enjoyed sleeping with your husband at least once!'

'No, Stephen, *never*! I loved my husband, but not as a woman should love a man. He was more of a father figure to me. Sex was something I did for him, not for myself. That was why after his death I never sought involvement with a man. I couldn't stand the thought of having to . . . to . . .'

She threw him a beseeching look. 'Don't you

understand what I'm saying? When I met you and wanted you so much, I *was* shocked. I didn't make any connection between these alien, unexpected desires and love, because I'd never felt that type of love before. Love for me had always been something quiet, steady . . . safe. Not instant and wild and uncontrollable! When you burst into my life I seemed in danger of losing the peaceful secure life that I'd battled long and hard for. I fought my feelings like crazy, lying to you, lying to myself. I . . . I know I've made a mess of things, Stephen, but I do love you. So much that the thought of life without you is unbearable.'

All the time she had been speaking he had stared at her, his face a mixture of wonder and wariness. For what seemed an interminable span of time, a breathless silence hung in the air, till at last Stephen expelled a ragged sigh. 'You do realise, Rhea, that what you've just said has a flaw in logic. You say you love me. But given your history, it's equally possible that now you've discovered the pleasure, the joy of sex, it's *that* that you've been missing. Not me.'

'How can you say that?' Rhea cried. 'I could go to bed with any number of men. I wouldn't need to come here today with my heart on my sleeve, my pride in shreds. Oh, Stephen, why don't you just say you don't love me? That's the bottom line, isn't it?'

She turned away, her despair reaching such mammoth proportions that as she took a step the room swirled before her blurring eyes. She made a grab for the chair, sending it toppling over, a whimpering cry rushing from her lungs as the floor started rising towards her.

Stephen caught her just before she hit the carpet, sinking to the floor with her and cradling her in his arms. 'Not love you?' he rasped as she struggled back from the threatening blackness to blink dazedly up into his torn face. 'Not love you?' he repeated, stretching out with his back against the desk, curling her body up in his lap and arms. 'Oh, my darling Rhea, my sweet darling Rhea... You're the only woman I've ever loved. Don't you know that?'

She could only stare up at him, hardly daring to believe those longed-for words.

'I was madly attracted to you right from that first day in the church,' he sighed. 'There you were, a vision of loveliness sitting at that organ, your face a perfect oval of innocence, this virginal quality seemingly at odds with the sensual abandonment of your beautiful hair. I wanted to touch it, and you, very badly ...'

He reached around the back of her head, pulling the pins from her hair, letting the waves cascade over his arm. Her breath caught in her throat as he began spreading her hair out, his fingers running through it with an unconscious eroticism.

'It gave me an awful jolt,' he was saying, 'when I realised you were a married woman with a child. It shattered all my plans. In my mind I already had you in my bed, determined to taste all the promise your glances bespoke. My God, Rhea, do you realise how you looked at me that day? It was like nothing I've ever experienced before. One moment your eyes were filled with a yearning, a passion that was totally compelling. And then ... such alarm, such fear. In a way, it was almost a relief to find out you were spoken for. I told myself later I'd imagined your desire, that you'd been amazed perhaps that I tried to pick you up, disgusted even. That was certainly verified later when I came to get Laura . . . You have to admit I did disgust you over Laura.'

'I was wrong,' Rhea whispered, unable to say more. She wished he would stop playing with her hair, stop letting his fingertips brush against her neck. She felt as if her skin were burning up. Her clothes were sticking to her.

'Not totally wrong,' Stephen surprised her by saying. 'I have been a selfish man, pleasing no other person in my life but myself. I wanted money, success, power. And relationships without strings, without commitment. I only ever took out independent career women, women whom I would never be tempted to fall in love with . . .'

He began untying the belt that secured her wrap-around dress, making her throat dry up completely. Her heart began to thud against the walls of her chest, making her breasts rise and fall with telling speed.

'I suppose, after Laura's mother, I had a somewhat cynical attitude towards love. I was deeply hurt by the way she treated me, convincing me she loved me and then dumping me cold. I was only twenty-one at the time. Our dear Naomi was a very experienced thirty-seven.'

'Thirty-*seven*?' Rhea sat up straight, her astonishment having the effect of halting Stephen's fingers on her belt, which was not her intention.

'She looked a well-preserved twenty-eight when I

met her,' he explained. 'It was during the last year of my economics-law degree. I had a part-time job in a stockbrokers' firm. Naomi was one of their hot-shot investment advisers. Being young and naïve—and presumably virile—I was the perfect candidate as the father of her planned child. Shortly after our brief affair she just disappeared, resigned from the company and left, leaving no forwarding address. No farewell tears, no goodbye, no telling stupid old Stevie boy he was about to become a daddy. Naomi wasn't large on sharing, it seemed.'

Rhea heard the bitterness in his voice and realised that Naomi Hatfield's desertion had affected him very deeply. No wonder he was so hurt by that night at the penthouse! It would have looked as if the two women in his life he had really cared about were only interested in his body.

'Not like *you*,' he rasped, tipping her back into the crook of his arm. 'You're all woman, Rhea—giving, loving, warm. But still sexy . . . very sexy . . .' He bent to kiss her, their tongues meeting in an explosion of longing. 'I knew I was in love with you,' he murmured into her trembling mouth, 'when I kept getting so angry with you. I wanted you to love me back, but I was so sure you despised me.'

He lifted his mouth away to look down at her, frustration in his eyes. 'Remember when you were at my place and I received a phone call? It was from a woman named Madeline, an actress I'd been seeing last year.'

'Yes,' Rhea nodded, 'I know about Madeline.'

'You do?'

Rhea had realised earlier on, when Stephen had accused her of confusing sex with love, that she could never tell him about the two times she had seen him before they officially met. He might not understand the subtleties behind her instant attraction. He would only see lust. So she smiled softly and said, 'Laura told Emily, who told me.'

'Women!' groaned Stephen.

'You don't seem to be able to do without them,' she said teasingly, but the comment made him frown.

'You don't still think me some kind of Casanova, Rhea, do you?'

'I don't care what you've been, Stephen,' she murmured understandingly. 'It's what you're going to be I'm interested in.'

She could see, though, that her answer irritated him. 'But I never was that type of man. Yes, there were women — I admit that. I'm a normal male. But not all that many women, and only one at a time. As I told you once before, I'm a busy man. Madeline was the only female in my life before you came into it, and we had already ended our relationship, though I see now that Madeline found this hard to accept. However, when I found out about Laura, Madeline had told me she had little patience with children.'

He sighed. 'Perhaps I should have broken off all contact with her straight away, but I needed some sort of support. Finding out about Naomi and Laura had been a shock. My life seemed one mad rush to fit everything in, and to be truthful I was depressed over Laura's attitude. I thought she hated me and would be happier away from me. Madeline sounded as if she really cared when she suggested boarding school. But when I met you and saw what a truly caring woman thought about the situation I realised she'd just been manipulating things for her own advantage, that she hadn't come to terms with our new friendship, and I sent her packing.'

'Yet you went out with her again,' Rhea inserted quietly.

'Strictly a platonic date, I assure you. I wouldn't even have agreed to that if a certain lady hadn't just rejected me rather brutally.'

A guilty blush flamed into her face.

'A lady I loved quite desperately.' He stroked her cheek and kissed her again before letting his hand drift down to her waist.

Rhea suppressed a groan. Dared she take his hand in hers and move it to her aching breast? No, no, she couldn't. He would think she only wanted sex from him.

But there was no need for her to do anything, for he was in tune with her desires, his fingers moving to her belt to complete what he had begun an eternity ago.

'You will marry me, won't you?' he whispered as he flicked the silk ties to either side of her body.

Rhea could only blink in amazement at his words. That he loved her had completed most of her dream. To have him ask her to marry him was almost too much.

A quivering sigh fluttered from her lips as she pressed her eyes shut. When she opened them to look at Stephen he was busily concentrating on peeling back her dress.

Rhea had chosen her underwear that day without daring to investigate why, the matching set having been part of her trousseau. But she had never worn them.

They had lain in a drawer, waiting, so it seemed now, for the moment when she would wear them for the man she loved. And they were indeed sexy garments, the ivory silk petticoat lending a warm glow to her softly tanned skin, the inserts of lace giving tempting glimpses of the womanly lushness of her body. Stephen's gaze ran hungrily over her body, bringing an even warmer glow.

'You haven't given me an answer,' he said thickly.

'Yes,' she whispered when one of his hands began tracing the swollen curves of her breasts, her back arching to press them more firmly into his palm. He groaned and moved his hand in erotic circles, rubbing her nipples into agonisingly hard peaks. 'Yes,' she repeated on a sob of pleasure.

As always Stephen took his time, sliding the straps from her shoulders with almost annoying slowness, his fingers brushing her bare skin as they attended to the front clasp on her bra. This he discarded, but he left the petticoat to fall around her hips, making no attempt to strip her further. Rhea noted with amazement that she even still had her shoes on.

She kicked them off, then twisted in his lap till she faced him, sliding her bare arms up around his neck. 'Love me, Stephen,' she whispered shakily, hoping he wouldn't misunderstand. But she wanted him, *needed* him at that moment, more than she had ever done.

He dragged in a shuddering breath, then suddenly yanked her hard against him, kissing her long and deep till they were both breathless. Rhea was momentarily worried when he set her aside, but when he began stripping with almost indecent haste she threw any remaining qualms and inhibitions out of the window and wriggled out of the rest of her clothes.

His naked form was beside hers on the floor within seconds, drawing her back on to his lap, fitting his throbbing hardness into her body with a forceful and almost shocking speed. Rough hands wrapped her legs around his hips, then he was rocking her back and forth in a passionate, primitive mating that was unlike any Rhea had ever conceived of. It was so much more overwhelming because she knew Stephen was normally a lover of the subtle, the slow, a true savourer of sensual pleasure.

But this was not like that. This was a demonstration of a raw, naked emotion that was beyond any elongated, erotic exploration. This was a physical union at its most basic, a man taking a woman with no thought of expertise, no idea of delaying satisfaction till every vestige of delight had been teased from it. This was a compelling, instinctive response to a deep and true love, a love that demanded not so much a making love, but a making one.

It underlined to Rhea the intense nature of Stephen's feelings. With her at this moment he could not be the man he usually was; he could not control, or direct, or wait . . .

The realisation of such a compulsive need exploded through her like the ultimate intoxication, increasing her own already inflamed desire. Her mouth sought his with a fierce response, her nails digging into his back as she moved with him, wildly, savagely, quickly bringing about a shuddering mutual release of soul-shattering intensity. They sagged into each other, the melding of their flesh completed, only their minds left to wonder dazedly as they drew back to gaze at each other in an awestruck silence, their chests still heaving with the effort of their spent passion.

At last Stephen's hand reached out to push some madly tangled locks of hair from her face. 'If it's always going to be like this,' he choked out, 'then I'll be dead within a week!'

With a shuddering sigh they both sank to the floor, holding and stroking each other into a calmer state in an almost shocked silence.

'Stephen,' Rhea whispered at last.

'Hmm?'

'I . . . I hate to bring this up, at such a time . . . but I think I should mention it . . .'

'What?'

'The first time we made love, it was almost perfectly safe. And this time too . . . But if we don't take precautions soon . . .'

She lifted her head from his chest to see the smile form on his face. 'You don't mind if I get pregnant?'

'What do you think, Mrs Chase?' he murmured, drawing her back down to him. 'Where's Emily?' he asked, distracting her with the change of subject.

'Staying with her grandmother for a couple of days.'

'Then you can stay with me tonight? All night?'

Rhea should have got over blushing by now, but it seemed she hadn't. 'Yes,' she whispered, hiding her face at the base of his neck.

Stephen scrambled to his feet, lifting her naked body into his arms and carrying her from the office.

'Where are we going?' she gasped.

'Upstairs to bed,' he told her as he pushed through the glass doors with his elbow. 'I'm too old for this floor nonsense.'

'But ... but what about your work? Melanie said you were going to Brisbane tomorrow.'

'Postponed as of now!'

She giggled as he directed her big toe to press the button for the penthouse lift, linking her arms tightly around his neck while he angled her body into the small enclosed space. Rhea was enjoying the sensation of being held naked against his equally naked body. It made her feel tiny and vulnerable and female, his strong arms carrying her as though she were a feather.

But along with these new feelings of submissive pleasure was a sense of feminine power. Stephen loved her, loved her and wanted her with a passion he could scarcely control. Her new womanly instincts told her that she only had to slide her skin suggestively against his, give him a certain look and he would be set upon a path from which there was no drawing back.

As the doors slid shut to enclose them in a temporary cocoon, Rhea glanced up at Stephen through smoky, half-closed eyes. She twisted slightly in his arms so that her still hard nipple grazed his. 'You know, Stephen,' she whispered huskily, 'I've never made love in an elevator ...'

CHAPTER FIFTEEN

RHEA was running late. Which was forgivable, since she was the bride. But Emily and Laura were getting agitated at her constant checking that everything was perfect with her appearance.

'Come on, Mum,' Emily urged. 'Dad will be having a pink fit if we're not at the church soon!'

Rhea warmed to the way her daughter had already accepted Stephen as her stepfather, despite only one month having gone by since they had announced their engagement.

'Yes, Rhea,' Bill chimed in, 'it's time we left, but may I say before we do how radiant you look?'

Rhea's mirror agreed. There was a bloom in her cheeks that made her look like the traditional blushing bride, though the image was certainly helped by the dress she had made. It was an elaborate gown in dazzling white satin, with a fitted, off-the-shoulder bodice, a nipped-in waist and a wide flouncing skirt. The veil was long at the back with a delicate orange-blossom head-piece and a shorter veil covering her face.

Rhea had rejected any idea of dressing down for her second wedding. It was Stephen's first, and the girls had been keen to be proper bridesmaids.

'I think she's the most beautiful bride in the whole world,' breathed Laura, gazing up at her soon-to-be mother in loving awe.

Emotion curled around Rhea's heart, bringing a lump to her throat. 'Not as beautiful as my two bridesmaids,' she complimented. Emily looked startlingly grown-up in floor-length lilac chiffon; Laura, like a Dresden doll in the same style in sweetest pink. Both had matching picture hats and flowers.

'If we don't leave now, Rhea,' Bill warned, 'I'll have to answer to your mother!'

She smiled at her stepfather, linking her arm through his and letting him lead her outside, the girls rushing forward to carry the train of her veil. 'Have I ever told you I love you?' she whispered to him as he helped her into the bridal car.

His glance carried shock, then a wealth of emotion. He made no reply, just took and patted her hand, clearly unable to speak.

The church looked marvellous, spruced up by a coat of white paint paid for by Stephen. The grounds had benefited too, having been mown and tidied by his gardener the day before.

Rhea was not surprised to see several reporters waiting for her in the churchyard, resigning herself to the fact she was marrying a man of considerable standing. Though, from what she had seen of Stephen, he was not a flaunter of his fame and fortune, keeping a low-key profile as much as possible. A lover of publicity would certainly not have chosen to be married in Bangaloo Creek Church.

But as the reporters crowded forward, snapping photographs and jotting down notes, Rhea realised that being Mrs Stephen Chase would take some getting used to. Yet she was not in any way nervous about this marriage, a fact that would have surprised the Rhea of a few months ago. She had changed in so many ways since meeting and loving Stephen, feeling much more confident in herself as a person and a woman.

The bridal chorus started up as soon as she appeared in the doorway, a young man playing the organ. Stephen had hired him with the same efficiency he had done everything in the meagre four weeks they had had to make all the arrangements. His capacity for hard work and getting things done was a bit overwhelming, not to mention the miles he covered most weeks. He was always going here, flying there on some business deal or other. But at least it was mostly in Australia, rarely overseas. And, to be honest, Rhea had no wish to change him. She loved Stephen as he was, human dynamo and all. And Emily adored him, never more so than on the day after their engagement when he had shown up with the most beautiful chestnut pony Rhea had ever seen.

The pony hadn't been his only purchase that day either. Her old van was mysteriously whisked away, with a brand new white sedan taking its place. Stephen had brushed aside any objection with a firm look, then a seductive kiss. 'Can't have my fiancée breaking down on one of these lonely roads, can I?' he said reasonably.

Rhea sighed contentedly with her memories, then looked down the aisle, catching her breath as Stephen turned to gaze back down at her. How handsome he looked! How wonderful! How . . . *nervous*?

The thought made her smile. Her Stephen—nervous? The same Stephen who had already put her farm up for auction, moved her goats to his place, had proper kennels built for the dogs and brought his parents down to mind the children while they went on the honeymoon he had booked in Tahiti?

But nervous he most certainly looked.

She started the slow walk down the aisle, throwing smiles at all the people who had come to wish her well. She saved a special beam for Stephen's parents, who were a delightful old couple, and seemed to genuinely like her.

'What rubbish!' Stephen had snapped when she had dared voice her worry that they might think her not good enough for him. 'I'm a simple farm boy myself. No airs and graces about my family!'

And there weren't, Rhea agreed as she cast a warm eye over his three brothers and two sisters, who had come to the wedding, with spouses and countless children in tow. If Stephen was as potent as his siblings Rhea was going to be kept busy!

Which thought had her gently touch her stomach behind her bouquet of flowers. She was only a couple of days late, but there was no doubt in her mind that she had already conceived Stephen's child. Despite his busy schedule his passion for her had not waned. It took her breath away to think of the many times they had made love already, not to mention the mad places!

As she approached the altar she caught a glimpse of her mother out of the corner of her eye, looking burstingly happy. Rhea grinned at her before bringing her attention back to Stephen.

For a second, he seemed taken aback by her unabashed happiness, but then the sight of his bride, smiling widely up at him, broke his strain, and he grinned back at her.

He took her arm quite eagerly and they turned together to face the priest.

'We are gathered together here . . .'

Rhea darted a glance up at Stephen as the words rolled over them, drawing his gaze. They looked into each other's eyes, the mutual emotion in their depths echoing the words of the ceremony.

'Stephen Richard, wilt thou have this woman to thy wedded wife . . .? Wilt thou love her, comfort her, honour, and keep her in sickness and in health; and, foresaking all other, keep thee only unto her, so long as ye both shall live?'

His eyes caressed her as he said, 'I will.'

'Rhea Catherine, wilt thou have this man to thy wedded husband . . .'

It was a beautiful simple ceremony ending with the traditional, 'I pronounce that they be man and wife together.'

Then the priest cleared his throat. 'Er . . . You may kiss the bride.'

Stephen turned and slowly lifted her veil, his face having taken on a more serious expression. 'I love you, Rhea,' he murmured.

His mouth met hers, sweetly, reverentially, yet smouldering with an impatient, barely contained passion. Rhea melted against him, knowing that what they had together was something so special that not even death would bring a halt to it. As long as their children and their children's children lived, they would be a testimony to a love that was as rare as the most priceless jewel, a love that encompassed all that a man and woman could ever possibly hope for.

It was certainly all that Rhea had hoped for, she thought blissfully as her lips parted and she began to kiss him back.

Debbie Macomber is one of the most popular romance authors writing today. She's written more than seventy romances and several best-selling 'mainstream' women's fiction novels. Not surprisingly, Debbie has won a number of awards for her books. She lives in Washington State with her husband, Wayne, and their dog, Peterkins. They have four grown children, and are also proud grandparents. Debbie loves to hear from readers. You can reach her at: PO Box 1458, Port Orchard, Washington 98366, USA.

YOURS AND MINE
by
DEBBIE MACOMBER

CHAPTER ONE

"MOM, I FORGOT to tell you, I need two dozen cupcakes for tomorrow morning."

Joanna Parsons reluctantly opened her eyes and lifted her head from the soft feather pillow, squinting at the illuminated dial of her clock radio. "Kristen, it's after eleven."

"I know, Mom, I'm sorry. But I've *got* to bring cupcakes."

"No, you don't," Joanna said hopefully. "There's a package of Oreos on the top shelf of the cupboard. You can take those."

"Oreos! You've been hiding Oreos from me again! Just what kind of mother are you?"

"I was saving them for an emergency—like this."

"It won't work." Crossing her arms over her still-flat chest, eleven-year-old Kristen sat on the edge of the mattress and heaved a loud, discouraged sigh.

"Why not?"

"It's got to be cupcakes, home-baked chocolate ones."

"That's unfortunate, since you seem to have forgotten to mention the fact earlier. And now it's about four hours too late for baking anything. Including chocolate cupcakes." Joanna tried to be fair with Kristen, but being a single parent wasn't easy.

"Mom, I know I forgot," Kristen cried, her young voice rising in panic, "but I've got to bring cupcakes to class tomorrow. It's important! Really important!"

"Convince me." Joanna used the phrase often. She didn't want to seem unyielding and hard-nosed. After all, she'd probably forgotten a few important things in her thirty-odd years, too.

"It's Mrs. Eagleton's last day as our teacher—remember I told you her husband got transferred and she's moving to Denver? Everyone in the whole class hates to see her go, so we're throwing a party."

"Who's *we*?"

"Nicole and me," Kristen answered quickly. "Nicole's bringing the napkins, cups and punch, and I'm supposed to bring homemade cupcakes. Chocolate cupcakes. Mom, I've just got to. Nicole would never forgive me if I did something stupid like bring store-bought cookies for a teacher as wonderful as Mrs. Eagleton."

Kristen had met Nicole almost five months before at the beginning of the school year, and the two girls had been as thick as gnats in August from that time on. "Shouldn't the room mother be organizing this party?" That made sense to Joanna; surely there was an adult who would be willing to help.

"We don't have one this year. Everyone's mother is either too busy or working."

Joanna sighed. Oh, great, she was going to end up baking cupcakes until the wee hours of the morning. "All right," she muttered, giving in to her daughter's pleading. Mrs. Eagleton *was* a wonderful teacher, and Joanna was as sorry as Kristen to see her leave.

"We just couldn't let Mrs. Eagleton move to Denver without doing something really nice for her," Kristen pressed.

Although Joanna agreed, she felt that Oreos or Fig Newtons should be considered special enough, since it was already after eleven. But Kristen obviously had her heart set on home-baked cupcakes.

"Mom?"

Even in the muted light, Joanna recognized the plea in her daughter's dark brown eyes. She looked so much like Davey that a twinge of anguish worked its way through Joanna's heart. They'd been divorced six years now, but the pain of that failure had yet to fade. Sometimes, at odd moments like these, she still recalled how good it had felt to be in his arms and how much she'd once loved him. Mostly, though, Joanna remembered how naive she'd been to trust him so completely. But she'd come a long way in the six years since her divorce. She'd gained a new measure of independence and self-respect, forging a career for herself at Columbia Basin Savings and Loan. And now she was close to achieving her goal of becoming the first female senior loan officer.

"All right, honey." Joanna sighed, dragging her thoughts back to her daughter. "I'll bake the cupcakes. Only next time, please let me know before we go to bed, okay?"

Kristen's shoulders slumped in relief. "I owe you one, Mom."

Joanna resisted the urge to remind her daughter that the score was a lot higher than one. Tossing aside the thick warm blankets, she climbed out of bed and reached for her long robe.

Kristen, flannel housecoat flying behind her like a flag unfurling, raced toward the kitchen, eager to do what she could to help. "I'll turn on the oven and get everything ready," she called.

"All right," Joanna said with a yawn as she sent her foot searching under the bed for her slippers. She was mentally scanning the contents of her cupboards, wondering if she had a chocolate cake mix. Somehow she doubted it.

"Trouble, Mom," Kristen announced when Joanna entered the well-lighted kitchen. The eleven-year-old stood on a chair in front of the open cupboards above the refrigerator, an Oreo between her teeth. Looking only mildly guilty, she ate the cookie whole, then shook her head. "We don't have cake mix."

"I was afraid of that."

"I guess we'll have to bake them from scratch," Kristen suggested, reaching for another Oreo.

"Not this late, we won't. I'll drive to the store." There was an Albertson's that stayed open twenty-four hours less than a mile away.

Kristen jumped down from the chair. The pockets of her bathrobe were stuffed full of cookies, but her attempt to conceal them failed. Joanna pointed toward the cookie jar, and dutifully Kristen emptied her pockets.

When Kristen had finished, Joanna yawned again and ambled back into her bedroom.

"Mom, if you're going to the store, I suppose I should go with you."

"No, honey, I'm just going to run in and out. You stay here."

"Okay," Kristen agreed quickly.

The kid wasn't stupid, Joanna thought wryly. Winters in eastern Washington were often merciless, and temperatures in Spokane had been well below freezing all week. To be honest, she wasn't exactly thrilled about braving the elements herself. She pulled on her calf-high boots over two pairs of heavy woollen socks. Because the socks were so thick, Joanna could only zip the boots up to her ankles.

"Mom," Kristen said, following her mother into the bedroom, a thoughtful expression on her face. "Have you ever thought of getting married again?"

Surprised, Joanna looked up and studied her daughter. The question had come from out of nowhere, but her answer was ready. "Never." The first time around had been enough. Not that she was one of the walking wounded, at least she didn't think of herself that way. Instead, her divorce had made her smart, had matured her. Never again would she look to a man for happiness; Joanna was determined to build her own. But the unexpectedness of Kristen's question caught her off guard. Was Kristen telling her something? Perhaps her daughter felt she was missing out because there were only the two of them. "What makes you ask?"

The mattress dipped as she sat beside Joanna. "I'm not exactly sure," she confessed. "But you could remarry, you know. You've still got a halfway decent figure."

Joanna grinned. "Thanks . . . I think."

"I mean, it's not like you're really old and ugly."

"Coming from you, that's high praise indeed, considering that I'm over thirty."

"I'm sure if you wanted to, you could find another man. Not like Daddy, but someone better."

It hurt Joanna to hear her daughter say things like that about Davey, but she couldn't disguise from Kristen how selfish and hollow her father was. Nor could she hide Davey's roving eye when it came to the opposite sex. Kristen spent one month every summer with him in Seattle and saw for herself the type of man Davey was.

After she'd finished struggling with her boots, Joanna clumped into the entryway and opened the hall cupboard.

"Mom!" Kristen cried, her eyes round with dismay.

"What?"

"You can't go out looking like that!" Her daughter was pointing at her, as though aghast at the sight.

"Like what?" Innocently Joanna glanced down at the dress-length blue wool coat she'd slipped on over her rose-patterned flannel pajamas. Okay, so the bottoms showed, but only a little. And she was willing to admit that the boots would look better zipped up, but she was more concerned with comfort than fashion. If the way she looked didn't bother her, then it certainly shouldn't bother Kristen. Her daughter had obviously forgotten why Joanna was venturing outside in the first place.

"Someone might see you."

"Don't worry, I have no intention of taking off my coat." She'd park close to the front door of the store, run inside, head for aisle three, grab a cake mix and be back at the car in four minutes flat. Joanna didn't exactly feel like donning tights for the event.

"You might meet someone," Kristen persisted.

"So?" Joanna stifled a yawn.

"But your hair... Don't you think you should curl it?"

"Kristen, listen. The only people who are going to be in the grocery store are insomniacs and winos and maybe a couple of pregnant women." It was highly unlikely she'd run into anyone from the bank.

"But what if you got in an accident? The policeman would think you're some kind of weirdo."

Joanna yawned a second time. "Honey, anyone who would consider making cupcakes in the middle of the night has a mental problem as it is. I'll fit right in with everyone else, so quit worrying.''

"Oh, all right," Kristen finally agreed.

Draping her bag strap over her shoulder, Joanna opened the front door and shivered as the arctic wind of late January wrapped itself around her. Damn, it was cold. The grass was so white with frost that she wondered, at first, if it had snowed. To ward off the chill, she wound Kristen's purple striped scarf around her neck to cover her ears and mouth and tied it loosely under her chin.

The heater in her ten-year-old Ford didn't have a chance to do anything but spew out frigid air as she huddled over the steering wheel for the few minutes it took to drive to the grocery store. According to her plan, she parked as close to the store as possible, turned off the engine and dashed inside.

Just as she'd predicted, the place was nearly deserted, except for a couple of clerks working near the front, arranging displays. Joanna didn't give them more than a fleeting glance as she headed toward the aisle where baking goods were shelved.

She was reaching for the first chocolate cake mix to come into sight when she heard footsteps behind her.

"Mrs. Parsons! Hello!" The shrill excited voice seemed to ring like a Chinese gong throughout the store.

Joanna hunched down as far as she could and cast a furtive glance over her shoulder. Dear Lord, Kristen had been right. She was actually going to bump into someone who knew her.

"It's me—Nicole. You remember me, don't you?"

Joanna attempted a smile as she turned to face her daughter's best friend. "Hi, there," she said weakly, and raised her right hand to wave, her wrist limp. "It's good to see you again." So she was lying. Anyone with a sense of decency would have pretended not to recognise her and casually looked the other way. Not Nicole. It seemed as though all the world's eleven-year-olds were plotting against her tonight. One chocolate cake mix; that was all she wanted. That and maybe a small tub of ready-made frosting. Then she could return home, get those cupcakes baked and climb back into bed where most sane people were at this very moment.

"You look different," Nicole murmured thoughtfully, her eyes widening as she studied Joanna.

Well, that was one way of putting it.

"When I first saw you, I thought you were a bag lady."

Loosening the scarf that obscured the lower half of her face, Joanna managed a grin.

"What are you doing here this late?" the girl wanted to know next, following Joanna as she edged her way to the checkout stand.

"Kristen forgot to tell me about the cupcakes."

Nicole's cheerful laugh resounded through the store like a yell echoing in an empty sports stadium. "I was watching Johnny Carson with my dad when I remembered I hadn't bought the juice and stuff for the party. Dad's waiting for me in the car right now."

Nicole's father allowed her to stay up that late on a school night? Joanna did her utmost to hide her disdain. From what Kristen had told her, she knew Nicole's parents were also divorced and her father had custody of Nicole. The poor kid probably didn't know what the word discipline meant. No doubt her father was one of those weak-willed liberal parents so involved in their own careers that they didn't have any time left for their children. Imagine a parent letting an eleven-year-old wander around a grocery store at this time of night! The mere thought was enough to send chills of parental outrage racing up and down Joanna's backbone. She placed her arm around Nicole's shoulders as if to protect her from life's harsher realities. The poor sweet kid.

The abrupt whoosh of the automatic door was followed by the sound of someone striding impatiently into the store. Joanna glanced up to discover a tall man, wearing a well-cut dark coat, glaring in their direction.

"Nicole, what's taking so long?"

"Dad," the girl said happily, "this is Mrs. Parsons—Kristen's mom."

Nicole's father approached, obviously reluctant to acknowledge the introduction, his face remote and unsmiling.

Automatically Joanna straightened, her shoulders stiffening with the action. Nicole's father was exactly as she'd pictured him just a few moments earlier. Polished, worldly, and too darn handsome for his own good. Just like Davey. This was exactly the type of man she went out of her way to avoid. She'd been burned once, and no relationship was worth what she'd endured. This brief encounter with Nicole's father told Joanna all she needed to know.

"Tanner Lund," he announced crisply, holding out his hand.

"Joanna Parsons," Joanna said, and gave him hers for a brisk cold shake. She couldn't take her hand away fast enough.

His eyes narrowed as they studied her, and the look he gave her was as disapproving as the one she offered him. Slowly his gaze dropped to the unzipped boots flapping at her ankles and the worn edges of the pajamas visible below her wool coat.

"I think it's time we met, don't you?" Joanna didn't bother to disguise her disapproval of the man's attitude toward child-rearing. She'd had Nicole over after school several times, but on the one occasion Kristen had visited her friend, the child was staying with a baby-sitter.

A hint of a smile appeared on his face, but it didn't reach his eyes. "Our meeting is long overdue, I agree."

He seemed to be suggesting that he'd made a mistake in allowing his daughter to have anything to do with someone who dressed the way she did.

Joanna's gaze shifted to Nicole. "Isn't it late for you to be up on a school night?"

"Where's Kristen?" he countered, glancing around the store.

"At home," Joanna answered, swallowing the words that said home was exactly where an eleven-year-old child belonged on a school night—or any other night for that matter.

"Isn't she a bit young to be left alone while you run to a store?"

"N-not in the least."

Tanner frowned and his eyes narrowed even more. His disapproving gaze demanded to know what kind of mother left a child alone in the house at this time of night.

Joanna answered him with a scornful look of her own.

"It's a pleasure to meet you, Mr. Lund," she said coolly, knowing her eyes relayed a conflicting message.

"The pleasure's mine."

Joanna was all the more aware of her dishevelled appearance. Uncombed and uncurled, her auburn hair hung limply to her shoulders. Her dark eyes were nice enough, she knew, fringed in long curling lashes. She considered them her best asset, and purposely glared at Tanner, hoping her eyes were as cold as the blast from her car heater had been.

Tanner placed his hands on his daughter's shoulders and drew her protectively to his side. Joanna was infuriated by the action. If Nicole needed shielding, it was from an irresponsible father!

Okay, she reasoned, so her attire was a bit outlandish. But that couldn't be helped; she was on a mission that by rights should win her a nomination for the mother-of-the-year award. The way Tanner Lund had implied that *she* was the irresponsible parent was something Joanna found downright insulting.

"Well," Joanna said brightly, "I have to go. Nice to see you again, Nicole." She swept two boxes of cake mix into her arms and grabbed what she hoped was some frosting.

"You, too, Mrs. Parsons," the girl answered, smiling up at her.

"Mr. Lund."

"Mrs. Parsons."

The two nodded politely at each other, and, clutching her packages, Joanna walked regally to the checkout stand. She made her purchase and started back toward the car. The next time Kristen invited Nicole over, Joanna mused on the short drive home, she intended to spend lots of extra time with the girls. Now she knew how badly Nicole needed someone to nurture her, to give her the firm but loving guidance every child deserved.

The poor darling.

CHAPTER TWO

JOANNA EXPERTLY LOWERED the pressure foot of her sewing machine over the bunched red material, then used both hands to push the fabric slowly under the bobbing needle. Straight pins, tightly clenched between her lips, protruded from her mouth. Her concentration was intense.

"Mom." A breathless Kristen bounded into the room.

Joanna intercepted her daughter with one upraised hand until she finished stitching the seam.

Kristen stalked around the kitchen table several times, like a shark circling its kill. "Mom, hurry, this is really important."

"Wlutt?" Joanna asked, her teeth still clamped on the pins.

"Can Nicole spend the night?"

Joanna blinked. This wasn't the weekend, and Kristen knew the rules; she had permission to invite friends over only on Friday and Saturday nights. Joanna removed the pins from her mouth before she answered. "It's Wednesday."

"I know what day it is." Kristen rolled her eyes towards the ceiling and slapped the heel of her hand against her forehead.

Allowing his daughter to stay over at a friend's house on a school night was exactly the kind of irresponsible parenting Joanna expected from Tanner Lund. Her estimation of the man was dropping steadily, though that hardly seemed possible. Earlier in the afternoon, Joanna had learned that Nicole didn't even plan to tell her father she and Kristen were going to be performing in the school talent show. The man revealed absolutely no interest in his daughter's activities. Joanna felt so bad about Tanner Lund's attitude that she'd volunteered to sew a second costume so Nicole would have something special to wear for this important event. And now it seemed that Tanner was in the habit of farming out his daughter on school nights, as well.

"Mom, hurry and decide. Nicole's on the phone."

"Honey, there's school tomorrow."

Kristen gave her another scornful look.

"The two of you will stay up until midnight chattering, and then in the morning class will be a disaster. The answer is no!"

Kristen's eager face fell. "I promise we won't talk. Just this once, Mom. Oh, please!" She folded her hands prayerfully, and her big brown eyes pleaded with Joanna. "How many times do I ask you for something?"

Joanna stared incredulously at her daughter. The list was endless.

"All right, forget I asked that. But this is important, Mom, real important—for Nicole's sake."

Every request was argued as urgent. But knowing what she did about the other little girl's home life made refusing all the more difficult. "I'm sorry, Kristen, but not on a school night."

Head drooping, Kristen shuffled toward the phone. "Now Nicole will have to spend the night with Mrs. Wagner, and she hates that."

"Who's Mrs. Wagner?"

Kristen turned to face her mother and released a sigh intended to evoke sympathy. "Her baby-sitter."

"Her father makes her spend the night at a baby-sitter's?"

"Yes. He has a business meeting with Becky."

Joanna stiffened and felt a sudden chill. "Becky?"

"His business partner."

I'll just bet! Joanna's eyes narrowed with outrage. Tanner Lund was a lowlife, kicking his own daughter out into the cold so he could bring a woman over. The man disgusted her.

"Mrs. Wagner is real old and she makes Nicole eat health food. She has a black-and-white TV, and the only programs she'll let Nicole watch are nature shows. Wouldn't you hate that?"

Joanna's mind was spinning. Any child would detest being cast from her own bed and thrust upon the not always tender mercies of a baby-sitter. "How often does Nicole have to spend the night with Mrs. Wagner?"

"Lots."

Joanna could well believe it. "How often is 'lots'?"

"At least twice a month. Sometimes even more often than that."

That poor neglected child. Joanna's heart constricted at the thought of sweet Nicole being ruthlessly handed over to a woman who served soybean burgers.

"Can she, Mom? Oh, please?" Again Kristen folded her hands, pleading with her mother to reconsider.

"All right," Joanna conceded, "but just this once."

Kristen ran across the room and hurled her arms around Joanna's neck, squeezing for all she was worth. "You're the greatest mother in the whole world."

Joanna snorted softly. "I've got to be in the top ten percent, anyway," she said, remembering the cupcakes.

"ABSOLUTELY NOT," Tanner said forcefully as he laid a neatly pressed shirt in his open suitcase. "Nicole, I won't hear of it."

"But, Dad, Kristen is my very best friend."

"Believe me, sweetheart, I'm pleased you've found a soulmate, but when I'm gone on these business trips I need to know you're being well taken care of." And supervised, he added mentally. What he knew about Kristen's mother wasn't encouraging. The woman was a scatterbrain who left her young daughter unattended while she raided the supermarket for nighttime goodies—and then had the nerve to chastise him because Nicole was up a little late. In addition to being a busybody, Joanna Parsons dressed like a fruitcake.

"Dad, you don't understand what it's like for me at Mrs. Wagner's."

Undaunted, Tanner continued packing his suitcase. He wasn't any happier about leaving Nicole than she was, but he didn't have any choice. As a relatively new half owner of Spokane Aluminum, he was required to do a certain amount of traveling. More these first few months than would be necessary later. His business trips were essential, since they familiarised him with the clients and their needs. He would have to absorb this information as quickly as possible in order to determine if the plant was going to achieve his and John Becky's five-year goal. In a few weeks, he expected to hire an assistant who would assume some of this responsibility, but for now the task fell into his hands.

Nicole slumped onto the edge of the bed. "The last time I spent the night at Mrs. Wagner's she served baked beef heart for dinner."

Involuntarily Tanner cringed.

"And, Dad, she made me watch a special on television that was all about fungus."

Tanner gritted his teeth. So the old lady was a bit eccentric, but she looked after Nicole competently, and that was all that mattered.

"Do you know what Kristen's having for dinner?"

Tanner didn't care to guess. It was probably something like strawberry ice cream and caramel-flavored popcorn. "No, and I don't want to know."

"It isn't sweet-and-sour calf liver, I can tell you that."

Tanner's stomach turned at the thought of liver in any kind of sauce. "Nicole, the subject is closed. You're spending the night with Mrs. Wagner."

"It's spaghetti and meatballs and three-bean salad and milk and French bread, that's what. And Mrs. Parsons said I could help Kristen roll the meatballs—but that's all right, I'll call and tell her that you don't want me to spend the night at a home where I won't be properly looked after."

"Nicole—"

"Dad, don't worry about it, I understand."

Tanner sincerely doubted that. He placed the last of his clothes inside the suitcase and closed the lid.

"At least I'm *trying* to understand why you'd send me to someplace like Mrs. Wagner's when my very best friend *invited* me to spend the night with her."

Tanner could feel himself weakening. It was only one night and Kristen's weird mother wasn't likely to be a dangerous influence on Nicole in that short a time.

"Spaghetti and meatballs," Nicole muttered under her breath. "My all-time favourite food."

Now that was news to Tanner. He'd thought pizza held that honour. He'd never known his daughter to turn down pizza at any time of the day or night.

"And they have a twenty-inch colour television set."

Tanner hesitated.

"With remote control."

Would wonders never cease? "Will Kristen's mother be there the entire night?" he asked.

"Of course."

His daughter was looking at him as though he'd asked if Mrs. Parsons were related to ET. "Where will you sleep?"

"Kristen has a double bed." Nicole's eyes brightened. "And we've already promised Mrs. Parsons that we'll go straight to bed at nine o'clock and hardly talk."

It was during times such as this that Tanner felt the full weight of parenting descend upon his shoulders. Common sense told him Nicole would be better off with Mrs. Wagner, but he understood her complaints about the older woman as well. "All right, Nicole, you can stay at Kristen's."

His daughter let out a whoop of sheer delight.

"But just this once."

"Oh, Dad, you're the greatest." Her arms locked around his waist, and she squeezed with all her might, her nose pressed against his flat stomach.

"Okay, okay, I get the idea you're pleased with my decision," Tanner said with a short laugh.

"Can we leave now?"

"Now?" Usually Nicole wanted to linger at the apartment until the last possible minute.

"Yes. Mrs. Parsons really did say I could help roll the meatballs, and you know what else?"

"What?"

"She's sewing me and Kristen identical costumes for the talent show."

Tanner paused—he hadn't known anything about his daughter needing a costume. "What talent show?"

"Oops." Nicole slapped her hand over her mouth. "I wasn't going to tell you because it's on Valentine's day and I know you won't be able to come. I didn't want you to feel bad."

"Nicole, it's more important that you don't hide things from me."

"But you have to be in Seattle."

She was right. He'd hate missing the show, but he was scheduled to meet with the Foreign Trade Commission on the fourteenth regarding a large shipment of aluminum to Japan. "What talent do you and Kristen have?" he asked, diverting his disappointment for the moment.

"We're lip-synching a song from Heart. You know, the rock group?"

"That sounds cute. A fitting choice, too, for a Valentine's Day show. Perhaps you two can be persuaded to give me a preview before the grand performance."

Her blue eyes became even brighter in her excitement. "That's a great idea! Kristen and I can practise while you're away, and we'll show you when you come back."

It was an acceptable compromise.

Nicole dashed out of his bedroom and returned a couple of minutes later with her backpack. "I'm ready anytime you are," she announced.

Tanner couldn't help but notice that his daughter looked downright cheerful. More cheerful than any of the other times he'd been forced to leave her. Normally she put on a long face and moped around, making him feel guilty about abandoning her to the dreaded Mrs. Wagner.

By the time he picked up his briefcase and luggage, Nicole was waiting at the front door.

"Are you going to come in and say hello to Mrs. Parsons?" Nicole asked when Tanner eased his Mercedes into Kristen's driveway fifteen minutes later. Even in the fading late-afternoon light, he could see that the house was newly painted, white with green shutters at the windows. The lawn and flower beds seemed well maintained. He could almost picture rose bushes in full bloom. It certainly wasn't the type of place he'd associated with Kristen's loony mother.

"Are you coming in or not?" Nicole asked a second time, her voice impatient.

Tanner had to mull over the decision. He wasn't eager to meet that unfriendly woman who wore unzipped boots and flannel pajamas again.

"Dad!"

Before Tanner could answer, the door opened and Kristen came bowling out of the house at top speed. A gorgeous redhead followed sedately behind her. Tanner felt his jaw sag and his mouth drop open. No, it couldn't be! Tall, cool, sophisticated, this woman looked as though she'd walked out of the pages of a fashion magazine. It couldn't be Joanna Parsons—no way. A relative perhaps, but certainly not the woman he'd met in the grocery store that night.

Nicole had already climbed out of the car. She paused as though she'd forgotten something, then ran around to his side of the car. When Tanner rolled down his window, she leaned over and gave him one of her famous bear hugs, hurling her arms around his neck and squeezing enthusiastically. "Bye, Dad."

"Bye, sweetheart. You've got the phone number of my hotel to give Mrs. Parsons?"

Nicole patted her jeans pocket. "It's right here."

"Be good."

"I will."

When Tanner looked up, he noted that Joanna was standing behind her daughter, her hands resting on Kristen's shoulders. Cool, disapproving eyes surveyed him. Yup, it was the same woman all right. Joanna Parsons's gaze could freeze watermelon at a Fourth of July picnic.

CHAPTER THREE

"WOULD YOU LIKE more spaghetti, Nicole?" Joanna asked for the second time.

"No, thanks, Mrs. Parsons."

"You asked her that already," Kristen commented, giving her mother a puzzled look. "After we've done the dishes, Nicole and I are going to practise our song."

Joanna nodded. "Good idea, but do your homework first."

Kristen exchanged a knowing look with her friend, and the two grinned at each other.

"I'm really glad you're letting me stay the night, Mrs. Parsons," Nicole said, as she carried her empty plate to the kitchen sink. "Dinner was great. Dad tries, but he isn't much of a cook. We get take-out food a lot." She wandered back to the table and fingered the blue-quilted place mat. "Kristen told me you sewed these, too. They're pretty."

"Thank you. The pattern is really very simple."

"They have to be," Kristen added, stuffing the last slice of toasted French bread into her mouth. "Cause Mom let me do a couple of them."

"You made two of these?"

"Yeah," Kristen said, after she'd finished chewing. Pride beamed from her dark brown eyes. "We've made lots of things together since we bought the house. Do you have any idea how expensive curtains can be? Mom made the entire set in my room—that's why everything matches."

"The bedspread, too?"

"Naturally." Kristen made it sound like they'd whipped up the entire set over a weekend, when the project had actually taken the better part of two weeks.

"Wow."

From the way Nicole was staring at her, Joanna half expected the girl to fall to her knees in homage. She felt a stab of pity for Nicole, who seemed to crave a mother's presence. But she had to admit she was thrilled by her own daughter's pride in their joint accomplishments.

"Mom sews a lot of my clothes," Kristen added, licking the butter from her fingertips. "I thought you knew that."

"I ... No, I didn't."

"She's teaching me, too. That's the best part. So I'll be able to make costumes for our next talent show." Kristen's gaze flew from Nicole to her mother then back to Nicole. "I bet my mom would teach you how to sew. Wouldn't you, Mom?"

"Ah ..."

"Would you really, Mrs. Parsons?"

Not knowing what else to say, Joanna agreed with a quick nod of her head. "Why not? We'll have fun learning together." She gave an encouraging smile, but she wondered a bit anxiously if she was ready for a project like this.

"That would be great." Nicole slipped her arm around Kristen's shoulders. Her gaze dropped as she hesitated. "Dinner was really good, too," she said again.

"I told you what a great cook my mom is," Kristen boasted.

Nicole nodded, but kept her eyes trained to the floor. "Could I ask you something, Mrs. Parsons?"

"Of course."

"Like I said, Dad tries real hard, but he just isn't a very good cook. Would it be rude to ask you for the recipe for your spaghetti sauce?"

"Not at all. I'll write it out for you tonight."

"Gee, thanks. It's so nice over here. I wish Dad would let me stay here all the time. You and Kristen do such neat things, and you eat real good, too."

Joanna could well imagine the kind of meals Tanner Lund served his daughter. She already knew that he frequently ordered out, and the rest probably came from the frozen-food section of the local grocery. That was if he didn't have an array of willing females who did his cooking for him. Someone like this Becky person, the woman he was with now.

"Dad makes great tacos though," Nicole was saying. "They're his specialty. He said I might be able to have a slumber party for my birthday in March, and I want him to serve tacos then. But I might ask him to make spaghetti instead—if he gets the recipe right."

"You get to have a slumber party?" Kristen cried, her eyes widening. "That's great! My mom said I could have two friends over for the night on my birthday, but only two, because that's all she can mentally handle."

Joanna pretended an interest in her leftover salad, stirring her fork through the dressing that sat in the bottom of the bowl. It was true; there were limits to her mothering abilities. A house full of screaming eleven- and twelve-year-olds was more than she dared contemplate on a full stomach.

While Nicole finished clearing off the table, Kristen loaded the dishwasher. Working together, the two completed their tasks in only a few minutes.

"We're going to my room now. Okay, Mom?"

"Sure, honey, that's fine," Joanna said, placing the leftovers in the refrigerator. She paused, then decided to remind the pair a second time. "Homework before anything else."

"Of course," answered Kristen.

"Naturally," added Nicole.

Both vanished down the hallway that led to Kristen's bedroom. Watching them, Joanna grinned. The friendship with Nicole had been good for Kristen, and Joanna intended to shower love and attention on Nicole in the hope of compensating her for her unsettled home life.

Once Joanna had finished wiping down the kitchen counters, she made her way to Kristen's bedroom. Dutifully knocking—since her daughter made emphatic comments about privacy these days—she let herself in. Both girls were sitting cross-legged on the bed, spelling books open on their laps.

"Need any help?"

"No, thanks, Mom."

Still Joanna lingered, looking for an excuse to stay and chat. "I was placed third in the school spelling bee when I was your age."

Kristen glanced speculatively toward her friend. "That's great, Mom."

Warming to her subject, Joanna hurried to add, "I could outspell every boy in the class."

Kristen closed her textbook. "Mrs. Andrews, our new teacher, said the school wasn't going to have a spelling bee this year."

Joanna walked into the room and sat on the edge of the bed. "That's too bad, because I know you'd do well."

"I only got a B in spelling, Mom. I'm okay, but it's not my best subject."

A short uneasy silence followed while both girls studied Joanna, as though waiting for her to either leave or make a formal announcement.

"I thought we'd pop popcorn later," Joanna said, flashing a cheerful smile.

"Good." Kristen nodded and her gaze fell pointedly to her textbook. This was followed by another long moment of silence.

"Mom, I thought you said you wanted us to do our homework."

"I do."

"Well, we can't very well do it with you sitting here watching us."

"Oh." Joanna leaped off the bed. "Sorry."

"That's all right."

"Let me know when you're done."

"Why?" Kristen asked, looking perplexed.

Joanna shrugged. "I . . . I thought we might all sit around and chat. Girl talk, that sort of thing." Without being obvious about it, she'd hoped to offer Nicole maternal advice and some much needed affection. The thought of the little girl's father and what he was doing that very evening was so distasteful that Joanna had to force herself not to frown.

"Mom, Nicole and I are going to practise our song once we've finished our homework. Remember?"

"Oh, right. I forgot." Sheepishly, she started to walk away.

"I really appreciate your sewing my costume, Mrs. Parsons," Nicole added.

"It's no trouble, Nicole. I'm happy to do it."

"Speaking of the costumes," Kristen muttered, "didn't you say something about wanting to finish them before the weekend?"

"I did?" The look Kristen gave her suggested she must have. "Oh, right, now I remember."

The girls, especially her daughter, seemed relieved when Joanna left the bedroom. This wasn't going well. She'd planned on spending extra time with them, but it was clear they weren't keen on having her around. Taking a deep breath, Joanna headed for the living room, feeling a little piqued. Her ego should be strong enough to handle rejection from two eleven-year-old girls.

She settled in the kitchen and brought out her sewing machine again. The red costumes for the talent show were nearly finished. She ran her hand over the polished cotton and let her thoughts wander. She and Kristen had lived in the house only since September. For the six years following the divorce, Joanna had been forced to raise her daughter in a small apartment. Becoming a home owner had been a major step for her and she was proud of the time and care that had gone into choosing their small one-storey house. It had required some repairs, but nothing major, and the sense of accomplishment she'd experienced when she signed her name to the mortgage papers had been well worth the years of scrimping. The house had only two bedrooms, but there was plenty of space in the backyard for a garden, something Joanna had insisted on. She thought that anyone studying her might be amused. On the one hand, she was a woman with basic traditional values, and on the other, a goal-setting businesswoman struggling to succeed in a male-dominated field. Her boss would have found it difficult to understand that the woman who'd set her sights on the position of senior loan officer liked the feel of wet dirt under her fingernails. And he would have been surprised to learn that she could take a simple piece of bright red cotton and turn it into a dazzling costume for a talent show.

An hour later, when Joanna was watching television and finishing up the hand stitching on the costumes, Kristen and Nicole rushed into the living room, looking pleased about something.

"You girls ready for popcorn?"

"Not me," Nicole said, placing her hands over her stomach. "I'm still full from dinner."

Joanna nodded. The girl obviously wasn't accustomed to eating nutritionally balanced meals.

"We want to do our song for you."

"Great." Joanna scooted close to the edge of the sofa, eagerly awaiting their performance. Kristen plugged in her ghetto blaster and snapped in the cassette, then hurried to her friend's side, striking a pose until the music started.

"I can tell already that you're going to be great," Joanna said, clapping her hands to the lively beat.

She was right. The two did astonishingly well, and when they'd finished Joanna applauded loudly.

"We did okay?"

"You were fabulous."

Kristen and Nicole positively glowed.

When they returned to Kristen's bedroom, Joanna followed them. Kristen turned around and seemed surprised to find her mother there.

"Mom," she hissed between clenched teeth, "what's with you tonight? You haven't been yourself since Nicole arrived."

"I haven't?"

"You keep following us around."

"I do?"

"Really, Mom, we like you and everything, but Nicole and I want to talk about boys and stuff, and we can't very well do that with you here."

"Oh, Mrs. Parsons, I forgot to tell you," Nicole inserted, obviously unaware of the whispered conversation going on between Kristen and her mother. "I told my dad about you making my costume for the talent show, and he said he wants to pay you for your time and expenses."

"You told your dad?" Kristen asked, and whirled around to face her friend. "I thought you weren't going to because he'd feel guilty. Oh, I get it! That's how you got him to let you spend the night. Great idea!"

Joanna frowned. "What exactly does that mean?"

The two girls exchanged meaningful glances and Nicole looked distinctly uncomfortable.

"What does what mean?" Kristen repeated the question in a slightly elevated voice Joanna recognized immediately. Her daughter was up to one of her schemes again.

Nicole stepped in front of her friend. "It's my fault, Mrs. Parsons. I wanted to spend the night here instead of with Mrs. Wagner, so I told Dad that Kristen had invited me."

"Mom, you've got to understand. Mrs. Wagner won't let Nicole watch anything but educational television, and you know there are special shows we like to watch."

"That's not the part I mean," Joanna said, dismissing their rushed explanation. "I want to know what you meant by not telling Mr. Lund about the talent show because he'd feel guilty."

"Oh...that part." The two girls glanced at each other, as though silently deciding which one would do the explaining.

Nicole raised her gaze to Joanna and sighed, her thin shoulders moving up and down expressively. "My dad won't be able to attend the talent show because he's got a business meeting in Seattle, and I knew he'd feel terrible about it. He really likes it when I do things like the show. It gives him something to tell my grandparents about, like I was going to be the next Madonna or something."

"He has to travel a lot to business meetings," Kristen added quickly.

"Business meetings?"

"Like tonight," Kristen went on to explain.

"Dad has to fly someplace with Mr. Becky. He owns half the company and Dad owns the other half. He said it had to do with getting a big order, but I never listen to stuff like that, although Dad likes to explain every little detail so I'll know where he's at and what he's doing."

Joanna felt a numbing sensation creeping slowly up her spine. "Your dad owns half a company?"

"Spokane Aluminum is the reason we moved here from West Virginia."

"Spokane Aluminum?" Joanna's voice rose half an octave. "Your dad owns half of Spokane Aluminum?" The company was one of the largest employers in the Northwest. A shockingly large percentage of their state's economy was directly or indirectly tied to this company. A sick feeling settled in Joanna's stomach. Not only was Nicole's father wealthy, he was socially prominent, and all the while she'd been thinking... Oh, dear heavens. "So your father's out of town tonight?" she asked, feeling the warmth invade her face.

"You knew that, Mom." Kristen gave her mother another one of those searching gazes that suggested Joanna might be losing her memory—due to advanced age, no doubt.

"I...I thought—" Abruptly she bit off what she'd been about to say. When Kristen had said something about Tanner being with Becky, she'd assumed it was a woman. But of course it was *John* Becky, whose name was familiar to everyone in that part of the country. Joanna remembered reading in the *Review* that Becky had taken on a partner, but she hadn't made the connection. Perhaps she'd misjudged Tanner Lund, she reluctantly conceded. Perhaps she'd been a bit too eager to view him in a bad light.

"Before we came to Spokane," Nicole was saying now, "Dad and I had a long talk about the changes the move would make in our lives. We made a list of the good things and a list of the bad things, and then we talked about them. One bad thing was that Dad would be gone a lot, until he can hire another manager. He doesn't feel good about leaving me with strangers, and we didn't know a single person in Spokane other than Mr. Becky and his wife, but they're real old—over forty, anyway. He even went and interviewed Mrs. Wagner before I spent the night there the first time."

The opinion Joanna had formed of Tanner Lund was crumbling at her feet. Evidently he wasn't the irresponsible parent she'd assumed.

"Nicole told me you met her dad in the grocery store when you bought the mix for the cupcakes." Kristen shook her head as if to say she was thoroughly disgusted with her mother for not taking her advice that night and curling her hair before she showed her face in public.

"I told my dad you don't dress that way all the time," Nicole added, then shifted her gaze to the other side of the room. "But I don't think he believed me until he dropped me off tonight."

Joanna began to edge her way toward the bedroom door. "Your father and I seem to have started off on the wrong foot," she said weakly.

Nicole bit her lower lip. "I know. He wasn't real keen on me spending the night here, but I talked him into it."

"Mom?" Kristen asked, frowning. "What did you say to Mr. Lund when you met him at the store?"

"Nothing," she answered, taking a few more retreating steps.

"She asked my dad what I was doing up so late on a school night, and he told me later that he didn't like her attitude," Nicole explained. "I didn't get a chance to tell you that I'm normally in bed by nine-thirty, but that night was special because Dad had just come home from one of his trips. His plane was late and I didn't remember to tell him about the party stuff until after we got home from Mrs. Wagner's."

"I see," Joanna murmured, and swallowed uncomfortably.

"You'll get a chance to settle things with Mr. Lund when he picks up Nicole tomorrow night," Kristen stated, and it was obvious that she wanted her mother to make an effort to get along with her best friend's father.

"Right," Joanna muttered, dreading the confrontation. She never had been particularly fond of eating crow.

CHAPTER FOUR

JOANNA WAS BREADING PORK CHOPS the following evening when Kristen barrelled into the kitchen, leaving the door swinging in her wake. "Mr. Lund's here to pick up Nicole. I think you should invite him and Nicole to stay for dinner... and explain about, you know, the other night."

Oh, sure, Joanna mused. She often invited company owners and acting presidents over for an evening meal. Pork chops and mashed potatoes weren't likely to impress someone like Tanner Lund.

Before Kristen could launch into an argument, Joanna shook her head and offered the first excuse that came to mind. "There aren't enough pork chops to ask him tonight. Besides, Mr. Lund is probably tired from his trip and anxious to get home."

"I bet he's hungry, too," Kristen pressed. "And Nicole thinks you're a fabulous cook, and—"

A sharp look from her mother cut her off. "Another night, Kristen!"

Joanna brushed the bread crumbs off her fingertips and untied her apron. Inhaling deeply, she paused long enough to run a hand through her hair and check her reflection in the window above the sink. No one was going to mistake her for Miss America, but her appearance was passable. Okay, it was time to hold her head high, spit the feathers out of her mouth and get ready to down some crow.

Joanna forced a welcoming smile onto her lips as she stepped into the living room. Tanner stood awkwardly just inside the front door, as though prepared to beat a hasty retreat if necessary. "How was your trip?" she ventured, straining to make the question sound cheerful.

"Fine. Thank you." His expression didn't change.

"Do you have time for a cup of coffee?" she asked next, doing her best to disguise her unease. She wondered quickly if she'd unpacked her china cups yet. After their shaky beginning, Joanna wasn't quite sure if she could undo the damage. But standing in the entryway wouldn't work. She needed to sit down for this.

He eyed her suspiciously. Joanna wasn't sure she should even try to explain things. In time he'd learn she wasn't a candidate for the loony bin—just as she'd stumbled over the fact that he wasn't a terrible father. Trying to tell him that she was an upstanding member of the community after he'd seen her dressed in a wool coat draped over pajamas, giving him looks that suggested he be reported to Children's Protective Services, wasn't exactly a task she relished.

Tanner glanced at his wristwatch and shook his head. "I haven't got time to visit tonight. Thanks for the invitation, though."

Joanna almost sighed aloud with relief.

"Did Nicole behave herself?"

Joanna nodded. "She wasn't the least bit of trouble. Nicole's a great kid."

A smile cracked the tight edges of his mouth. "Good."

Kristen and Nicole burst into the room. "Is Mr. Lund going to stay, Mom?"

"He can't tonight..."

"Another time..."

They spoke simultaneously, with an equal lack of enthusiasm.

"Oh." The girls looked at each other and frowned, their disappointment noticeable.

"Have you packed everything, Nicole?" Tanner asked, not hiding his eagerness to leave.

The eleven-year-old nodded reluctantly. "I think so."

"Don't you think you should check my room one more time?" Kristen suggested, grabbing her friend's hand and leading her back toward the hallway.

"Oh, right. I suppose I should." The two disappeared before either Joanna or Tanner could call them back.

The silence between them hummed so loudly Joanna swore she could have waltzed to it. But since the opportunity had presented itself, she decided to get the unpleasant task of explaining her behavior out of the way while she still had her nerve.

"I think I owe you an apology," she murmured, her face flushing.

"An apology?"

"I thought...you know... The night we met, I assumed you were an irresponsible parent because Nicole was up so late. She's now told me that you'd just returned from a trip."

"Yes, well, I admit I did feel the sting of your disapproval."

This wasn't easy. Joanna swallowed uncomfortably and laced her fingers together forcing herself to meet his eyes. "Nicole explained that your flight was delayed and she forgot to mention the party supplies when you picked her up at the baby-sitter's. She said she didn't remember until you got all the way home."

Tanner's mouth relaxed a bit more. "Since we're both being truthful here, I'll admit that I wasn't overly impressed with you that night, either."

Joanna dropped her gaze. "I can imagine. I hope you realise I don't usually dress like that."

"I gathered as much when I dropped Nicole off yesterday afternoon."

They both paused to share a brief smile and Joanna instantly felt better. It hadn't been easy to blurt all this out, but she was relieved that they'd finally cleared the air.

"Since Kristen and Nicole are such good friends, I thought, well, that I should set things right between us. From everything Nicole's said, you're doing an excellent job of parenting."

"From everything she's told me, the same must be true of you."

"Believe me, it isn't easy raising a preteen daughter," Joanna announced. She rubbed her palms together a couple of times, searching for something brilliant to add.

Tanner shook his head. "Isn't that the truth?"

They laughed then, and because they were still awkward with each other the sound was rusty.

"Now that you mention it, maybe I could spare a few minutes for a cup of coffee."

"Sure." Joanna led the way into the kitchen. While Tanner sat down at the table, she filled a mug from the pot keeping warm on the plate of the automatic coffee maker and placed it carefully in front of him. Now that she knew him a bit better, she realised he'd prefer that to a dainty china cup. "How do you take it?"

"Just black, thanks."

She pulled out the chair across the table from him, still feeling a little ill at ease. Her mind was whirling. She didn't want to give Tanner a second wrong impression

now that she'd managed to correct the first one. Her
worry was that he might interpret her friendliness as a sign
of romantic interest, which it wasn't. Building a new relationship was low on her priority list. Besides, they simply weren't on the same economic level. She worked for a
savings-and-loan institution and he was half owner of the
largest employer in the area. The last thing she wanted was
for Tanner to think of her as a gold digger.

Joanna's thoughts were tumbling over themselves as she
struggled to find a diplomatic way of telling him all this
without sounding like some kind of man hater. And
without sounding presumptuous.

"I'd like to pay you," Tanner said, cutting into her re-
flections. His cheque-book was resting on the table, Cross
pen poised above it.

Joanna blinked, not understanding. "For the coffee?"

He gave her an odd look. "For looking after Nicole."

"No, please." Joanna shook her head dismissively. "It
wasn't the least bit of trouble for her to stay the night.
Really."

"What about the costume for the talent show? Surely
I owe you something for that."

"No." Once more she shook her head for emphasis.
"I've had that material tucked away in a drawer for ages.
If I hadn't used it for Nicole's costume, I'd probably have
ended up giving it away later."

"But your time must be worth something."

"It was just as easy to sew up two as one. I was happy
to do it. Anyway, there'll probably be a time in the future
when I need a favour. I'm worthless when it comes to
electrical outlets and even worse with plumbing."

Joanna couldn't believe she'd said that. Tanner Lund
wasn't the type of man to do his own electrical repairs.

"Don't be afraid to ask," he told her. "If I can't fix it, I'll find someone who can."

"Thank you," she said, relaxing. Now that she was talking to Tanner, she decided he was both pleasant and forthright, not at all the coldly remote or self-important man his wealth might have led her to expect.

"Mom," Kristen cried as she charged into the kitchen, "did you ask Mr. Lund yet?"

"About what?"

"About coming over for dinner some time."

Joanna felt the heat shoot up her neck and face until it reached her hairline. Kristen had made the invitation sound like a romantic tryst the three of them had been planning the entire time Tanner was away.

Nicole, entering the room behind her friend, provided a timely interruption.

"Dad, Kristen and I want to do our song for you now."

"I'd like to see it. Do you mind, Joanna?"

"Of course not."

"Mom finished the costumes last night. We'll change and be back in a minute," Kristen said, her voice high with excitement. The two scurried off. The minute they were out of sight, Joanna stood up abruptly and refilled her cup. Actually she was looking for a way to speak frankly to Tanner, without embarrassing herself—or him. She thought ironically that anyone looking at her now would be hard put to believe she was a competent loan officer with a promising future.

"I think I should explain something," she began, her voice unsteady.

"Yes?" Tanner asked, his gaze following her movements around the kitchen.

Joanna couldn't seem to stand in one place for long. She moved from the coffeepot to the refrigerator, finally stopping in front of the stove. She linked her fingers behind her back and took a deep breath before she trusted herself to speak. "I thought it was important to clear up any misunderstanding between us, because the girls are such good friends. When Nicole's with Kristen and me, I want you to know she's in good hands."

Tanner gave her a polite nod. "I appreciate that."

"But I have a feeling that Kristen—and maybe Nicole, too—would like for us to get to know each other, er, better, if you know what I mean." Oh Lord, that sounded so stupid. Joanna felt herself grasping at straws. "I'm not interested in a romantic relationship, Tanner. I've got too much going on in my life to get involved, and I don't want you to feel threatened by the girls and their schemes. Forgive me for being so blunt, but I'd prefer to have this out in the open." She'd blurted it out so fast, she wondered if he'd understood. "This dinner invitation was Kristen's idea, not mine. I don't want you to think I had anything to do with it."

"An invitation to dinner isn't exactly a marriage proposal."

"True," Joanna threw back quickly. "But you might think...I don't know. I guess I don't want you to assume I'm interested in you—romantically, that is." She slumped back into the chair, pushed her hair away from her forehead and released a long sigh. "I'm only making matters worse, aren't I?"

"No. If I understand you correctly, you're saying you'd like to be friends and nothing more."

"Right." Pleased with his perceptiveness, Joanna straightened. Glad he could say in a few simple words what had left her breathless.

"The truth of the matter is, I feel much the same way," Tanner went on to explain. "I was married once and it was more than enough."

Joanna found herself nodding enthusiastically. "Exactly. I like my life the way it is. Kristen and I are very close. We just moved into this house and we've lots of plans for redecorating. My career is going nicely."

"Likewise. I'm too busy with this company to get involved in a relationship, either. The last thing I need right now is a woman to complicate my life."

"A man would only come between Kristen and me at this stage."

"How long have you been divorced?" Tanner asked, folding his hands around his coffee mug.

"Six years."

The information appeared to satisfy him, and he nodded slowly, as though to say he trusted what she was telling him. "It's been five for me."

She nodded, too. Like her, he hadn't immediately jumped into another relationship, nor was he looking for one. No doubt he had his reasons; Joanna knew she had hers.

"Friends?" Tanner asked, and extended his hand for her to shake.

"And nothing more," Joanna added, placing her hand in his.

They exchanged a smile.

"SINCE MR. LUND can't be here for the talent show on Wednesday, he wants to take Nicole and me out for dinner next Saturday night," Kristen announced. "Nicole said to ask you if it was all right."

"That's fine," Joanna returned absently, scanning the front page of the Saturday evening newspaper. It had been more than a week since she'd spoken to Tanner. She felt good about the way things had gone that afternoon; they understood each other now, despite their rather uncertain start.

Kristen darted back into the kitchen, returning a minute later. "I think it would be best if you spoke to Mr. Lund yourself, Mom."

"Okay, honey." She'd finished reading Dear Abby and had just turned to the comics section, looking for Garfield, her favourite cat.

"Mom!" Kristen cried impatiently. "Mr. Lund's on the phone now. You can't keep him waiting like this. It's impolite."

Hurriedly Joanna set the paper aside. "For heaven's sake, why didn't you say so earlier?"

"I did. Honestly, Mom, I think you're losing it."

Whatever *it* was sounded serious. The minute Joanna was inside the kitchen, Kristen thrust the telephone receiver into her hand.

"This is Joanna," she said.

"This is Tanner," he answered right away. "Don't feel bad. Nicole claims I'm losing *it* too."

"I'd take her more seriously if I knew what *it* was."

"Yeah, me too," Tanner said, and she could hear the laughter in his voice. "Listen, is dinner next Saturday evening all right with you?"

"I can't see a problem at this end."

"Great. The girls suggested that ice-cream parlour they're always talking about."

"The Pink Palace," Joanna said, and managed to swallow a chuckle. Tanner was really letting himself in for a crazy night with those two. Last year Kristen had talked Joanna into dinner there for her birthday. The hamburgers had been as expensive as T-bone steaks, and tough as rawhide. The music was so loud it had impaired Joanna's hearing for an entire week afterward. And the place was packed with teenagers. On the bright side, though, the ice cream was pretty good.

"By the way," Joanna said, "Nicole's welcome to stay here when you're away next week."

"Joanna, that's great. I didn't want to ask, but the kid's been at me ever since the last time. She was worried I was going to send her back to Mrs. Wagner."

"It'll work best for her to stay here, since that's the night of the talent show."

"Are you absolutely sure?"

"Absolutely. It's no trouble at all. Just drop her off—and don't worry."

"Right." He sounded relieved. "And don't wear anything fancy next Saturday night."

"Saturday night?" Joanna asked, lost for a moment.

"Yeah. Didn't you just tell me it was all right for the four of us to go to dinner?"

CHAPTER FIVE

"I REALLY APPRECIATE THIS, Joanna," Tanner said. Nicole stood at his side, overnight bag clenched in her hand, her eyes round and sad.

"It's no problem, Tanner. Really."

Tanner hugged his daughter tightly. He briefly closed his eyes and Joanna could feel his regret. He was as upset about missing his daughter's talent-show performance as Nicole was not to have him there.

"Be good, sweetheart."

"I will."

"And I want to hear all the details about tonight when I get back, okay?"

Nicole nodded and attempted a smile.

"I'd be there if I could."

"I know, Dad. Don't worry about it. There'll be plenty of other talent shows. Kristen and I were thinking that if we do really good, we might take our act on the road, the way Daisy Gilbert does."

"Daisy who?" Tanner asked, and raised questioning eyes to Joanna, as if he expected her to supply the answer.

"A singer," was the best Joanna could do. Kristen had as many cassette tapes as Joanna had runs in her tights. She found it impossible to keep her daughter's favourite rock stars straight. Apparently Tanner wasn't any more knowledgeable than she was.

"Not just *any* singer, Mom," Kristen corrected impatiently. "Daisy's special. She's only a little older than Nicole and me, and if she can be a rock star at fifteen, then so can we."

Although Joanna hated to squelch such optimism, she suspected that the girls might be missing one minor skill if they hoped to find fame and fortune as professional singers. "But you don't sing."

"Yeah, but we lip-synch real good."

"Come on, Nicole," Kristen said, reaching for her friend's overnight bag. "We've got to practise."

The two disappeared down the hallway and Joanna was left alone with Tanner.

"You have the telephone number for the hotel and the meeting place?" he asked.

"I'll call if there's a problem. Don't worry, Tanner, I'm sure everything's going to be fine."

He nodded, but a tight scowl darkened his face.

"For heaven's sake, stop looking so guilty."

His eyes widened in surprise. "It shows?"

"It might as well be flashing from a marquee."

Tanner grinned and rubbed the side of his jaw with his left hand. "There are only two meetings left that I'll have to deal with personally. Becky's promised to handle the others. You know, when I bought into the company and committed myself to these trips, I didn't think leaving Nicole would be this traumatic. We both hate it—at least, she did until she spent the night here with you and Kristen the last time."

"She's a special little girl."

"Thanks," Tanner said, looking suitably proud. It was obvious that he worked hard at being a good father, and Joanna felt a twinge of conscience for the assumptions she'd made about him earlier.

"Listen," she murmured, then took a deep breath, wondering how best to approach the subject of dinner. "About Saturday night..."

"What about it?"

"I thought, well, it would be best if it were just you and the girls."

Already he was shaking his head, his mouth set in firm lines of resolve. "It wouldn't be the same without you. I owe you, Joanna, and since you won't accept payment for keeping Nicole, then the least you can do is agree to dinner."

"But—"

"If you're worried about this seeming too much like a date—don't. We understand each other."

Her responding smile was decidedly weak. "Okay, if that's the way you want it. Kristen and I'll be ready Saturday at six."

"Good."

JOANNA WAS PUTTING the finishing touches to her make-up before the talent show when the telephone rang.

"I'll get it," Kristen yelled, racing down the hallway as if answering the phone before the second ring was a matter of life and death.

Joanna rolled her eyes toward the ceiling at the importance telephone conversations had recently assumed for Kristen. She half expected the call to be from Tanner, but then she heard Kristen exclaim, "Hi, Grandma!" Joanna smiled softly, pleased that her mother had remembered the talent show. Her parents were retired and lived in Colville, a town about sixty miles north of Spokane. She knew they would have attended the talent show themselves had road conditions been better. In winter, the families tended to keep in touch by phone because driving could be hazardous. No doubt her mother was calling now to wish Kristen luck.

Bits and pieces of the conversation drifted down the hallway as Kristen chatted excitedly about the show, Nicole's visit and their song.

"Mom, it's Grandma!" Kristen yelled. "She wants to talk to you."

Joanna finished blotting her lipstick and hurried to the phone. "Hi, Mom," she said cheerfully. "It's nice of you to call."

"What's this about you going out on a date Saturday night?"

"Who told you that?" Joanna demanded, groaning silently. Her mother had been telling her for years that she ought to remarry. Joanna felt like throttling Kristen for even mentioning Tanner's name. The last thing she needed was for her parents to start pressuring her about this relationship.

"Why, Kristen told me all about it, and sweetie, if you don't mind my saying so, this man sounds just perfect for you. You're both single parents. He has a daughter, you have a daughter, and the girls are best friends. The arrangement is ideal."

"Mother, please, I don't know what Kristen told you, but Tanner only wants to thank me for watching Nicole while he's away on business. Dinner on Saturday night is not a date!"

"He's taking you to dinner?"

"Me and Kristen and his daughter."

"What was his name again?"

"Tanner Lund," Joanna answered, desperate to change the subject. "Hasn't the weather been nasty this week? I'm really looking forward to spring. I was thinking about planting some annuals along the back fence."

"Tanner Lund," her mother repeated, slowly drawling out his name. "Now that has a nice solid feel to it. What's he like, sweetie?"

"Oh, honestly, Mother, I don't know. He's a man. What more do you want me to say?"

Her mother seemed to approve that piece of information. "I find it interesting that that's the way you view him. I think he could be the one, Joanna."

"Mother, please, how many times do I have to tell you? I'm not going to remarry. Ever!"

A short pause followed her announcement. "We'll see, sweetie, we'll see."

" AREN'T YOU GOING to wear a dress, Mom?" Kristen gave her another of those scathing glances intended to melt a mother's confidence into puddles of doubt. Joanna had deliberated for hours on what to wear for this evening out with Tanner and the girls. If she chose a dress, something simple and classic like the ones she wore to the office, she might look too formal for a casual outing. The only other dresses she owned were party dresses, and those were so outdated they were almost back in style.

Dark wool pants and a wheat-colored Irish cableknit sweater had seemed the perfect solution. Or so Joanna had thought until Kristen looked at her and frowned.

"Mom, tonight is important."

"We're going to the Pink Palace, not the Spokane House."

"I know, but Mr. Lund is so nice." Her daughter's gaze fell on the bouquet of pink roses on the dining-room table, and she reverently stroked a bloom. Tanner had arranged for the flowers to be delivered to Nicole and Kristen the night of the talent show. "You can't wear slacks to dinner with the man who sent me my first real flowers," she announced in tones of finality.

Joanna hesitated. "I'm sure this is what Mr. Lund expects," she said with far more confidence than she felt.

"You think so?"

She hoped so! She smiled, praying that her air of certainty would be enough to appease her sceptical daughter. Still, she had to agree with Kristen: Tanner *was* nice. More than nice—that was such a weak word. With every meeting, Joanna's estimation of the man grew. He'd called on Friday to thank her for minding Nicole, who'd gone straight home from school on Thursday afternoon since her father was back, and mentioned he was looking forward to Saturday. He was thoughtful, sensitive, personable, and a wonderful father. Not to mention one of the best-looking men she'd ever met. It was unfortunate, really, that she wasn't looking for a husband, because Tanner Lund could easily be a prime candidate.

The word husband bounced in Joanna's mind like a ricocheting bullet. She blamed her mother for that. What she'd told her was true—Joanna was finished with marriage, finished with love. Davey had taught her how difficult it was for most men to remain faithful, and Joanna had no intention of repeating those painful lessons. Besides, if a man ever did become part of her life again, it would be someone on her own social and economic level. Not like Tanner Lund. But that didn't mean she was completely blind to male charms. On the contrary, she saw handsome men every day, worked with several, and had even dated a few. However, it was Tanner Lund she found herself thinking about lately, and that bothered Joanna. It bothered her a lot.

The best thing to do was nip this near relationship in the bud. She'd go to dinner with him this once, but only this once, and that would be the end of it.

"They're here!" The drape swished back into place as Kristen bolted away from the large picture window.

Calmly Joanna opened the hall closet and retrieved their winter coats. She might appear outwardly composed, but her fingers were shaking. The prospect of seeing Tanner left her trembling, and that fact drained away what little confidence she'd managed to accumulate over the past couple of days.

Both Tanner and Nicole came to the front door. Kristen held out her hands, and Nicole gripped them eagerly. Soon the two were jumping up and down like pogo sticks gone berserk.

"I can tell we're in for a fun evening," Tanner muttered under his breath.

He looked wonderful, Joanna admitted grudgingly. The kind of man every woman dreams about—well, almost every woman. Joanna longed to think of herself as immune to the handsome Mr. Lund. Unfortunately she wasn't.

Since their last meeting, she'd tried to figure out when her feelings for Tanner had changed. The roses had done it, she decided. Ordering them for Kristen and Nicole had been so thoughtful, and the girls had been ecstatic at the gesture.

When they'd finished lip-synching their song, they'd bowed before the auditorium full of appreciative parents. Then the school principal, Mr. Holliday, had stood at their side and presented them each with a beautiful bouquet of long-stemmed pink roses. Flowers Tanner had wired because he couldn't be there to watch their act.

"Are you ready?" Tanner asked, holding open the door for Joanna.

She nodded. "I think so."

Although it was early, a line had already begun to form outside the Pink Palace when they arrived. The minute they pulled into the parking lot, they were accosted by a loud, vibrating rock-and-roll song that might have been an old Jerry Lee Lewis number.

"It looks like we'll have to wait," Joanna commented. "That lineup's getting longer by the minute."

"I had my secretary make reservations," Tanner told her. "I heard this place really grooves on a Saturday night."

"Grooves!" Nicole repeated, smothering her giggles behind her cupped palm. Kristen laughed with her.

Turner leaned his head close to Joanna's. "It's difficult to reason with a generation that grew up without Janis and Jimi!"

Janis Joplin and Jimi Hendrix were a bit before Joanna's time, too, but she knew what he meant.

The Pink Palace was exactly as Joanna remembered. The popular ice-cream parlor was decorated in a fifties theme, with old-fashioned circular booths and outdated jukeboxes. The waitresses wore billowing pink skirts with a French poodle design and roller-skated between tables, taking and delivering orders. Once inside, Joanna, Tanner and the girls were seated almost immediately and handed huge menus. Neither girl bothered to read through the selections, having made their choices in the car. They'd both decided on cheeseburgers and banana splits.

By the time the waitress, chewing on a thick wad of bubble gum, skated to a stop at their table, Joanna had made her selection, too.

"A cheeseburger and a banana split," she said, grinning at the girls.

"Same here," Tanner said, "and coffee, please."

"I'll have a cup, too," Joanna added.

The teenager wrote down their order and glided toward the kitchen.

Joanna opened her purse and brought out a small wad of cotton wool.

"What's that for?" Tanner wanted to know when she pulled it apart into four fluffy balls and handed two of them to him, keeping the other pair for herself.

She pointed to her ears. "The last time I was here, I was haunted for days by a ringing in my ears that sounded suspiciously like an old Elvis tune."

Tanner chuckled and leaned across the table to shout, "It does get a bit loud, doesn't it?"

Kristen and Nicole looked from one parent to the other then shouted together, "If it's too loud, you're too old!"

Joanna raised her hand. "Guilty as charged."

Tanner nodded and shared a smile with Joanna. The smile did funny things to her stomach, and Joanna pressed her hands over her abdomen in a futile effort to quell her growing awareness of Tanner. A warning light flashed in her mind, spelling out danger.

Joanna wasn't sure what had come over her, but whatever it was, she didn't like it.

Their meal arrived, and for a while, at least, Joanna could direct her attention to that. The food was better than she remembered. The cheeseburgers were juicy and tender and the banana splits divine. She promised herself she'd eat cottage cheese and fruit every day at lunch for the next week to balance all the extra calories from this one meal.

While Joanna and Tanner exchanged only the occasional remark, the girls chattered happily throughout dinner. When the waitress skated away with the last of their empty plates, Tanner suggested a movie.

"Great idea!" Nicole cried, enthusiastically seconded by Kristen.

"What do you think, Joanna?" asked Tanner.

She started to say that the evening had been full enough—until she found two eager young faces looking hopefully at her. She couldn't finish her sentence; it just wasn't in her to dash their good time.

"Sure," she managed instead, trying to insert a bit of excitement into her voice.

"*Teen Massacre* is showing at the mall," Nicole said, shooting a glance in her father's direction. "Donny Rosenburg saw it and claims it scared him out of his wits, but then Donny doesn't have many."

Kristen laughed and nodded, apparently well-acquainted with the witless Donny.

Without the least bit of hesitation, Tanner shook his head. "No way, Nicole."

"Come on, Dad, everyone's seen it. The only reason it got an adult rating is because of the blood and gore, and I've seen that lots of times."

"Discussion is closed." He spoke without raising his voice, but the authority behind his words was enough to convince Joanna she'd turn up the loser if she ever crossed Tanner Lund. Still, she knew she wouldn't hesitate if she felt he was wrong, but in this case she agreed with him completely.

Nicole's lower lip jutted out rebelliously, and for a minute Joanna thought the girl might try to argue her case. But she wasn't surprised when Nicole yielded without further argument.

Deciding which movie to see involved some real negotiating. The girls had definite ideas of what was acceptable, as did Tanner and Joanna. Like Tanner, Joanna
wasn't about to allow her daughter to see a movie with an
adult rating, even if it was "only because of the blood and
gore."

They finally compromised on a comedy that starred a
popular teen idol. The girls thought that would be "all
right," but they made it clear that *Teen Massacre* was their
first choice.

Half an hour later they were inside the theater, and
Tanner asked, "Anyone for popcorn?"

"Me," Kristen said.

"Me, too, and could we both have a Coke and
chocolate-covered raisins, too?" Nicole asked.

Tanner rolled his eyes and, grinning, glanced toward
Joanna. "What about you?"

"Nothing." She didn't know where the girls were going
to put all this food, but she knew where it would end up
if she were to consume it. Her hips! She sometimes suspected that junk food didn't even pass through her stomach, but attached itself directly to her hip bones.

"You're sure?"

"Positive."

Tanner returned a moment later with three large boxes
of popcorn and other assorted treats.

As soon as they'd emptied Tanner's arms of all but one
box of popcorn, the girls started into the auditorium.

"Hey, you two, wait for us," Joanna called after them,
bewildered by the way they'd hurried off without waiting
for her and Tanner.

Kristen and Nicole stopped abruptly and turned
around, a look of pure horror on their young faces.

"You're not going to sit with us, are you, Mom?" Kristen wailed. "You just can't!"

"Why not?" This was news to Joanna. Sure, it had been a while since she'd gone to a movie with her daughter, but Kristen had always sat with her in the past.

"Someone might see us," her daughter went on to explain, in tones of exaggerated patience. "No one sits with their parents any more. Not even woosies."

"Woosies?"

"Sort of like nerds, only worse!" Kristen said.

"Sitting with us is obviously a social embarrassment to be avoided at all costs," Tanner muttered.

"Can we go now, Mom?" Kristen pleaded. "I don't want to miss the previews."

Joanna nodded, still a little stunned. She enjoyed going out to a movie now and again, usually accompanied by her daughter and often several of Kristen's friends. Until tonight, no one had openly objected to sitting in the same row with her. However, now that Joanna thought about it, Kristen hadn't been interested in going to the movies for the past couple of months.

"I guess this is what happens when they hit sixth grade," Tanner said, holding the auditorium door for Joanna.

She walked down the center aisle and paused by an empty row near the back, checking with Tanner before she entered. Neither of them sat down, though, until they'd located the girls. Kristen and Nicole were three rows from the front and had slid down so far that their eyes were level with the seats ahead of them.

"Ah, the joys of fatherhood," Tanner commented, after they'd taken their places. "Not to mention motherhood."

Joanna still felt a little taken aback by what had happened. She thought she had a close relationship with Kristen, and yet her daughter had never said a word about not wanting to be anywhere near her in a movie theatre. She knew this might sound like a trivial concern to some, but she couldn't help worrying that the solid foundation she'd spent a decade reinforcing had started to crumble.

"Joanna?"

She turned to Tanner and tried to smile, but the attempt was unconvincing.

"What's wrong?"

Joanna fluttered her hand weakly, unable to find her voice. "Nothing." That came out sounding as though she might burst into tears any second.

"Is it Kristen?"

She nodded wildly.

"Because she didn't want to sit with us?"

Her hair bounced against her shoulders as she nodded again.

"The girls wanting to be by themselves bothers you?"

"No...yes. I don't know what I'm feeling. She's growing up, Tanner, and I guess it just hit me right between the eyes."

"It happened to me last week," Tanner said thoughtfully. "I found Nicole wearing a pair of tights. Hell, I didn't even know they made them for girls her age."

"They do, believe it or not," Joanna informed him. "Kristen did the same thing."

He shook his head as though he couldn't quite grasp the concept. "But they're only eleven."

"Going on sixteen."

"Has Kristen tried pasting on those fake fingernails yet?" Tanner shuddered in exaggerated disgust.

Joanna covered her mouth with one hand to hold back an attack of giggles. "Those press-on things turned up every place imaginable for weeks afterward."

Tanner turned sideways in his seat. "What about makeup?" he asked urgently.

"I caught her trying to sneak out of the house one morning last month. She was wearing the brightest eye shadow I've ever seen in my life. Tanner, I swear if she'd been standing on a shore, she could have guided lost ships into port."

He smiled, then dropped his gaze, looking uncomfortable. "So you do let her wear makeup?"

"I'm holding off as long as I can," Joanna admitted. "At the very least, she'll have to wait until seventh grade. That was when my mother let me. I don't think it's so unreasonable to expect Kristen to wait until junior high."

Tanner relaxed against the back of his seat and nodded a couple of times. "I'm glad to hear that. Nicole's been after me to 'wake up and smell the coffee,' as she puts it, for the past six months. Hell, I didn't know who to ask about these things. It really isn't something I'm comfortable discussing with my secretary."

"What about her mother?"

His eyes hardened. "She only sees Nicole when it's convenient, and it hasn't been for the past three years."

"I . . . I didn't mean to pry."

"You weren't. Carmen and I didn't exactly part on the best of terms. She's got a new life now and apparently doesn't want any reminders of the past—not that I totally blame her. We made each other miserable. Frankly, Joanna, my feelings about getting married again are the same as yours. One failed marriage was enough for me."

The theatre lights dimmed then, and the sound track started. Tanner leaned back and crossed his long legs, balancing one ankle on the opposite knee.

Joanna settled back, too, grateful that the movie they'd selected was a comedy. Her emotions were riding too close to the surface this evening. She could see herself bursting into tears at the slightest hint of sadness—for that matter, joy. Bambi traipsing through the woods would have done her in just then.

Joanna was so caught up in her thoughts that when Tanner and the others around her let out a boisterous laugh, she'd completely missed whatever had been so hilarious.

Without thinking, she reached over and grabbed a handful of Tanner's popcorn. She discovered that the crunchiness and the buttery, salty flavor suited her mood. Tanner held the box on the arm between them to make sharing easier.

The next time Joanna sent her fingers digging, they encountered Tanner's. "Sorry," she murmured, pulling her hand free.

"No problem," he answered, tilting the box her way.

Joanna munched steadily. Before she knew it, the popcorn was gone and her fingers were laced with Tanner's, her hand firmly clasped in his.

The minute he reached for her hand, Joanna lost track of what was happening on the screen. Holding hands seemed such an innocent gesture, something teenagers did. He certainly didn't mean anything by it, Joanna told herself. It was just that her emotions were so confused lately, and she wasn't even sure why.

She liked Tanner, Joanna realised anew, liked him very much. And she thoroughly enjoyed Nicole. For the first time since her divorce, she could imagine getting involved with another man, and the thought frightened her. All right, it terrified her. This man belonged to a different world. Besides, she wasn't ready. Good grief, six years should have given her ample time to heal, but she'd been too afraid to lift the bandage.

When the movie was over, Tanner drove them home. The girls were tired, but managed to carry on a lively backseat conversation. The front seat was a different story. Neither Tanner nor Joanna had much to say.

"Would you like to come in for coffee?" Joanna asked when Tanner pulled into her driveway, although she was silently wishing he'd decline. Her nerves continued to clamor from the hand holding, and she wanted some time alone to organise her thoughts.

"Can we, Dad? Please?" Nicole begged. "Kristen and I want to watch the Saturday Night videos together."

"You're sure?" Tanner looked at Joanna, his brow creased with concern.

She couldn't answer. She wasn't sure of anything just then. "Of course," she forced herself to say. "It'll only take a minute or two to brew a pot."

"All right, then," Tanner said, and the girls let out whoops of delight.

Occasionally Joanna wondered if their daughters would ever get tired of one another's company. Probably, although they hadn't shown any signs of it yet. As far as she knew, the two girls had never had a serious disagreement.

Kristen and Nicole disappeared as soon as they got into the house. Within seconds, the television could be heard blaring rock music, which had recently become a familiar sound in the small one-storey house.

Tanner followed Joanna into the kitchen and stood leaning against the counter while she filled the automatic coffee maker with water. Her movements were jerky and abrupt. She felt awkward, ungraceful—as though this was the first time she'd ever been alone with a man. And that was a ridiculous way to feel, especially since the girls were practically within sight.

"I enjoyed tonight," Tanner commented, as she removed two cups from the cupboard.

"I did, too." She tossed him a lazy smile over her shoulder. But Tanner's eyes held hers, and it was as if she was seeing him for the first time. She half turned toward him, suddenly aware of how tall and lean he was, how thick and soft his dark hair. With an effort, Joanna looked from those mesmerising blue eyes and returned to the task of making coffee, although her fingers didn't seem willing to cooperate.

She stood waiting for the dark liquid to filter its way into the glass pot. Never had it seemed to take so long.

"Joanna."

Judging by the loudness of his voice, Tanner was standing directly behind her. A beat of silence followed before she turned around to face him.

Tanner's hands grasped her shoulders. "It's been a long time since I've sat in a movie and held a girl's hand."

She lowered her eyes and nodded. "Me, too."

"I felt like a kid again."

She'd been thinking much the same thing herself.

"I want to kiss you, Joanna."

She didn't need an analyst to inform her that kissing Tanner was something best avoided. She was about to tell him so when his hands gripped her waist and pulled her away from the support of the kitchen counter. A little taken aback, Joanna threw up her hands, as if to ward him off. But the minute they came into contact with the muscled hardness of his chest, they lost their purpose.

The moment Tanner's warm mouth claimed her lips, she felt an excitement that was almost shocking in its intensity. Her hands clutched the collar of his shirt as she eagerly gave herself up to the forgotten sensations. It had been so long since a man had kissed her like this.

The kiss was over much too soon. Far sooner than Joanna would have liked. The fire of his mouth had ignited a response in her she'd believed long dead. She was amazed at how readily it had sprung back to life. When Tanner dropped his arms and released her, Joanna felt suddenly weak, barely able to remain upright.

Her hand found her chest and she heaved a giant breath. "I... don't think that was a good idea."

Tanner's brows drew together, forming a ledge over his narrowed eyes. "I'm not sure I do, either, but it seemed right. I don't know what's happening between us, Joanna, and it's confusing the hell out of me."

"You? I'm the one who made it abundantly clear from the outset that I wasn't looking for a romantic involvement."

"I know, and I agree, but—"

"I'm more than pleased Kristen and Nicole are good friends, but I happen to like my life the way it is, thank you."

Tanner's frown grew darker, his expression both baffled and annoyed. "I feel the same way. It was a kiss, not a suggestion we live in sin."

"I... really wish you hadn't done that, Tanner."

"I apologise. Trust me, it won't happen again," he muttered, and buried his hands deep inside his pockets. "In fact it would probably be best if we forgot the entire incident."

"I agree totally."

"Fine then." He stalked out of the kitchen, but not before Joanna found herself wondering if she *could* forget it.

CHAPTER SIX

A KISS WAS REALLY such a minor thing, Joanna mused, slowly rotating her pencil between her palms. She'd made a criminal case out of nothing, and embarrassed both Tanner and herself.

"Joanna, have you had time to read over the Osborne loan application yet?" her boss, Robin Simpson asked, strolling up to her desk.

"Ah, no, not yet," Joanna said, her face flushing with guilt.

Robin frowned as he studied her. "What's been with you today? Every time I see you, you're gazing at the wall with a faraway look in your eye."

"Nothing's wrong." Blindly she reached toward her In basket and grabbed a file, although she hadn't a clue which one it was.

"If I didn't know better, I'd say you were daydreaming about a man."

Joanna managed a short, sarcastic laugh meant to deny everything. "Men are the last thing on my mind," she said flippantly. It was a half-truth. Men in the plural didn't interest her, but *man*, as in Tanner Lund, well, that was another matter.

Over the years Joanna had gone out of her way to avoid men she was attracted to—it was safer. She dated occasionally, but usually men who might be classified as pleasant, men for whom she could never feel anything beyond a mild friendship. Magnetism, charm and sex appeal were lost on her, thanks to a husband who'd possessed all three and systematically destroyed her faith in the possibility of a lasting relationship. At least, those qualities hadn't piqued her interest again, until she met Tanner. Okay, so her dating habits for the past few years had been a bit premeditated, but everyone deserved a night out now and again. It didn't seem fair to be denied the pleasure of a fun evening simply because she wasn't in the market for another husband. So she'd dated, not a lot, but some and nothing in the past six years had affected her as much as those few short hours with Nicole's father.

"Joanna!"

She jerked her head up to discover her boss still standing beside her desk. "Yes?"

"The Osborne file."

She briefly closed her eyes in a futile effort to clear her thoughts. "What about it?"

Robin glared at the ceiling and paused, as though pleading with the light fixture for patience. "Read it and get back to me before the end of the day—if that isn't too much to ask?"

"Sure," she grumbled, wondering what had put Robin in such a foul mood. She picked up the loan application and was halfway through it before she realised the name on it wasn't Osborne. Great! If her day continued like this, she could blame Tanner Lund for getting her fired.

When Joanna arrived home three hours later she was exhausted and short-tempered. She hadn't been herself all day, mainly because she'd been so preoccupied with thoughts of Tanner Lund and the way he'd kissed her. She was overreacting—she'd certainly been kissed before, so it shouldn't be such a big deal. But it was. Her behaviour demonstrated all the maturity of someone Kristen's age, she chided herself. She'd simply forgotten how to act with men; it was too long since she'd been involved with one. The day wasn't a complete waste, however. She'd made a couple of important decisions in the last few hours, and she wanted to clear the air with her daughter before matters got completely out of hand.

"Hi, honey."

"Hi."

Kristen's gaze didn't waver from the television screen where a talk-show host was interviewing a man—at least Joanna thought it was a man—whose brilliant red hair was so short on top it stuck straight up and so long in front it fell over his face, obliterating his left eye and part of his nose.

"Who's that?"

Kristen gave a deep sigh of wonder and adolescent love. "You mean you don't know? I've been in love with Simply Red for a whole year and you don't even know the lead singer when you see him?"

"No, I can't say that I do."

"Oh, Mom, honestly, get with it."

There *it* was again. First she was losing *it* and now she was supposed to get with *it*. Joanna wished her daughter would decide which she wanted.

"We need to talk."

Kristen reluctantly dragged her eyes away from her idol. "Mom, this is important. Can't it wait?"

Frustrated, Joanna sighed and muttered, "I suppose."

"Good."

Kristen had already tuned her out. Joanna strolled into the kitchen and realised she hadn't taken the hamburger out of the freezer to thaw. Great. So much for the tacos she'd planned to make for dinner. She opened and closed cupboard doors, rummaging around for something interesting. A can of tuna fish wasn't likely to meet with Kristen's approval. One thing about her daughter that the approach of the teen years hadn't disrupted was her healthy appetite.

Joanna stuck her head around the corner. "How does tuna casserole sound for dinner?"

Kristen didn't even look in her direction, just held out her arm and jerked her thumb toward the carpet.

"Soup and sandwiches?"

Once more Kristen's thumb headed downward, and Joanna groaned.

"Bacon, lettuce and tomato on toast with chicken noodle soup," she tried. "And that's the best I can do. Take it or leave it."

Kristen sighed. "If that's the final offer, I'll take it. But I thought we were having tacos."

"We were. I forgot to take out the hamburger."

"All right, BLTs," Kristen muttered, reversing the direction of her thumb.

Joanna was frying the bacon when Kristen joined her, sitting on a stool while her mother worked. "You wanted to talk to me about something?"

"Yes." Joanna concentrated on spreading mayonnaise over slices of whole-wheat toast, as she made an effort to gather her scattered thoughts. She cast about for several moments, trying to come up with a way of saying what needed to be said without making more of it than necessary.

"It must be something big," Kristen commented. "Did my teacher phone you at work or something?"

"No, should she have?" She raised her eyes and scrutinised Kristen's face closely.

Kristen gave a quick denial with a shake of her head. "No way. I'm a star pupil this year. Nicole and I are both doing great. Just wait until report-card time, then you'll see."

"I believe you." Kristen had been getting top marks all year, and Joanna was proud of how well her daughter was doing. "What I have to say concerns Nicole and—" she hesitated, swallowing tightly "—her father."

"Mr. Lund sure is good-looking, isn't he?" Kristen said enthusiastically, watching for Joanna's reaction.

Reluctantly Joanna nodded, hoping to sound casual. "I suppose."

"Oh, come on, Mom, he's a hunk."

"All right," Joanna admitted slowly. "I'll grant you that Tanner has a certain amount of . . . appeal."

Kristen grinned, looking pleased with herself.

"Actually it was Mr. Lund I wanted to talk to you about," Joanna continued, placing a layer of tomato slices on the toast.

"Really?" The brown eyes opened even wider.

"Yes, well, I wanted to tell you that I . . . I don't think it would be a good idea for the four of us to go on doing things together."

Abruptly Kristen's face fell with surprise and disappointment. "Why not?"

"Well . . . because he and I are both really busy." Even to her own ears, the statement sounded illogical, but it was difficult to tell her own daughter that she was frightened of her attraction to the man. Difficult to explain why nothing could come of it.

"Because you're both busy? Come on, Mom, that doesn't make any sense."

"All right, I'll be honest." She wondered whether an eleven-year-old could grasp the complexities of adult relationships. "I don't want to give Nicole's dad the wrong idea," she said carefully.

Kristen leaned forward, setting her elbows on the kitchen counter and resting her face in both hands. Her gaze looked sharp enough to shatter diamonds. "The wrong idea about what?" she asked.

"Me," Joanna said, swallowing uncomfortably.

"You?" Kristen repeated thoughtfully, a frown creasing her smooth brow. She relaxed then and released a huge sigh. "Oh, I see. You think Mr. Lund might think you're in the marriage market."

Joanna pointed a fork at her daughter. "Bingo!"

"But, Mom, I think it would be great if you and Nicole's dad got together. In fact, Nicole and I were talking about it just today. Think about all the advantages. We could all be a real family, and you could have more babies... I don't know if I ever told you this, but I'd really like a baby brother, and so would Nicole. And if you married Mr. Lund we could take family vacations together. You wouldn't have to work, because... I don't know if you realise this, but Mr. Lund is pretty rich. You could stay home and bake cookies and sew and stuff."

Joanna was so surprised that it took her a minute to find her voice. Openmouthed, she waved the fork jerkily around. "No way, Kristen." Joanna's knees felt rubbery, and before she could slip to the floor, she slumped into a chair. All this time she'd assumed she was a good mother, giving her daughter everything she needed physically and emotionally, making up to Kristen as much as she could for her father's absence. But she apparently hadn't done enough. And Kristen and Nicole were scheming to get Joanna and Tanner together. As in married!

Something had to be done.

She decided to talk to Tanner, but an opportunity didn't present itself until much later that evening when Kristen was in bed, asleep. At least Joanna hoped her daughter was asleep. She dialled his number and prayed Nicole wouldn't answer.

Thankfully she didn't.

"Tanner, it's Joanna," she whispered, cupping her hand over the mouthpiece, taking no chance that Kristen could overhear their conversation.

"What's the matter? Have you got laryngitis?"

"No," she returned hoarsely, straining her voice. "I don't want Kristen to hear me talking to you."

"I see. Should I pretend you're someone else so Nicole won't tell on you?" he whispered back.

"Please." She didn't appreciate the humor in his voice. Obviously he had yet to realise the seriousness of the situation. "We need to talk."

"We do?"

"Trust me, Tanner. You have no idea what I just learned. The girls are planning on us getting married."

"Married?" he shouted.

That, Joanna had known, would get a reaction out of him.

"When do you want to meet?"

"As soon as possible." He still seemed to think she was joking, but she couldn't blame him. If the situation were reversed, no doubt she would react the same way. "Kristen said something about the two of them swimming Wednesday night at the community pool. What if we meet at Denny's for coffee after you drop Nicole off?"

"What time?" He said it as though they were planning a reconnaissance mission deep into enemy territory.

"Seven-ten." That would give them both a few extra minutes to make it to the restaurant.

"Shall we synchronise our watches?"

"This isn't funny, Tanner."

"I'm not laughing."

But he was, and Joanna was furious with him. "I'll see you then."

"Seven-ten, Wednesday night at Denny's," he repeated. "I'll be there."

ON THE EVENING of their scheduled meeting, Joanna arrived at the restaurant before Tanner. She already regretted suggesting they meet at Denny's, but it was too late to change that now. There were bound to be other customers who would recognise either Tanner or her, and Joanna feared that word of their meeting could somehow filter back to the girls. She'd been guilty of underestimating them before; she wouldn't make the same mistake a second time. If Kristen and Nicole did hear about this private meeting, they'd consider it justification for further interference.

Tanner strolled into the restaurant and glanced around. He didn't seem to recognise Joanna, and she moved her sunglasses down her nose and gave him an abrupt wave.

He took one look at her, and even from the other side of the room she could see he was struggling to hold in his laughter.

"What's with the scarf and sunglasses?"

"I'm afraid someone might recognise us and tell the girls." It made perfect sense to her, but obviously not to him. Joanna forgave him since he didn't know the extent of the difficulties facing them.

But all he said was, "I see." He inserted his hands in the pockets of his overcoat and walked lazily past her, whistling. "Should I sit here or would you prefer the next booth?"

"Don't be silly."

"I'm not going to comment on that."

"For heaven's sake," Joanna hissed, "sit down before someone notices you."

"Someone notices me? Lady, you're wearing sunglasses at night, in the dead of winter, and with that scarf tied around your chin you look like an immigrant fresh off the boat."

"Tanner," she said, "this is not the time to crack jokes."

A smile lifted his features as he slid into the booth opposite her. He reached for a menu. "Are you hungry?"

"No." His attitude was beginning to annoy her. "I'm just having coffee."

"Nicole cooked dinner tonight, and frankly I'm starving."

When the waitress appeared he ordered a complete dinner. Joanna asked for coffee.

"Okay, what's up, Sherlock?" he asked, once the coffee had been poured.

"To begin with I...I think Kristen and Nicole saw you kiss me the other night."

He made no comment, but his brow puckered slightly.

"It seems the two of them have been talking, and from what I gather they're interested in getting us, er, together."

"I see."

To Joanna's dismay, Tanner didn't seem to be the slightest bit concerned by her revelation.

"That troubles you?"

"Tanner," she said, leaning toward him, "to quote my daughter, 'Nicole and I have been talking and we thought it would be great if you and Mr. Lund got together. You could have more babies and we could go on vacations and be a real family and you could stay home and bake cookies and stuff.'" She waited for his reaction, but his face remained completely impassive.

"What kind of cookies?" he asked finally.

"Tanner, if you're going to turn this into a joke, I'm leaving." As far as Joanna was concerned, he deserved to be tormented by two dedicated eleven-year-old match-makers! She started to slide out of the booth, but he stopped her with an upraised hand.

"All right, I'm sorry."

He didn't sound too contrite, and she gave a weak sigh of disgust. "You may consider this a joking matter, but I don't."

"Joanna, we're both mature adults," he stated calmly. "We aren't going to let a couple of eleven-year-old girls manipulate us!"

"Yes, but—"

"From the first, we've been honest with each other. That isn't going to change. You have no interest in remarriage—to me or anyone else—and I feel the same way. As long as we continue as we are now, the girls don't have a prayer."

"It's more than that," Joanna said vehemently. "We need to look past their schemes to the root of the problem."

"Which is?"

"Tanner, obviously we're doing something wrong as single parents."

He frowned. "What makes you say that?"

"Isn't it obvious? Kristen, and it seems equally true for Nicole, wants a complete family. What Kristen is really saying is that she longs for a father. Nicole is telling you she'd like a mother."

The humour drained out of Tanner's eyes, replaced with a look of real concern. "I see. And you think this all started because Kristen and Nicole saw us kissing?"

"I don't know," she murmured, shaking her head. "But I do know my daughter, and when she wants something, she goes after it with the force of a bulldog and won't let up. Once she's got it in her head that you and I are destined for each other, it's going to be pretty difficult for her to accept that all we'll ever be is friends."

"Nicole can get that way about certain things," he said thoughtfully.

The waitress delivered his roast beef sandwich and refilled Joanna's coffee cup.

Maybe she'd overreacted to the situation, but she couldn't help being worried. "I suppose you think I'm making more of a fuss about this than necessary," she said, flustered and a little embarrassed.

"About the girls manipulating us?"

"No, about the fact that we've both tried so hard to be good single parents, and obviously we're doing something wrong."

"I will admit that part concerns me."

"I don't mind telling you, Tanner, I've been in a panic all week, wondering where I've failed. We've got to come to terms with this. Make some important decisions."

"What do you suggest?"

"To start with, we've got to squelch any hint of personal involvement. I realize a certain amount of contact will be unavoidable with the girls being such close friends." She paused and chewed on her bottom lip. "I don't want to disrupt their relationship."

"I agree with you there. Being friends with Kristen has meant a good deal to Nicole."

"You and I went months without talking to each other," Joanna said, recalling that they'd only recently met. "There's no need for us to see each other now, is there?"

"That won't work."

"Why not?"

"Nicole will be spending the night with you again next Thursday—that is, unless you'd rather she didn't."

"Of course she can stay."

Tanner nodded, looking relieved. "To be honest, I don't think she'd go back to Mrs. Wagner's anymore without raising a big fuss."

"Taking care of Nicole is one thing, but the four of us doing anything together is out of the question."

Once more he nodded, but he didn't look pleased with the suggestion. "I think that would be best, too."

"We can't give them any encouragement."

Pushing his plate aside, Tanner reached for his water glass, cupping it with both hands. "You know, Joanna, I think a lot of you." He paused, then gave her a teasing smile. "You have a habit of dressing a little oddly every now and then, but other than that I respect your judgment. I'd like to consider you a friend."

She decided to let his comment about her choice of clothing slide. "I'd like to be your friend, too," she told him softly.

He grinned, and his gaze held hers for a long uninterrupted moment before they both looked away. "I know you think that kiss the other night was a big mistake, and I suppose you're right, but I'm not sorry it happened." He hesitated, as though waiting for her to argue with him, and when she didn't, he continued. "It's been a lot of years since I held a woman's hand at a movie or kissed her the way I did you. It was good to feel that young and innocent again."

Joanna dropped her gaze to her half-filled cup. It had felt right for her, too. So right that she'd been frightened out of her wits ever since. She could easily fall in love with Tanner, and that would be the worst possible thing for her. She just wasn't ready to take those risks again. They came from different worlds, too, and she'd never fit comfortably in his. Yet every time she thought about that kiss, she started to shake from the inside out.

"In a strange sort of way we need each other," Tanner went on, his look thoughtful. "Nicole needs a strong loving woman to identify with, to fill a mother's role, and she thinks you're wonderful."

"And Kristen needs to see a man who can be a father, putting the needs of his family before his own."

"I think it's only natural for the two of them to try to get us together," Tanner added. "It's something we should be prepared to deal with in the future."

"You're right," Joanna agreed, understanding exactly what he meant. "We need each other to help provide what's lacking in our daughters' lives. But we can't get involved with each other." She didn't know any other way to say it but bluntly.

"I agree," he said, with enough conviction to lay aside any doubt Joanna might still hold.

They were silent for a long moment.

"Why?"

Strangely, Joanna knew immediately what he was asking. She had the same questions about what had happened between him and Nicole's mother.

"Davey was—is—the most charming personable man I've ever met. I was fresh out of college and so in love with him I didn't stop to think." She paused and glanced away, not daring to look at Tanner. Her voice had fallen so low it was almost a whisper. "We were engaged when my best friend, Carol, told me Davey had made a pass at her. Fool that I was, I didn't believe her. I thought she was jealous that Davey had chosen me to love and marry. I was sick that my friend would stoop to anything so underhand. I always knew Carol found him attractive—most women did—and I was devastated that she would lie that way. I trusted Davey so completely that I didn't even ask him about the incident. Later, after we were married, there were a lot of times when he said he was working late, a lot of unexplained absences, but I didn't question those, either. He was building his career in real estate, and if he had to put in extra hours, well, that was understandable. All those nights I sat alone, trusting him when he claimed he was working, believing with all my heart that he was doing his utmost to build a life for us . . . and then learning he'd been with some other woman."

"How'd you find out?"

"The first time?"

"You mean there was more than once?"

She nodded, hating to let Tanner know how many times she'd forgiven Davey, how many times she'd taken him back after he'd pleaded and begged and promised it would never happen again.

"I was blind to his wandering eye for the first couple of years. What they say about ignorance being bliss is true. When I found out, I was physically sick. When I realised how I'd fallen for his lies, it was even worse, and yet I stuck it out with him, trusting that everything would be better, everything would change . . . someday. I wanted so badly to believe him, to trust him, that I accepted anything he told me, no matter how implausible it sounded.

"The problem was that the more I forgave him, the lower my self-esteem dropped. I became convinced it was all my fault. I obviously lacked something, since he...felt a need to seek out other women."

"You know now that's not true, don't you?" His voice was so gentle, so caring, that Joanna battled down a rush of emotion.

"There'd never been a divorce in my family," she told him quietly. "My parents have been married nearly forty years, and my brothers all have happy marriages. I think that was one of the reasons I held on so long. I just didn't know how to let go. I'd be devastated and crushed when I learned about his latest affair, yet I kept coming back for more. I suppose I believed Davey would change. Something magical would happen and all our problems would disappear. Only it never did. One afternoon—I don't even know what prompted it.... All I knew was that I couldn't stay in the marriage any longer. I packed Kristen's and my things and walked out. I've never been back, never wanted to go back."

Tanner reached for her hand, and his fingers wrapped warmly around hers. A moment passed before he spoke, and when he did, his voice was tight with remembered pain. "I thought Carmen was the sweetest, gentlest woman in the world. As nonsensical as it sounds, I think I was in love with her before I even knew her name. She was a college cheerleader and a homecoming queen, and I felt like a nobody. By chance, we met several years after graduation when I'd just begun making a name for myself. I'd bought my first company, a small aluminum window manufacturer back in West Virginia. And I was working night and day to see it through those first rough weeks of transition.

"I was high on status," Tanner admitted, his voice filled with regret. "Small-town boy makes good—that kind of stuff. She'd been the most popular girl in my college year, and dating her was the fulfilment of a fantasy. She'd recently broken up with a guy she'd been involved with for two years and had something to prove herself, I suppose." He focused his gaze away from Joanna. "Things got out of hand and a couple of months later Carmen announced she was pregnant. To be honest, I was happy about it, thrilled. There was never any question whether I'd marry her. By then I was so in love with her I couldn't see straight. Eight months after the wedding, Nicole was born..." He hesitated, as though gathering his thoughts. "Some women are meant to be mothers, but not Carmen. She didn't even like to hold Nicole, didn't want anything to do with her. I'd come home at night and find that Carmen had neglected Nicole most of the day. But I made excuses for her, reasoned everything out in my own mind—the unexplained bruises on the baby, the fear I saw in Nicole's eyes whenever her mother was around. It got so bad that I started dropping Nicole off at my parents', just so I could be sure she was being looked after properly."

Joanna bit the corner of her lip at the raw pain she witnessed in Tanner's eyes. She was convinced he didn't speak of his marriage often, just as she rarely talked about Davey, but this was necessary if they were to understand each other.

"To be fair to Carmen, I wasn't much of a husband in those early months. Hell, I didn't have time to be. I was feeling like a big success when we met, but that didn't last long. Things started going wrong at work and I damn near lost my shirt.

"Later," he continued slowly, "I learned that the entire time I was struggling to hold the company together, Carmen was seeing her old boyfriend, Sam Dailey."

"Oh, Tanner."

"Nicole's my daughter, there was no doubting that. But Carmen had never really wanted children, and she felt trapped in the marriage. We separated when Nicole was less than three years old."

"I thought you said you'd only been divorced five years?"

"We have. It took Carmen a few years to get around to the legal aspect of things. I wasn't in any rush, since I had no intention of ever marrying again."

"What's happened to Carmen since? Did she remarry?"

"Eventually. She lived with Sam for several years, and the last thing I heard was they'd split up and she married a professional baseball player."

"Does Nicole ever see her mother?" Joanna remembered that he'd said his ex-wife saw Nicole only when it was convenient.

"She hasn't in the past three years. The thing I worry about most is having Carmen show up someday, demanding that Nicole come to live with her. Nicole doesn't remember anything about those early years—thank God—and she seems to have formed a rosy image of her mother. She keeps Carmen's picture in her bedroom and every once in a while I'll see her staring at it wistfully." He paused and glanced at his watch. "What time were we supposed to pick up the kids?"

"Eight."

"It's five after now."

"Oh, good grief." Joanna slung her bag over her shoulder as they slid out of the booth and hurried towards the cash register. Tanner insisted on paying for her coffee, and Joanna didn't want to waste time arguing.

They walked briskly toward their cars, parked beside each other in the lot. "Joanna," he called, as she fumbled with her keys. "I'll wait a couple of minutes so we don't both arrive at the same time. Otherwise the girls will probably guess we've been together."

She flashed him a grateful smile. "Good thinking."

"Joanna." She looked at him questioningly as he shortened the distance between them. "Don't misunderstand this," he said softly. He pulled her gently into the circle of his arms, holding her close for a lingering moment. "I'm sorry for what Davey did to you. The man's a fool." Tenderly he brushed his lips over her forehead, then turned and abruptly left her.

It took Joanna a full minute to recover enough to get into her car and drive away.

CHAPTER SEVEN

"MOM," KRISTEN SCREECHED, "the phone's for you."

Joanna was surprised. A call for her on a school night was rare enough, but one that actually got through with Kristen and Nicole continually on the line was a special occasion.

"Who is it, honey?" No doubt someone interested in cleaning her carpets or selling her a cemetery plot.

"I don't know," Kristen said, holding the phone to her shoulder. She lowered her voice to whisper, "But whoever it is sounds weird."

"Hello." Joanna spoke into the receiver as Kristen wandered toward her bedroom.

"Can you talk?" The husky male voice was unmistakably Tanner's.

"Y-yes." Joanna looked toward Kristen's bedroom to be certain her daughter was out of earshot.

"Can you meet me tomorrow for lunch?"

"What time?"

"Noon at the Sea Galley."

"Should we synchronise our watches?" Joanna couldn't resist asking. It had been a week since she'd last talked to Tanner. In the meantime she hadn't heard a word from Kristen about getting their two families together again. That in itself was suspicious, but Joanna had been too busy at work to think about it.

"Don't be cute, Joanna. I need help."

"Buy me lunch and I'm yours." She hadn't meant that quite the way it sounded and was grateful Tanner didn't comment on her slip of the tongue.

"I'll see you tomorrow then."

"Right."

A smile tugged at the edges of her mouth as she replaced the telephone receiver. Her hand lingered there for a moment as an unexpected tide of happiness washed over her.

"Who was that, Mom?" Kristen asked, poking her head around her bedroom door.

"A . . . friend, calling to ask if I could meet . . . her for lunch."

"Oh." Kristen's young face was a study in scepticism. "For a minute there I thought it sounded like Mr. Lund trying to fake a woman's voice."

"Mr. Lund? That's silly," Joanna said with a forced little laugh, then deftly changed the subject. "Kristen, it's nine-thirty. Hit the hay, kiddo."

"Right, Mom. 'Night."

"'Night, sweetheart."

"Enjoy your lunch tomorrow."

"I will."

Joanna hadn't had a chance to walk away from the phone before it pealed a second time. She gave a guilty start and reached for it.

"Hello," she said hesitantly, half expecting to hear Tanner's voice again.

But it was her mother's crisp clear voice that rang over the wire. "Joanna, I hope this isn't too late to call."

"Of course not, Mom," Joanna answered quickly. "Is everything all right?"

Her mother ignored the question and asked one of her own instead. "What was the name of that young man you're dating again?"

"Mother," Joanna said with an exasperated sigh, "I'm not seeing anyone. I told you that."

"Tanner Lund, wasn't it?"

"We went out to dinner *once* with both our daughters, and that's the extent of our relationship. If Kristen let you assume anything else, it was just wishful thinking on her part. One dinner, I swear."

"But, Joanna, he sounds like such a nice young man. He's the same Tanner Lund who recently bought half of Spokane Aluminum, isn't he? I saw his name in the paper this morning and recognised it right away. Sweetie, your dad and I are so pleased you're dating such a famous successful man."

"Mother, please!" Joanna cried. "Tanner and I are friends. How many times do I have to tell you, we're not dating? Kristen and Tanner's daughter, Nicole, are best friends. I swear that's all there is to—"

"Joanna," her mother interrupted. "The first time you mentioned his name, I heard something in your voice that's been missing for a good long while. You may be able to fool yourself, but not me. You like this Tanner." Her voice softened perceptively.

"Mother, nothing could possibly come of it even if I was attracted to him—which I'm not." Okay, so that last part wasn't entirely true. But the rest of it certainly was.

"And why couldn't it?" her mother insisted.

"You said it yourself. He's famous, in addition to being wealthy. I'm out of his league."

"Nonsense," her mother responded in a huff.

Joanna knew better than to get into a war of words with her stubborn parent.

"Now don't be silly. You like Tanner Lund, and I say it's about time you let down those walls you've built around yourself. Joanna, sweetie, you've been hiding behind them for six years now. Don't let what happened with Davey ruin your whole life."

"I'm not going to," Joanna promised.

There was a long pause before her mother sighed and answered, "Good. You deserve some happiness."

AT PRECISELY NOON the following day, Joanna drove into the Sea Galley parking lot. Tanner was already there, waiting for her by the entrance.

"Hi," she said with a friendly grin, as he walked toward her.

"What, no disguises?"

Joanna laughed, embarrassed now by that silly scarf and sunglasses she'd worn when they met at Denny's. "Kristen doesn't know anyone who eats here."

"I'm grateful for that."

His smile was warm enough to tunnel through snow drifts, and as much as Joanna had warned herself not to be affected by it, she was.

"It's good to see you," Tanner added, taking her arm to escort her into the restaurant.

"You, too." Although she hadn't seen him in almost a week, Tanner was never far from her thoughts. Nicole had stayed with her and Kristen when Tanner flew to New York for two days in the middle of the previous week. The Spokane area had been hit by a fierce snowstorm the evening he left. Joanna had felt nervous the entire time about his traveling in such inclement weather, yet she hadn't so much as asked him about his flight when he arrived to pick up Nicole. Their conversation had been brief and pleasantly casual, but her relief that he'd got home safely had kept her awake for hours. Later, she'd been furious with herself for caring so much.

The Sea Galley hostess seated them right away and handed them thick menus. Joanna ordered a shrimp salad and coffee. Tanner echoed her choice.

"Nicole's birthday is next week," he announced, studying her face carefully. "She's handing out the party invitations today at school."

Joanna smiled and nodded. But Tanner's eyes held hers, and she saw something unidentifiable flicker there.

"In a moment of weakness, I told her she could have a slumber party."

Joanna's smile faded. "As I recall, Nicole did mention something about this party," she said, trying to sound cheerful. The poor guy didn't know what he was in for. "You're obviously braver than I am."

"You think it was a bad move?"

Joanna made a show of closing her eyes and nodding vigorously.

"I was afraid of that," Tanner muttered, and he rearranged the silverware around his place setting a couple of times. "I know we agreed it probably wouldn't be a good idea for us to do things together. But I need some advice—from a friend."

"What can I do?"

"Joanna, I haven't the foggiest idea about entertaining a whole troop of girls. I can handle contract negotiations and make split-second business decisions, but I panic at the thought of all those squealing little girls sequestered in my apartment for all those hours."

"How do you want me to help?"

"Would you consider..." He gave her a hopeful look, then shook his head regretfully. "No. I can't ask that of you. Besides, we don't want to give the girls any more ideas about the two of us. What I really need is some suggestions for keeping all these kids occupied. What do other parents do?''

"Other parents know better."

Tanner wiped a lock of dark brown hair from his brow and frowned. "I was afraid of that."

"What time are the girls supposed to arrive?"

"Six."

"Tanner, that's too early."

"I know, but Nicole insists I serve my special tacos, and she has some screwy idea about all the girls crowding into the kitchen to watch me."

Now it was Joanna's turn to frown. "That won't work. You'll end up with ten different pairs of hands trying to help. There'll be hamburger and cheese from one end of the place to the other."

"I thought as much. Good Lord, Joanna, how did I get myself into this mess?"

"Order pizza," she tossed out, tapping her index finger against her bottom lip. "Everyone loves that."

"Pizza. Okay. What about games?"

"A scavenger hunt always comes in handy when things get out of hand. Release the troops on your unsuspecting neighbours."

"So far we've got thirty minutes of the first fourteen hours filled."

"Movies," Joanna suggested next. "Lots of movies. You can phone early and reserve a couple of new releases and add an old favourite like *Pretty in Pink*, and the girls will be in seventh heaven."

His eyes brightened. "Good idea."

"And if you really feel adventurous, take them roller-skating."

"Roller-skating? You think they'd like that?"

"They'd love it, especially if word leaked out that they were going to be at the rink Friday night. That way, several of the boys from the sixth-grade class can just happen to be there, too."

Tanner nodded, and a smile quirked the corners of his mouth. "And you think that'll keep everyone happy?"

"I'm sure of it. Wear 'em out first, show a movie or two second, with the lights out, of course, and I guarantee you by midnight everyone will be sound asleep."

Their salads arrived and Tanner stuck his fork into a fat succulent shrimp, then paused. "Now what was it you said last night about buying you lunch and making you mine?"

"It was a slip of the tongue," she muttered, dropping her gaze to her salad.

"Just my luck."

They laughed, and it felt good. Joanna had never had a relationship like this with a man. She wasn't on her guard the way she normally was, fearing that her date would put too much stock in an evening or two out. Because their daughters were the same age, they had a lot in common. They were both single parents doing their damnedest to raise their daughters right. The normal dating rituals and practised moves were unnecessary with him. Tanner was her friend, and it renewed Joanna's faith in the opposite sex to know there were still men like him left. Their friendship reassured her—but the undeniable attraction between them still frightened her.

"I really appreciate your suggestions," he said, after they'd both concentrated on their meals for several moments. "I've had this panicky feeling for the past three days. I suppose it wasn't a brilliant move on my part to call you at home, but I was getting desperate."

"You'll do fine. Just remember, it's important to keep the upper hand."

"I'll try."

"By the way, when *is* Hell Night?" She couldn't resist teasing him.

He gave a heartfelt sigh. "Next Friday."

Joanna slowly ate a shrimp. "I think Kristen figured out it was you on the phone last night."

"She did?"

"Yeah. She started asking questions the minute I hung up. She claimed my 'friend' sounded suspiciously like Mr. Lund faking a woman's voice."

Tanner cleared his throat and answered in a high falsetto. "That should tell you how desperate I was."

Joanna laughed and speared another shrimp. "That's what friends are for."

CHAPTER EIGHT

"MOM, HURRY or we're going to be late." Kristen paced the hallway outside her mother's bedroom door while Joanna finished dressing.

"Have you got Nicole's gift?"

"Oh." Kristen dashed into her bedroom and returned with a gaily wrapped oblong box. They'd bought the birthday gift the night before, a popular board game, which Kristen happened to know Nicole really wanted.

"I think Mr. Lund is really nice to let Nicole have a slumber party, don't you?"

"Really brave is a more apt description. How many girls are coming?"

"Fifteen."

"Fifteen!" Joanna echoed in a shocked voice.

"Nicole originally invited twenty, but only fifteen could make it."

Joanna slowly shook her head. He'd had good reason to feel panicky. With all these squealing, giddy preadolescent girls, the poor man would be certifiable by the end of the night. Either that or a prime candidate for extensive counselling.

When they arrived, the parking area outside Tanner's apartment building looked like the scene of a rock concert. There were enough parents dropping off kids to cause a minor traffic jam.

"I can walk across the street if you want to let me out here," Kristen suggested, anxiously eyeing the group of girls gathering outside the building.

"I'm going to find a parking place," Joanna said, scanning the side streets for two adjacent spaces—so that she wouldn't need to struggle to parallel park.

"You're going to find a place to leave the car? Why?" Kristen wanted to know, her voice higher pitched and more excited than usual. "You don't have to come in, if you don't want. I thought you said you were going to re-finish that old chair Grandpa gave us last summer."

"I was," Joanna murmured with a short sigh, "but I have the distinct impression that Nicole's father is going to need a helping hand."

"I'm sure he doesn't, Mom. Mr. Lund is a really or-ganised person. I'm sure he's got everything under control."

Kristen's reaction surprised Joanna. She would have expected her daughter to encourage the idea of getting the two of them together.

She finally found a place to park and they hurried across the street, Kristen apparently deep in thought.

"Actually, Mom, I think helping Mr. Lund might be a good idea," she said after a long pause. "He'll probably be grateful."

Joanna wasn't nearly as confident by this time. "I have a feeling I'm going to regret this later."

"No, you won't." Joanna could tell Kristen was about to launch into another one of her little speeches about babies, vacations and homemade cookies. Thankfully she didn't get the chance, since they'd entered the building and encountered a group of Kristen's other friends.

Tanner was standing in the doorway of his apartment, already looking frazzled when Joanna arrived. Surprise flashed through his eyes when he saw her.

"I've come to help," she announced, peeling off her jacket and pushing up the sleeves of her thin sweater. "This group is more than one parent can reasonably be expected to control."

He looked for a moment as though he wanted to fall to the ground and kiss her feet. "Bless you."

"Believe me, Tanner, you owe me for this." She glanced around at the chaos that dominated the large apartment. The girls had already formed small groups and were arguing loudly with each other over some subject of earth-shattering importance—like Bruce Springsteen's age, or the real colour of Billy Idol's hair.

"Is the pizza ready?" Joanna asked him, raising her voice in order to be heard over the din of squeals, shouts and rock music.

Tanner nodded. "It's in the kitchen. I ordered eight large ones. Do you think that'll be enough?"

Joanna rolled her eyes. "I suspect you're going to be eating leftover pizza for the next two weeks."

The girls proved her wrong. Never had Joanna seen a hungrier group. They were like school of piranha attacking a hapless victim, and within fifteen minutes everyone had eaten her fill. There were one or two slices left of four of the pizzas, but the others had vanished completely.

"It's time for a movie," Joanna decided, and while the girls voted on which film to see first Tanner started dumping dirty paper plates and pop cans into a plastic garbage sack. When the movie was finished, Joanna calculated, it would be time to go skating.

Peace reigned once Tom Cruise appeared on the television screen and Joanna joined Tanner in the bright cheery kitchen.

He was sitting dejectedly at the round table, rubbing a hand across his forehead. "I feel a headache coming on."

"It's too late for that," she said with a soft smile. "Actually I think everything is going very well. Everyone seems to be having a good time, and Nicole is a wonderful hostess."

"You do? She is?" He gave her an astonished look. "I keep having nightmares about pillow fights and lost dental appliances."

"Hey, it isn't going to happen." Not while they maintained control. "Tanner, I meant what I said about the party going well. In fact, I'm surprised at how smoothly everything is falling into place. The kids really are having a good time, and as long as we keep them busy there shouldn't be any problems."

He grinned, looking relieved. "I don't know about you, but I could use a cup of coffee."

"I'll second that."

He poured coffee into two pottery mugs and carried them to the table. Joanna sat across from him, propping her feet on the opposite chair. Sighing, she leaned back and cradled the steaming mug.

"The pizza was a good idea." He reached for a piece and shoved the box in her direction.

Now that she had a chance to think about it, Joanna realized she'd been so busy earlier, serving the girls, she hadn't managed to eat any of the pizza herself. She straightened enough to reach for a napkin and a thick slice dotted with pepperoni and spicy Italian sausage.

"What made you decide to give up your evening to help me out?" Tanner asked, watching her closely. "Kristen told Nicole that you had a hot date tonight. You were the last person I expected to see."

Joanna wasn't sure what had changed her mind about tonight and staying to help Tanner. Pity, she suspected. "If the situation were reversed, you'd lend me a hand," she replied, more interested in eating than conversation at the moment.

Tanner frowned at his pizza. "You missed what I was really asking."

"I did?"

"I was trying to be subtle about asking if you had a date tonight."

Joanna found that question odd. "Obviously I didn't."

"It isn't so obvious to me. You're a single parent, so there aren't that many evenings you can count on being free of responsibility. I would have thought you'd use this time to go out with someone special, flap your wings and that sort of thing." His frown grew darker.

"I'm too old to flap my wings," she said with a soft chuckle. "Good grief, I'm over thirty."

"So you aren't dating anyone special?"

"Tanner, you know I'm not."

"I don't know anything of the sort." Although he didn't raise his voice, Joanna could sense his disquiet.

"All right, what's up?" She didn't like the looks he was giving her. Not one bit.

"Nicole."

"Nicole?" she repeated.

"She was telling me that other day that you'd met someone recently. 'A real prince' is the phrase she used. Someone rich and handsome who was crazy about you— she claimed you were seeing a lot of this guy. Said you were falling madly in love."

Joanna dropped her feet to the floor with a loud thud and bolted upright so fast she nearly tumbled out of the chair. She was furiously chewing her pepperoni-and-sausage pizza, trying to swallow it as quickly as she could. All the while, her finger was pointing, first toward the living room where the girls were innocently watching *Top Gun* and then at Tanner who was staring at her in fascination.

"Hey, don't get angry with me," he said. "I'm only repeating what Kristen supposedly told Nicole and what Nicole told me."

She swallowed the piece of pizza in one huge lump. "They're plotting again, don't you see? I should have known something was up. It's been much too quiet lately. Kristen and Nicole are getting devious now, because the direct approach didn't work." Flustered, she started pacing the kitchen floor.

"Settle down, Joanna. We're smarter than a couple of school kids."

"That's easy for you to say." She pushed her hair away from her forehead and continued to pace. Little wonder Kristen hadn't been keen on the idea of her helping Tanner tonight. Joanna whirled around to face him. "Well, aren't you going to say something?" To her dismay, she discovered he was doing his best not to chuckle. "This isn't a laughing matter, Tanner Lund. I wish you'd take this seriously!"

"I am."

Joanna snorted softly. "You are not!"

"We're mature adults, Joanna. We aren't going to allow two children to dictate our actions."

"Is that a fact?" She braced both hands against her hips and glared at him. "I'm pleased to hear you're such a tower of strength, but I'll bet a week's pay that it wasn't your idea to have this slumber party. You probably rejected the whole thing the first time Nicole suggested it, but after having the subject of a birthday slumber party brought up thirty times in about thirty minutes you weakened, and that was when Nicole struck the fatal blow. If your daughter is anything like mine, she probably used every trick in the book to talk you into this party idea. Knowing how guilty you felt about all those business trips, I suppose Nicole brought them up ten or twelve times. And before you knew what hit you, there were fifteen little girls spending the night at your apartment.''

Tanner paled.

"Am I right?'' she insisted.

He shrugged and muttered disparagingly, "Close enough.''

Slumping into the chair, Joanna pushed the pizza box aside and forcefully expelled her breath. "I don't mind telling you, I'm concerned about this. If Kristen and Nicole are plotting against us, then we've got to form some kind of plan of our own before they drive us out of our minds. We can't allow them to manipulate us like this.''

"I think you may be right.''

She eyed him hopefully. "Any suggestions?'' If he was smart enough to manage a couple of thousand employees, surely he could figure out a way to keep two eleven-year-olds under control.

Slouched in his chair, his shoulders sagging, Tanner shook his head. "None. What about you?''

"Communication is the key.''

"Right.''

"We've got to keep in touch with each other and keep tabs on what's going on with these two. Don't believe a thing they say until we check it out with the other.''

"We've got another problem, Joanna," Tanner said, looking in every direction but hers.

"What?"

"It worked."

"What worked?" she asked irritably. Why was he speaking in riddles?

"Nicole's telling me that you'd been swept off your feet by this rich guy."

"Yes?" He still wasn't making any sense.

"The purpose of that whole fabrication was to make me jealous—and it worked."

"It worked?" An icy numb feeling swept through her. Swallowing became difficult.

Tanner nodded. "I kept thinking about how much I liked you. How much I enjoyed talking to you. And then I decided that when this slumber party business was over, I was going to risk asking you out to dinner."

"But I've already told you I'm not interested in a romantic relationship. One marriage was more than enough for me."

"I don't think that's what bothered me."

"Then what did?"

It was obvious from the way his eyes darted around the room that he felt uncomfortable. "I kept thinking about another man kissing you, and frankly, Joanna, that's what bothered me most."

The kitchen suddenly went so quiet that Joanna was almost afraid to breathe. The only noise was the faint sound of the movie playing in the other room.

Joanna tried to put herself in Tanner's place, wondering how she'd feel if Kristen announced that he'd met a gorgeous blonde and was dating her. Instantly she felt her stomach muscles tighten. There wasn't the slightest doubt in Joanna's mind that the girls' trick would have worked on her, too. Just the thought of Tanner's kissing another woman produced a curious ache, a pain that couldn't be described—or denied.

"Kissing you that night was the worst thing I could have done," Tanner conceded reluctantly. "I know you don't want to talk about it. I don't blame you—"

"Tanner," she interjected in a low hesitant voice, which hardly resembled her own. "It would have worked with me, too."

His eyes were dark and piercing. "Are you certain?"

She nodded, feeling utterly defeated yet strangely excited. "I'm afraid so. What are we going to do now?"

The silence returned as they stared at one another.

"The first thing I think we should do is experiment a little," he suggested in a flat emotionless voice. Then he released a long sigh. "Almost three weeks have passed since the night we took the girls out, and we've both had plenty of time to let that kiss build in our minds. Right?"

"Right," Joanna agreed. She'd attempted to put that kiss completely out of her mind, but it hadn't worked, and there was no point in telling him otherwise.

"It seems to me," Tanner continued thoughtfully, "that we should kiss again, for the sake of research, and find out what we're dealing with here."

She didn't need him to kiss her again to know she was going to like it. The first time had been ample opportunity for her to recognise how strongly she was attracted to Tanner Lund, and she didn't need another kiss to remind her.

"Once we know, we can decide where to go from there. Agreed?"

"Okay," she said impulsively, ignoring the small voice that warned of danger.

He stood up and held out his hand. She stared at it for a moment, uncertain. "You want to kiss right now?"

"Do you know of a better time?"

She shook her head. Good grief, she couldn't believe she was doing this. Tanner stretched out his arms and she walked into them with all the finesse of tumbleweed. The way she fit so snugly, so comfortably into his embrace worried her already. And he hadn't even kissed her yet.

Tanner held her lightly, his eyes wide and curious as he stared down at her. First he cocked his head to the right, then abruptly changed his mind and moved it to the left.

Joanna's movements countered his until she was certain they looked like a pair of ostriches who couldn't make up their minds.

"Are you comfortable?" he asked, and his voice was slightly hoarse.

Joanna nodded. She wished he'd hurry up and do it before one of the girls came crashing into the kitchen and found them. With their luck, it would be either Kristen or Nicole. Or both.

"You ready?" he asked.

Joanna nodded again. He was looking at her almost anxiously as though they were waiting for an imminent explosion. And that was exactly the way it felt when Tanner's mouth settled on hers, even though the kiss was infinitely gentle, his lips sliding over hers like a soft summer rain, barely touching.

They broke apart, momentarily stunned. Neither spoke, and then Tanner kissed her again, moving his mouth over her parted lips in undisguised hunger. His hand clutched the thick hair at her nape as she raised her arms and tightened them around his neck, leaning into him, absorbing his strength.

Tanner groaned softly and deepened the kiss until it threatened to consume Joanna. She met his fierce urgency with her own, arching closer to him, holding onto him with everything that was in her.

An unabating desire flared to life between them as he kissed her again and again, until they were both breathless and shaking.

"Joanna," he groaned, and dragged in several deep breaths. After taking a long moment to compose himself, he asked, "What do you think?" The question was murmured into her hair.

Joanna's chest was heaving, as though she'd been running and was desperate for oxygen. "I . . . I don't know," she lied, silently calling herself a coward.

"I do."

"You do?"

"Good Lord, Joanna, you taste like heaven. We're in trouble here. Deep trouble."

CHAPTER NINE

THE POP MUSIC at the roller-skating rink blared from huge speakers and vibrated around the room. A disc jockey announced the tunes from a glass-fronted booth and joked with the skaters as they circled the polished hardwood floor.

"I can't believe I let you talk me into this," Joanna muttered, sitting beside Tanner as she laced up her rented high-top white skates.

"I refuse to be the only one over thirty out there," he replied, but he was smiling, obviously pleased with his persuasive talents. No doubt he'd take equal pleasure in watching her fall flat on her face. It had been years since Joanna had worn a pair of roller skates. *Years.*

"It's like riding a bicycle," Tanner assured her with that maddening grin of his. "Once you know how, you never forget."

Joanna grumbled under her breath, but she was actually beginning to look forward to this. She'd always loved roller-skating as a kid, and there was something about being with Tanner that brought out the little girl in her. *And the woman,* she thought, remembering their kiss.

Nicole's friends were already skating with an ease that made Joanna envious. Slowly, cautiously, she joined the crowd circling the rink.

"Hi, Mom." Kristen zoomed past at the speed of light.

"Hi, Mrs. Parsons," Nicole shouted, following her friend.

Staying safely near the side, within easy reach of the handrail, Joanna concentrated on making her feet work properly, wheeling them back and forth as smoothly as possible. But instead of the gliding motion achieved by the others, her movements were short and jerky. She didn't acknowledge the girls' greetings with anything more than a raised hand and was slightly disconcerted to see the other skaters giving her a wide berth. They obviously recognised danger when they saw it.

Tanner glided past her, whirled around and deftly skated backward, facing Joanna. She looked up and threw him a weak smile. She should have known Tanner would be as confident on skates as he seemed to be at everything else—except slumber parties for eleven-year-old girls. Looking at him, one would think he'd been skating every day for years, although he claimed it was twenty years since he'd been inside a rink. It was clear from the expert way he soared across the floor that he didn't need to relearn anything—unlike Joanna, who felt as awkward as a newborn foal attempting to stand for the first time.

"How's it going?" he asked, with a cocky grin.

"Great. Can't you tell?" Just then, her right foot jerked out from under her and she groped desperately for the rail, managing to get a grip on it seconds before she went crashing to the floor.

Tanner was by her side at once. "You okay?"

"About as okay as anyone who has stood on the edge and looked into the deep abyss," she muttered.

"Come on, what you need is a strong hand to guide you."

Joanna snorted. "Forget it, fellow. I'll be fine in a few minutes, once I get my sea legs."

"You're sure?"

"Tanner, for heaven's sake, at least leave me with my pride intact!" Keeping anything intact at the moment was difficult, with her feet flaying wildly as she tried to pull herself back into an upright position.

"Okay, if that's what you want," he said shrugging, and sailed away from her with annoying ease.

Fifteen minutes later, Joanna felt steady enough to join the main part of the crowd circling the rink. Her movements looked a little less clumsy, a little less shaky, though she certainly wasn't in complete control.

"Hey, you're doing great," Tanner said, slowing down enough to skate beside her.

"Thanks," she said breathlessly, studying her feet in an effort to maintain her balance.

"You've got a gift for this," he teased.

She looked up at him and laughed outright. "Isn't that the truth! I wonder if I should consider a new career as a roller-skating waitress at the Pink Palace."

Amusement lifted the edge of his sensuous mouth. "Has anyone ever told you that you have an odd sense of humour?"

Looking at Tanner distracted Joanna, and her feet floundered for an instant. "Kristen does at least once a day."

Tanner chuckled. "I shouldn't laugh. Nicole tells me the same thing."

The disc jockey announced that the next song was for couples only. Joanna gave a sigh of relief and aimed her body toward the nearest exit. She could use the break; her calf muscles were already protesting the unaccustomed exercise. She didn't need roller-skating to remind her she wasn't a kid.

"How about it, Joanna?" Tanner asked, skating around her.

"How about what?"

"Skating together for the couples' dance. You and me and fifty thousand preteens sharing centre stage." He offered her his hand. The lights had dimmed and a mirrored ball hanging in the middle of the ceiling cast speckled shadows over the floor.

"No way, Tanner," she muttered, ignoring his hand.

"I thought not. Oh well, I'll see if I can get Nicole to skate with her dear old dad." Effortlessly he glided toward the group of girls who stood against the wall flirtatiously challenging the boys on the other side with their eyes.

Once Joanna was safely off the rink, she found a place to sit and rest her weary bones. Within a couple of minutes, Tanner lowered himself into the chair beside her, looking chagrined.

"I got beat out by Tommy Spenser," he muttered.

Joanna couldn't help it—she was delighted. Now Tanner would understand how she'd felt when Kristen announced she didn't want her mother sitting with her at the movies. Tanner looked just as dejected as Joanna had felt then.

"It's hell when they insist on growing up, isn't it?" she said, doing her best not to smile, knowing he wouldn't appreciate it.

He heaved an expressive sigh and gave her a hopeful look before glancing out at the skating couples. "I don't suppose you'd reconsider?"

The floor was filled with kids, and Joanna knew the minute she moved onto the hardwood surface with Tanner, every eye in the place would be on them.

He seemed to read her mind, because he added, "Come on, Joanna. My ego has just suffered a near-mortal wound. I've been rejected by my own flesh and blood."

She swallowed down a comment and awkwardly rose to her feet, struggling to remain upright. "When my ego got shot to bits at the movie theatre, all you did was share your popcorn with me."

He chuckled and reached for her hand. "Don't complain. This gives me an excuse to put my arm around you again." His right arm slipped around her waist, and she tucked her left hand in his as they moved side by side. She had to admit it felt incredibly good to be this close to him. Almost as good as it had felt being in his arms for those few moments in his kitchen.

Tanner must have been thinking the same thing, because he was unusually quiet as he directed her smoothly across the floor to the strains of a romantic ballad. They'd circled the rink a couple of times when Tanner abruptly switched position, skating backward and holding onto her as though they were dancing.

"Tanner," she said, surprise widening her eyes as he swept her into his arms. "The girls will start thinking . . . things if we skate like this."

"Let them."

His hands locked at the base of her spine and he pulled her close. Very close. Joanna drew a slow breath, savouring the feel of Tanner's body pressed so intimately against her own.

"Joanna, listen," he whispered. "I've been thinking."

So had she. Hard to do when she was around Tanner.

"Would it really be such a terrible thing if we were to start seeing more of each other? On a casual basis—it doesn't have to be anything serious. We're both mature adults. Neither of us is going to allow the girls to manipulate us into anything we don't want. And as far as the past is concerned, I'm not Davey and you're not Carmen."

Why, Joanna wondered, was the most important discussion she'd had in years taking place in a roller-skating rink with a top-forty hit blaring in one ear and Tanner whispering in the other? Deciding to ignore the thought, she said, "But the girls might start making assumptions, and I'm afraid we'd only end up disappointing them."

Tanner disagreed. "I feel our seeing each other might help more than it would hinder."

"How do you mean?" Joanna couldn't believe she was actually entertaining this suggestion. Entertaining was putting it mildly; her heart was doing somersaults at the prospect of seeing Tanner more often. She was thrilled, excited...and yet hesitant. The wounds Davey had inflicted went very deep.

"If we see each other more often we could include the girls, and that should lay to rest some of the fears we've had over their matchmaking efforts. And spending time with you will help satisfy Nicole's need for a strong mother figure. At the same time, I can help Kristen, by being a father figure."

"Yes, but—"

"The four of us together will give the girls a sense of belonging to a whole family," Tanner added confidently.

His arguments sounded so reasonable, so logical. Still, Joanna remained uncertain. "But I'm afraid the girls will think we're serious."

Tanner lifted his head enough to look into her eyes, and Joanna couldn't remember a time they'd ever been bluer or more intense. "I am serious."

She pressed her forehead against his collarbone and willed her body to stop trembling. Their little kissing experiment had affected her far more than she dared let him know. Until tonight, they'd both tried to disguise or deny their attraction for each other, but the kiss had exposed everything.

"I haven't stopped thinking about you from the minute we first met," he whispered, and touched his lips to her temple. "If we were anyplace else right now, I'd show you how crazy I am about you."

If they'd been anyplace else, Joanna would have let him. She wanted him to kiss her, needed him to, but she was more frightened by her reaction to this one man than she'd been by anything else in a very long while. "Tanner, I'm afraid."

"Joanna, so am I, but I can't allow fear to rule my life." Gently he brushed the loose wisps of curls from the side of her face. His eyes studied her intently. "I didn't expect to feel this way again. I've guarded against letting this happen, but here we are, and Joanna, I don't mind telling you, I wouldn't change a thing."

Joanna closed her eyes and listened to the battle raging inside her head. She wanted so badly to give this feeling between them a chance to grow. But logic told her that if she agreed to his suggestion, she'd be making herself vulnerable again. Even worse, Tanner Lund wasn't just any man—he was wealthy and successful, the half owner of an important company. And she was just a loan officer at a small local bank.

"Joanna, at least tell me what you're feeling."

"I . . . I don't know," she hedged, still uncertain.

He gripped her hand and pressed it over his heart, holding it there. "Just feel what you do to me."

Her own heart seemed about to hammer its way out of her chest. "You do the same thing to me."

He smiled ever so gently. "I know."

The music came to an end and the lights brightened. Reluctantly Tanner and Joanna broke apart, but he still kept her close to his side, tucking his arm around her waist.

"You haven't answered me, Joanna. I'm not going to hurt you, you know. We'll take it nice and easy at first and see how things develop."

Joanna's throat felt constricted, and she couldn't answer him one way or the other, although it was clear that he was waiting for her to make a decision.

"We've got something good between us," he continued, "and I don't want to just throw it away. I think we should find out whether this can last."

He wouldn't hurt her intentionally, Joanna realised, but the probability of her walking away unscathed from a relationship with this man was remote.

"What do you think?" he pressed.

She couldn't refuse him. "Maybe we should give it a try," she said after a long pause.

Tanner gazed down on her, bathing her in the warmth of his smile. "Neither of us is going to be sorry."

Joanna wasn't nearly as confident. She glanced away and happened to notice Kristen and Nicole. "Uh-oh," she murmured.

"What's wrong?"

"I just saw Kristen zoom over to Nicole and whisper into her ear. Then they hugged each other like long-lost sisters."

"I can deal with it if you can," he said, squeezing her hand.

Tanner's certainty lent her courage. "Then so can I."

CHAPTER TEN

JOANNA DIDN'T SLEEP WELL that night, or the following two. Tanner had suggested they meet for dinner the next weekend. It seemed an eternity, but there were several problems at work that demanded his attention. She felt as disappointed as he sounded that their first real date wouldn't take place for a week.

Joanna wished he hadn't given her so much time to think about it. If they'd been able to casually go to a movie the afternoon following the slumber party, she wouldn't have been so nervous about it.

When she arrived at work Monday morning, her brain was so muddled she felt as though she were walking in a fog. Twice during the weekend she'd almost called Tanner to suggest they call the whole thing off.

"Morning," her boss murmured absently, hardly looking up from the newspaper. "How was your weekend?"

"Exciting," Joanna told Robin, tucking her purse into the bottom drawer of her desk. "I went roller-skating with fifteen eleven-year-old girls."

"Sounds adventurous," Robin said, his gaze never leaving the paper.

Joanna poured herself a cup of coffee and carried it to her desk to drink black. The way she was feeling, she knew she'd need something strong to clear her head.

"I don't suppose you've been following what's happening at Spokane Aluminum?" Robin asked, refilling his own coffee cup.

It was a good thing Joanna had set her mug down when she did, otherwise it would have tumbled from her fingers. "Spokane Aluminum?" she echoed.

"Yes." Robin sat on the edge of her desk, allowing one leg to dangle. "There's another news item in the paper this morning on Tanner Lund. Six months ago, he bought out half the company from John Becky. I'm sure you've heard of John Becky?"

"Of...course."

"Apparently Lund came into this company and breathed new life into its sagging foreign sales. He took over management himself and has completely changed the company's direction...all for the better. I've heard nothing but good about this guy. Every time I turn around, I'm either reading how great he is, or hearing people talk about him. Take my word, Tanner Lund is a man who's going places."

Joanna couldn't agree more. And she knew for a fact where he was going Saturday night. He was taking her to dinner.

"MR. LUND'S HERE," Kristen announced the following Saturday, opening Joanna's bedroom door. "And does he ever look handsome!"

A dinner date. A simple dinner date, and Joanna was more nervous than a college graduate applying for her first job. She smoothed her hand down her red-and-white flowered dress and held in her breath so long her lungs ached.

Kristen rolled her eyes. "You look fine, Mom."

"I do?"

"As nice as Mr. Lund."

For good measure, Joanna paused long enough to dab more cologne behind her ears, then she squared her shoulders and turned to face the long hallway that led to the living room. "Okay, I'm ready."

Kristen threw open the bedroom door as though she expected royalty to emerge. By the time Joanna had walked down the hallway to the living room where Tanner was waiting, her heart was pounding and her hands were shaking. Kristen was right. Tanner looked marvellous in a three-piece suit and silk tie. He smiled when she came into the room, and stood up, gazing at her with an expression of undisguised delight.

"Hi."

"Hi." Their eyes met, and everything else faded away. Just seeing him again made Joanna's pulse leap into overdrive. No week had ever dragged more.

"Sally's got the phone number of the restaurant, and her mother said it was fine if she stayed here late," Kristen said, standing between them and glancing from one adult to the other. "I don't have any plans myself, so you two feel free to stay out as long as you want."

"Sally?" Joanna forced herself to glance at the babysitter.

"Yes, Mrs. Parsons?"

"There's salad and leftover spaghetti in the refrigerator for dinner, and some microwave popcorn in the cupboard for later."

"Okay."

"I won't be too late."

"But, Mom," Kristen cut in, a slight whine in her voice, "I just got done telling you that it'd be fine if you stayed out till the wee hours of the morning."

"We'll be back before midnight," Joanna informed the baby-sitter, ignoring Kristen.

"Okay," the girl said, as Kristen sighed expressively. "Have a good time."

Tanner escorted Joanna out to the car, which was parked in front of the house, and opened the passenger door. He paused, his hand still resting on her shoulder. "I'd like to kiss you now, but we have an audience," he said, nodding toward the house.

Joanna chanced a look and discovered Kristen standing in the living-room window, holding aside the curtain and watching them intently. No doubt she was memorising everything they said and did to report back to Nicole.

"I couldn't believe it when she agreed to let Sally come over. She's of the opinion lately that she's old enough to stay by herself."

"Nicole claims the same thing, but she didn't raise any objections about having a baby-sitter, either."

"I guess we should count our blessings."

Tanner drove to an expensive downtown restaurant overlooking the Spokane River, in the heart of the city.

Joanna's mouth was dry and her palms sweaty when the valet opened her door and helped her out. She'd never eaten at such a luxurious place in her life. She'd heard that their prices were outrageous. The amount Tanner intended to spend on one meal would probably outfit Kristen for an entire school year. Joanna felt faint at the very idea.

"Chez Michel is an exceptionally nice restaurant, Tanner, if you get my drift," she muttered under her breath after he handed the car keys to the valet. As a newcomer to town, he might not have been aware of just how expensive this place actually was.

"Yes, that's why I chose it," he said nonchalantly. "I was quite pleased with the food and the service when I was here a few weeks ago." He glanced at Joanna and her discomfort must have shown. "Consider it a small token of my appreciation for your help with Nicole's birthday party," he added, offering her one of his bone-melting smiles.

Joanna would have been more than content to eat at Denny's, and that thought reminded her again of how different they were.

She wished now that she'd worn something a little more elegant. The waiters seemed to be better dressed than she was. For that matter, so were the menus.

They were escorted to a table with an unobstructed view of the river. The maître d' held out Joanna's chair and seated her with flair. The first thing she noticed was the setting of silverware, with its bewildering array of forks, knives and spoons. After the maître d' left, she leaned forward and whispered to Tanner, "I've never eaten at a place that uses three teaspoons."

"Oh, quit complaining."

"I'm not, but if I embarrass you and use the wrong fork, don't blame me."

Unconcerned, Tanner chuckled and reached for the shiny gold menu.

Apparently Chez Michel believed in leisurely dining, because nearly two hours had passed by the time they were served their after-dinner coffee. The entire meal was everything Joanna could have hoped for, and more. The food was exceptional, but Joanna considered Tanner's company the best part of the evening. She'd never felt this much at ease with a man before. He made her smile, but he challenged her ideas, too. They talked about the girls and about the demands of being a parent. They discussed Joanna's career goals and Tanner's plans for his company. They covered a lot of different subjects, but didn't focus their conversation on any one.

Now that the meal was over, Joanna was reluctant to see the evening end. She lifted the delicate china cup, admiring its pattern, and took a sip of fragrant coffee. She paused, her cup raised halfway to her mouth, when she noticed Tanner staring at her. "What's wrong?" she asked, fearing part of her dessert was on her nose or something equally disastrous.

"Nothing."

"Then why are you looking at me like that?"

Tanner relaxed, leaned back in his chair, and grinned. "I'm sorry. I was just thinking how lovely you are, and how pleased I am that we met. It seems nothing's been the same since. I never thought a woman could make me feel the way you do, Joanna."

She looked quickly down, feeling a sudden shyness— and a wonderful warmth. Her life had changed, too, and she wasn't sure she could ever go back to the way things had been before. She was dreaming again, feeling again, trusting again, and it felt so good. And so frightening.

"I'm pleased, too," was her only comment.

"You know what the girls are thinking, don't you?"

Joanna could well imagine. No doubt those two would have them engaged after one dinner date. "They're probably expecting us to announce our marriage plans tomorrow morning," Joanna said, trying to make a joke of it.

"To be honest, I find some aspects of married life appealing."

Joanna smiled and narrowed her eyes suspiciously. "Come on, Tanner, just how much wine have you had?"

"Obviously too much, now that I think about it," he said, grinning. Then his face sobered. "All kidding aside,

I want you to know how much I enjoy your company. Every time I'm with you, I come away feeling good about life—you make me laugh again.''

"I'd make anyone laugh," she said, "especially if I'm wearing a pair of roller skates." She didn't know where their conversation was leading, but the fact that Tanner spoke so openly and honestly about the promise of their relationship completely unnerved her. She felt exactly the same things, but didn't have the courage to voice them.

"I'm glad you agreed we should start seeing each other," Tanner continued.

"Me, too." But she fervently hoped her mother wouldn't hear about it, although Kristen had probably phoned her grandmother the minute Joanna was out the door. Lowering her gaze, Joanna discovered that a bread crumb on the linen tablecloth had become utterly absorbing. She carefully brushed it onto the floor, an inch at a time. "It's worked out fine...so far. Us dating, I mean." It was more than fine. And now he was telling her how she'd brightened his life, as though *he* was the lucky one. That someone like Tanner Lund would ever want to date her still astonished Joanna.

She gazed up at him, her heart shining through her eyes, telling him without words what she was feeling.

Tanner briefly shut his eyes. "Joanna, for heaven's sake, don't look at me like that."

"Like what?"

"Like...that."

"I think you should kiss me," Joanna announced, once again staring down at the tablecloth. The instant the words slipped out she longed to take them back. She couldn't believe she'd said something like that to him.

"I beg your pardon?"

"Never mind," she said quickly, grateful he hadn't heard her.

He had. "Kiss you? Now? Here?"

Joanna shook her head, forcing a smile. "Forget I said that. It just slipped out. Sometimes my mouth disconnects itself from my brain."

Tanner didn't remove his gaze from hers as he raised his hand. Their waiter appeared almost immediately, and still looking at Joanna, he muttered, "Check, please."

"Right away, sir."

They were out of the restaurant so fast Joanna's head was spinning. Once they were seated in the car, Tanner paused, frowning, his hands clenched on the steering wheel.

"What's the matter?" Joanna asked anxiously.

"We goofed. We should have shared a baby-sitter."

The thought had fleetingly entered her mind earlier, but she'd discounted the idea because she didn't want to encourage the girls' scheming.

"I can't take you back to my place because Nicole will be all over us with questions, and it'll probably be the same story at your house with Kristen."

"You're right." Besides, her daughter would be sorely disappointed if they showed up this early. It wasn't even close to midnight.

"Just where am I supposed to kiss you, Joanna Parsons?"

Oh Lord, he'd taken her seriously. "Tanner...it was a joke."

He ignored her comment. "I don't know of a single lookout point in the city."

"Tanner, please." Her voice rose in embarrassment, and she could feel herself blushing.

Tanner leaned over and brushed his lips against her cheek. "I've got an idea for something we can do, but don't laugh."

"An idea? What?"

"You'll see soon enough." He eased his car onto the street and drove quickly through the city to the freeway on-ramp and didn't exit until they were well into the suburbs.

"Tanner?" Joanna said, looking around her at the unfamiliar streets. "What's out here?" Almost as soon as she'd spoken a huge white screen appeared in the distance. "A drive-in?" she whispered in disbelief.

"Have you got any better ideas?"

"Not a one." Joanna chuckled; she couldn't help it. He was taking her to a drive-in movie just so he could kiss her.

"I can't guarantee this movie. This is its opening weekend, and if I remember the ad correctly, they're showing something with lots of blood and gore."

"As long as it isn't *Teen Massacre*. Kristen would never forgive me if I saw it when she hadn't."

"If the truth be known, I don't plan to watch a whole lot of the movie." He darted an exaggerated leer in her direction and wiggled his eyebrows suggestively.

Joanna returned his look by demurely fluttering her lashes. "I don't know if my mother would approve of my going to a drive-in on a first date."

"With good reason," Tanner retorted. "Especially if she knew what I had in mind."

Although the weather had been mild and the sky was cloudless and clear, only a few cars were scattered across the wide lot.

Tanner parked as far away from the others as possible. He connected the speaker, but turned the volume so low it was almost inaudible. When he'd finished, he placed his arm around Joanna's shoulders, pulling her closer.

"Come here, woman."

Joanna leaned her head against his shoulder and pretended to be interested in the cartoon characters leaping across the large screen. Her stomach was playing jumping jacks with the dinner she'd just eaten.

"Joanna?" His voice was low and seductive.

She tilted her head to meet his gaze, and his eyes moved slowly over her upturned face, searing her with their intensity. The openness of his desire stole her breath away. Her heart was pounding, although he hadn't even kissed her yet. One hungry look from Tanner and she was melting at his feet.

Her first thought was to crack a joke. That had saved her in the past, but whatever she might have said or done was lost as Tanner lowered his mouth and tantalised the edges of her trembling lips, teasing her with soft, tempting nibbles, making her ache all the way to her toes for his kiss. Instinctively her fingers slid up his chest and around the back of his neck. Tanner created such an overwhelming need in her that she felt both humble and elated at the same time. When her hands tightened around his neck, his mouth hardened into firm possession.

Joanna thought she'd drown in the sensations that flooded her. She hadn't felt this kind of longing in years, and she trembled with the wonder of it. Tanner had awakened the deep womanly part of her that had lain dormant for so long. And suddenly she felt all that time without love come rushing up at her, overtaking her. Years of regret, years of doubt, years of rejection all pressed so heavily on her heart that she could barely breathe.

A sob was ripped from her throat, and the sound of it broke them apart. Tears she couldn't explain flooded her eyes and ran unheeded down her face.

"Joanna, what's wrong? Did I hurt you?"

She tried to break away, but Tanner wouldn't let her go. He brushed the hair from her face and tilted her head to lift her eyes to his, but she resisted.

He must have felt the wetness on her face, because he paused and murmured, "You're crying," in a tone that sounded as shocked as she felt. "Dear Lord, what did I do?"

Wildly she shook her head, unable to speak even if she'd been able to find the words to explain.

"Joanna, tell me, please."

"J-just hold me." Even saying that much required all her reserves of strength.

He did as she asked, wrapping his arms completely around her, kissing the crown of her head as she buried herself in his strong, solid warmth.

Still, the tears refused to stop, no matter how hard she tried to make them. They flooded her face and seemed to come from the deepest part of her.

"I can't believe I'm doing this," she said between sobs. "Oh, Tanner, I feel like such a fool."

"Go ahead and cry, Joanna. I understand."

"You do? Good. You can explain it to me."

She could feel his smile as he kissed the corner of her eye. She moaned a little and he lowered his lips to her cheek, then her chin, and when she couldn't bear it any longer, she turned her face, her mouth seeking his. Tanner didn't disappoint her, kissing her gently again and again until she was certain her heart would stop beating if he ever stopped holding her and kissing her.

"Good Lord, Joanna," he whispered after a while, gently extricating himself from her arms and leaning against the car seat, his eyes closed. His face was a picture of desire struggling for restraint. He drew in several deep breaths.

Joanna's tears had long since dried on her face and now her cheeks flamed with confusion and remorse.

A heavy silence fell between them. Joanna searched frantically for something witty to say to break the terrible tension.

"Joanna, listen—"

"No, let me speak first," she broke in, then hesitated. Now that she had his attention, she didn't know what to say. "I'm sorry, Tanner, really sorry. I don't know what came over me, but you weren't the one responsible for my tears. Well, no, you were, but not the way you think."

"Joanna, please," he said and his hands bracketed her face. "Don't be embarrassed by the tears. Believe me when I say I'm feeling the same things you are, only they come out in different ways."

Joanna stared up at him, not sure he could possibly understand.

"It's been so long for you— it has for me, too," Tanner went on. "I feel like a teenager again. And the drive-in has nothing to do with it."

Her lips trembled with the effort to smile. Tanner leaned his forehead against hers. "We need to take this slow. Very, very slow."

That was a fine thing for him to say, considering they'd been as hot as torches for each other a few minutes ago. If they continued at this rate, they'd end up in bed together by the first of the week.

"I've got a company party in a couple of weeks; I want you there with me. Will you do that?"

Joanna nodded.

Tanner drew her closer to his side and she tucked her head against his chest. His hand stroked her shoulder, as he kissed the top of her head.

"You're awfully quiet," he said after several minutes. "What are you thinking?"

Joanna sighed and snuggled closer, looping one arm around his middle. Her free hand was laced with his. "It just occurred to me that for the first time in my life I've met a real prince. Up until now, all I've done is make a few frogs happy."

Kristen hesitated, then asked, "When are you going out again?" The question hit an unexpected nerve. Joanna considered a moment. She had dated occasionally over the past several years, but nothing serious...

CHAPTER ELEVEN

KNEELING ON THE POLISHED linoleum floor of the kitchen, Joanna held her breath and tentatively poked her head inside the foam-covered oven. Sharp, lemon-scented fumes made her grimace as she dragged the wet sponge along the sides, peeling away a layer of blackened crust. She'd felt unusually ambitious for a Saturday and had worked in the yard earlier, planning her garden. When she'd finished that, she'd decided to tackle the oven, not questioning where this burst of energy had come from. Spring was in the air, but instead of turning her fancy to thoughts of love, it filled her mind with zucchini seeds and rows of tomato seedlings.

"I'm leaving now, Mom," Kristen called from behind her.

Joanna jerked her head free, gulped some fresh air and twisted toward her daughter. "What time will you be through at the library?" Kristen and Nicole were working together on a school project, and although they complained about having to do research, they'd come to enjoy it. Their biggest surprise was discovering all the cute junior-high boys who sometimes visited the library. In Kristen's words, it was an untapped gold mine.

"I don't know when we'll be through, but I'll call. And remember, Nicole is coming over afterwards."

"I remember."

Kristen hesitated, then asked, "When are you going out with Mr. Lund again?"

Joanna glanced over at the calendar. "Next weekend. We're attending a dinner party his company's sponsoring."

"Oh."

Joanna rubbed her forearm across her cheek, and glanced suspiciously at her daughter. "What does that mean?"

"What?"

"That little 'oh.'"

Kristen shrugged. "Nothing.... It's just that you're not seeing him as often as Nicole and I think you should. You like Mr. Lund, don't you?"

That was putting it mildly. "He's very nice," Joanna said cautiously. If she admitted to anything beyond a casual attraction, Kristen would assume much more. Joanna wanted her relationship with Tanner to progress slowly, one careful step at a time, not in giant leaps—though slow and careful didn't exactly describe what had happened so far!

"Nice?" Kristen exclaimed.

Her daughter's outburst caught Joanna by surprise.

"Is that all you can say about Mr. Lund?" Kristen asked, hands on her hips. "I've given the matter serious consideration and I think he's a whole lot more than just nice. Really, Mother."

Taking a deep breath, Joanna plunged her head back inside the oven, swiping her sponge furiously against the sides.

"Are you going to ignore me?" Kristen demanded.

Joanna emerged again, gasped and looked straight at her daughter. "Yes. Unless you want to volunteer to clean the oven yourself."

"I would, but I have to go to the library with Nicole."

Joanna noted the soft regret that filled her daughter's voice and gave her a derisive snort. The kid actually sounded sorry that she wouldn't be there to do her part. Kristen was a genius at getting out of work, and she always managed to give the impression of really wishing she could help her mother—if only she could fit it into her busy schedule.

A car horn beeped out front. "That's Mr. Lund," Kristen said, glancing toward the living room. "I'll give you a call when we're done."

"Okay, honey. Have a good time."

"I will."

With form an Olympic sprinter would envy, Kristen tore out of the kitchen. Two seconds later, the front door slammed. Joanna was only mildly disappointed that Tanner hadn't stopped in to chat. He'd phoned earlier and explained that after he dropped the girls off at the library, he was driving to the office for a couple of hours. An unexpected problem had arisen, and he needed to deal with it right away.

Actually Joanna had to admit she was more grateful than disappointed that Tanner hadn't stopped in. It didn't look as though she'd get a chance to see him before the company party. She needed this short separation to pull together her reserves. Following their dinner date and the drive-in movie afterward, Joanna felt dangerously close to falling in love with Tanner. Every time he came to mind, and that was practically every minute of every day, a rush of warmth and happiness followed. Without too much trouble, she could envision them finding a lifetime of happiness together. For the first time since her divorce she allowed herself the luxury of dreaming again, and although the prospect of remarriage excited and thrilled her, it also terrified her.

Fifteen minutes later, with perspiration beaded on her forehead and upper lip, Joanna heaved a sigh and sat back on her heels. The hair she'd so neatly tucked inside a scarf and tied at the back of her head, had fallen loose. She swiped a grimy hand at the auburn curls that hung limply over her eyes and ears. It was all worth it, though, since the gray-speckled sides of the oven, which had been encrusted with black grime, were now clearly visible and shining.

Joanna emptied the bucket of dirty water and hauled a fresh one back to wipe the oven one last time. She'd just knelt down when the doorbell chimed.

"Great," she muttered under her breath, casting a glance at herself. She looked like something that had crawled out of the bog in some horror movie. Pasting a smile on her face, she peeled off her rubber gloves and hurried to the door.

"Davey!" Finding her ex-husband standing on the porch was enough of a shock to knock the breath from Joanna's lungs.

"May I come in?"

"Of course." Flustered, she ran her hand through her hair and stepped aside to allow him to pass. He looked good—really good—but then Davey had never lacked in the looks department. From the expensive cut of his three-piece suit, she could tell that his real-estate business must be doing well, and of course that was precisely the impression he wanted her to have. She was pleased for him; she'd never wished him ill. They'd gone their separate ways, and although both the marriage and the divorce had devastated Joanna, she shared a beautiful child

with this man. If he had come by to tell her how successful he was, well, she'd just smile and let him.

"It's good to see you, Joanna."

"You, too. What brings you to town?" She struggled
to keep her voice even and controlled, hoping to hide her
discomfort at being caught unawares.

"I'm attending a conference downtown. I apologise for
dropping in unexpectedly like this, but since I was going
to be in Spokane, I thought I'd stop in and see how you
and Kristen are doing."

"I wish you'd phoned first. Kristen's at the library."
Joanna wasn't fooled—Davey hadn't come to see their
daughter, although he meant Joanna to think so. It was all
part of the game he played with her, wanting her to believe that their divorce had hurt him badly. Not calling to
let her know he planned to visit was an attempt to catch
her off guard and completely unprepared—which, of
course, she was. Joanna knew Davey, knew him well.
He'd often tried to manipulate her this way.

"I should have called, but I didn't know if I'd have the
time, and I didn't want to disappoint you if I found I
couldn't slip away."

Joanna didn't believe that for a minute. It wouldn't
have taken him much time or trouble to phone before he
left the hotel. But she didn't mention the fact, couldn't see
that it would have done any good.

"Come in and have some coffee." She led him into the
kitchen and poured him a mug, automatically adding the
sugar and cream she knew he used. She handed it to him
and was rewarded with a dazzling smile. When he wanted,
Davey Parsons could be charming, attentive and generous. The confusing thing about her ex-husband was that
he wasn't all bad. He'd gravely wounded her with his un-
faithfulness, but in his own way he'd loved her and

Kristen—as much as he could possibly love anybody beyond himself. It had taken Joanna a good many years to distance herself enough to appreciate his good points and to forgive him for the pain he'd caused her.

"You've got a nice place here," he commented, casually glancing around the kitchen. "How long have you lived here now?"

"Seven months."

"How's Kristen?"

Joanna was relieved that the conversation had moved to the only subject they still had in common—their daughter. She talked for fifteen minutes nonstop, telling him about the talent show and the other activities Kristen had been involved in since the last time she'd seen her father.

Davey listened and laughed, and then his gaze softened as he studied Joanna. "You're looking wonderful."

She grinned ruefully. "Sure I am," she scoffed. "I've just finished working in the yard and cleaning the oven."

"I wondered about the lemon perfume you were wearing."

They both laughed. Davey started to tease her about their early years together and some of the experimental meals she'd cooked and expected him to eat and praise. Joanna let him and even enjoyed his comments, for Davey could be warm and funny when he chose. Kristen had inherited her friendly, easygoing confidence from her father.

The doorbell chimed and still chuckling, Joanna stood up. "It's probably one of the neighbourhood kids. I'll just be a minute." She never ceased to be astonished at how easy it was to be with Davey. He'd ripped her heart in two, lied to her repeatedly, cheated on her, and still she couldn't be around him and not laugh. It always took him a few minutes to conquer her reserve, but he never failed. She was mature enough to recognise her ex-husband's faults, yet appreciate his redeeming qualities.

For the second time that day, Joanna was surprised by the man who stood on her front porch. "Tanner."

"Hi," he said with a sheepish grin. "The girls got off okay and I thought I'd stop in for a cup of coffee before heading to the office." His eyes smiled softly into hers. "I heard you laughing from out here. Do you have company? Should I come back later?"

"N-no, come in," she said, her pulse beating as hard and loud as jungle drums. Lowering her eyes, she automatically moved aside. He walked into the living room and paused, then raised his hand and gently touched her cheek in a gesture so loving that Joanna longed to fall into his arms. Now that he was here, she found herself craving some time alone with him.

Tanner's gaze reached out to her, but Joanna had trouble meeting it. A frown started to form, and his eyes clouded. "This is a bad time, isn't it?"

"No...not really." When she turned around, Davey was standing in the kitchen doorway watching them. The smile she'd been wearing felt shaky as she stood between the two men and made the introductions. "Davey, this is Tanner Lund. Tanner, this is Davey—Kristen's father."

For a moment, the two men glared at each other like angry bears who had claimed territory and were prepared to do battle to protect what was theirs. When they stepped towards each other, Joanna held her breath for fear neither one would make the effort to be civil.

Stunned, she watched as they exchanged handshakes and enthusiastic greetings.

"Davey's in town for a real-estate conference and thought he'd stop in to see Kristen," Joanna explained, her words coming out in such a rush that they nearly stumbled over themselves.

"I came to see you, too, Joanna," Davey added in a low sultry voice that suggested he had more on his mind than a chat over a cup of coffee.

She flashed him a heated look before marching into the kitchen, closely followed by both men. She walked straight to the cupboard, bringing down another cup, then poured Tanner's coffee and delivered it to the table.

"Kristen and my daughter are at the library," Tanner announced in a perfectly friendly voice, but Joanna heard the undercurrents even if Davey didn't.

"Joanna told me," Davey returned.

The two men remained standing, smiling at each other. Tanner took a seat first, and Davey promptly did the same.

"What do you do?" her ex-husband asked.

"I own half of Spokane Aluminum."

It was apparent to Joanna that Davey hadn't even bothered to listen to Tanner's reply because he immediately fired back in an aggressive tone, "I recently opened my own real-estate brokerage and have plans to expand within the next couple of years." He announced his success with a cocky slant to his mouth.

Watching the change in Davey's features as Tanner's identity began to sink in was so comical that Joanna nearly laughed out loud. Davey's mouth sagged open, and his eyes flew from Joanna to Tanner and then back to Joanna.

"Spokane Aluminum," Davey repeated slowly, his face unusually pale. "I seem to remember reading something about John Becky taking on a partner."

Joanna almost felt sorry for Davey. "Kristen and Tanner's daughter, Nicole, are best friends. They were in the Valentine's Day show together—the one I was telling you about. . . ."

To his credit, Davey regrouped quickly. "She gets all that performing talent from you."

"Oh, hardly," Joanna countered, denying it with a vigorous shake of her head. Of the two of them, Davey was the entertainer—crowds had never intimidated him. He could walk into a room full of strangers, and anyone who didn't know better would end up thinking Davey Parsons was his best friend.

"With the girls being so close, it seemed only natural for Joanna and me to start dating," Tanner said, turning to smile warmly at Joanna.

"I see," Davey answered. He didn't appear to have recovered from Tanner's first announcement.

"I sincerely hope you do understand," Tanner returned, all pretence of friendliness dropped.

Joanna resisted rolling her eyes toward the ceiling. Both of them were behaving like immature children, battling with looks and words as if she were a prize to be awarded the victor.

"I suppose I'd better think about heading out," Davey said after several awkward moments had passed. He stood up, noticeably eager to make his escape.

As a polite hostess, Joanna stood when Davey did. "I'll walk you to the door."

He sent Tanner a wary smile. "That's not necessary."

"Of course it is," Joanna countered.

To her dismay, Tanner followed them and stood conspicuously in the background while Davey made arrangements to phone Kristen later that evening. The whole time Davey was speaking, Joanna could feel Tanner's eyes burning into her back. She didn't know why he'd insisted on following her to the door. It was like saying he couldn't trust her not to fall into Davey's arms the minute he was out of sight, and that irritated her no end.

Once her ex-husband had left, she closed the door and whirled around to face Tanner. The questions were jammed in her mind. They'd only gone out on one date, for heaven's sake, and here he was, acting as though...as though they were engaged.

"I thought he broke your heart," Tanner said, in a cutting voice.

Joanna debated whether or not to answer him, then decided it would be best to clear the air. "He did."

"I heard you laughing when I rang the doorbell. Do you often have such a good time with men you're supposed to hate?"

"I don't hate Davey."

"Believe me, I can tell."

"Tanner, what's wrong with you?" That was a silly question, and she regretted asking it immediately. She already knew what was troubling Tanner. He was jealous. And angry. And hurt.

"Wrong with me?" He tossed the words back at her. "Nothing's wrong with me. I happen to stumble upon the woman I'm involved with cosying up to her ex-husband, and I don't mind telling you I'm upset. But nothing's wrong with me. Not one damn thing. If there's something wrong with anyone, it's you, lady."

Joanna held tightly onto her patience. "Before we start arguing, let's sit down and talk this out." She led him back into the kitchen, then took Davey's empty coffee mug and placed it in the sink, removing all evidence of his brief visit. She searched for a way to reassure Tanner that Davey meant nothing to her anymore. But she had to explain that she and her ex-husband weren't enemies, either; they couldn't be for Kristen's sake.

"First of all," she said, as evenly as her pounding heart would allow, "I could never hate Davey the way you seem to think I should. As far as I'm concerned, that would only be counterproductive. The people who would end up suffering are Kristen and me. Davey is incapable of being faithful to one woman, but he'll always be Kristen's father, and if for no other reason than that, I prefer to remain on friendly terms with him."

"But he cheated on you . . . used you."

"Yes." She couldn't deny it. "But, Tanner, I lived a lot of years with Davey. He's not all bad—no one is—and scattered between all the bad times were a few good ones. We're divorced now. What good would it do to harbour ill will toward him? None that I can see."

"He let it be known from the moment I walked into this house that he could have you back any time he wanted."

Joanna wasn't blind; she'd recognised the looks Davey had given Tanner, and the insinuations. "He'd like to believe that. It helps him deal with his ego."

"And you let him?"

"Not the way you're implying."

Tanner mulled that over for a few moments. "How often does he casually drop in unannounced like this?"

She hesitated, wondering whether she should answer his question. His tone had softened, but he was obviously still angry. She could sympathise, but she didn't like having to defend herself or her attitude toward Davey. "I haven't seen him in over a year. This is the first time he's been to the house."

Tanner's hands gripped the coffee mug so tightly that Joanna was amazed it remained intact. "You still love him, don't you?"

The question hit her square between the eyes. Her mouth opened and closed several times as she struggled for the words to deny it. Then she realised she couldn't. Lying to Tanner about this would be simple enough and it would keep the peace, but it would wrong them both. "I suppose in a way I do," she began slowly. "He's the father of my child. He was my first love, Tanner. And the only lover I've ever had. Although I'd like to tell you I don't feel a thing for him, I can't do that and be completely honest. But please, try to understand—"

"You don't need to say anything more." He stood abruptly, his back stiff. "I appreciate the fact that you told me the truth. I won't waste any more of your time. I wish you and Kristen a good life." With that he stalked out of the room, headed for the door.

Joanna was shocked. "Tanner...you make it sound like I'll never see you again."

"I think that would be best for everyone concerned," he replied, without looking at her.

"But . . . that's silly. Nothing's changed." She snapped her mouth closed. If Tanner wanted to act so childishly and ruin everything, she wasn't about to argue with him. He was the one who insisted they had something special, something so good they shouldn't throw it away because of their fears. And now he was acting like this! Fine. If that was the way he wanted it. It was better to find out how unreasonable he could be before anything serious developed between them. Better to discover now how quick-tempered he could be, how hurtful.

"I have no intention of becoming involved with a woman who's still in love with her loser of an ex-husband," he announced, his hands clenched at his sides. His voice was calm, but she recognised the tension in it. And the resolve.

Unable to restrain her anger any longer, Joanna marched across the room and threw open the front door.

"Smart move, Tanner," she said, her words coated with sarcasm. "You made a terrible mistake getting involved with a woman who refuses to hate." Now that she had a better look at him, she decided he wasn't a prince after all, only another frog.

Tanner didn't say a word as he walked past her, his strides filled with purpose. She closed the door and leaned against it, needing the support. Tears burned in her eyes and clogged her throat, but she held her head high and hurried back into the kitchen, determined not to give in to the powerful emotions that racked her, body and soul.

She finished cleaning up the kitchen, and took a long hot shower afterward. Then she sat quietly at the table, waiting for Kristen to phone so she could pick up the two girls. The call came a half hour later, but by that time she'd already reached for the cookies, bent on self-destruction.

On the way home from the library, Joanna stopped off at McDonald's and bought the girls cheeseburgers and chocolate milk shakes to take home for dinner. Her mind was filled with doubts. In retrospect, she wished she'd done a better job of explaining things to Tanner. The thought of never seeing him again was almost too painful to endure.

"Aren't you going to order anything, Mom?" Kristen asked, surprised.

"Not tonight." Somewhere deep inside, Joanna found the energy to smile.

She managed to maintain a light-hearted facade while Kristen and Nicole ate their dinner and chattered about the boys they'd seen at the library and how they were going to shock Mrs. Andrews with their well-researched report.

"Are you feeling okay?" Kristen asked, pausing in mid-sentence.

"Sure," Joanna lied, looking for something to occupy her hands. She settled for briskly wiping down the kitchen counters. Actually, she felt sick to her stomach, but she couldn't blame Tanner; she'd done that to herself with all those stupid cookies.

It was when she was putting the girls' empty McDonald's containers in the garbage that the silly tears threatened to spill over. She did her best to hide them and quickly carried out the trash. Nicole went to get a cassette from Kristen's bedroom, but Kristen followed her mother outside.

"Mom, what's wrong?"

"Nothing, sweetheart."

"You have tears in your eyes."

"It's nothing."

"You never cry," Kristen insisted.

"Something must have got into my eye to make it tear like this," she said, shaking her head. The effort to smile was too much for her. She straightened and placed her hands on Kristen's shoulders, then took a deep breath. "I don't want you to be disappointed if I don't see Mr. Lund again."

"He did this?" Kristen demanded, in a high shocked voice.

"No," Joanna countered immediately. "I already told you, I got something in my eye."

Kristen studied her with a frown, and Joanna tried to meet her daughter's gaze. If she was fool enough to make herself vulnerable to a man again, then she deserved this pain. She'd known better than to get involved with Tanner, but her heart had refused to listen.

A couple of hours later, Tanner arrived to pick up Nicole. Joanna let Kristen answer the door and stayed in the kitchen, pretending to be occupied there.

When the door swung open, Joanna assumed it was her daughter and asked, "Did Nicole get off all right?"

"Not yet."

Joanna jerked away from the sink at the husky sound of Tanner's voice. "Where are the girls?"

"In Kristen's room. I want to talk to you."

"I can't see how that would do much good."

"I've reconsidered."

"Bravo for you. Unfortunately so have I. You're absolutely right about it being better all around if we don't see each other again."

Tanner dragged his fingers through his hair and stalked to the other side of the room. "Okay, I'll admit it. I was jealous as hell when I walked in and found you having coffee with Davey. I felt you were treating him like some conquering hero returned from the war."

"Oh, honestly, it wasn't anything like that."

"You were laughing and smiling."

"Grievous sins, I'm sure."

Tanner clamped down his jaw so hard that the sides of his face went white. "All I can do is apologise, Joanna. I've already made a fool of myself over one woman who loved someone else, and frankly that caused me enough grief. I'm not looking to repeat the mistake with you."

A strained silence fell between them.

"I thought I could walk away from you and not feel any regrets, but I was wrong," he continued a moment later. "I haven't stopped thinking about you all afternoon. Maybe I overreacted. Maybe I behaved like a jealous fool."

"Maybe?" Joanna challenged. "Maybe? You were unreasonable and hurtful and...and I ate a whole row of Oreo cookies over you."

"What?"

"You heard me. I stuffed down a dozen cookies and now I think I'm going to be sick and it was all because of you. I've come too far to be reduced to that. One argument with you and I was right back into the Oreos! If you think you're frightened—because of what happened with Carmen—it's nothing compared to the fears I've been facing since the day we met. I can't deal with your insecurities, Tanner. I've got too damn many of my own."

"Joanna, I've already apologised. If you can honestly tell me there isn't any chance that you'll ever get back together with Davey, I swear to you I'll drop the subject and never bring it up again. But I need to know that much. I'm sorry, but I've got to hear you say it."

"I had a nice quiet life before you paraded into it," she went on, as though she hadn't heard him.

"Joanna, I asked you a question." His intense gaze cut straight through her.

"You must be nuts! I'd be certifiably insane to ever take Davey back. Our marriage—our entire relationship—was over the day I filed for divorce, and probably a lot earlier than that."

Tanner relaxed visibly. "I wouldn't blame you if you decided you never wanted to see me again, but I'm hoping you'll be able to forget what happened this afternoon so we can go back to being...friends again."

Joanna struggled against the strong pull of his magnetism for as long as she could, then nodded, agreeing to place this quarrel behind them.

Tanner walked toward her and she met him halfway, slipping easily into his embrace. She felt as if she belonged here, as if he were the man she would always be content with. He'd once told her he wouldn't ever hurt her the way her ex-husband had, but caring about him, risking a relationship with him, left her vulnerable all over again. She'd realised that this afternoon, learned again what it was to give a man the power to hurt her.

"I reduced you to gorging yourself with Oreos?" Tanner whispered the question into her hair.

She nodded wildly. "You fiend. I didn't mean to eat that many, but I sat at the table with the Oreos package and a glass of milk and the more I thought about what happened, the angrier I became, and the faster I shoved those cookies into my mouth."

"Could this mean you care?" His voice was still a whisper.

She nodded a second time. "I hate fighting with you. My stomach was in knots all afternoon."

"Good Lord, Joanna," he said, dropping several swift kisses on her face. "I can't believe what fools we are."

"We?" She tilted back her head and glared up at him, but her mild indignation drained away the moment their eyes met. Tanner was looking down at her with such tenderness, such concern, that every negative emotion she'd experienced earlier that afternoon vanished like rain falling into a clear blue lake.

He kissed her then, with a thoroughness that left her in no doubt about the strength of his feelings. Joanna rested against this warmth, holding onto him with everything that was in her. When he raised his head, she looked up at him through tear-filled eyes and blinked furiously in a futile effort to keep them at bay.

"I'm glad you came back," she said, when she could find her voice.

"I am, too." He kissed her once more, lightly this time, sampling her lips, kissing the tears from her face. "I wasn't worth a damn all afternoon." Once more he lowered his mouth to hers, creating a delicious sensation that electrified Joanna and sent chills racing down her spine.

Tanner's arms tightened as loud voices suddenly erupted from the direction of the living room.

"I never want to see you again," Joanna heard Kristen declare vehemently.

"You couldn't possibly want to see me any less than I want to see you," Nicole returned with equal volume and fury.

"What's that all about?" Tanner asked, his eyes searching Joanna's.

"I don't know, but I think we'd better find out."

Tanner led the way into the living room. They discovered Kristen and Nicole standing face to face, glaring at each other in undisguised antagonism.

"Kristen, stop that right now," Joanna demanded. "Nicole is a guest in our home and I won't have you talking to her in that tone of voice."

Tanner moved to his daughter's side. "And you're Kristen's guest. I expect you to be on your best behaviour whenever you're here."

Nicole crossed her arms over her chest and darted a venomous look in Kristen's direction. "I refuse to be friends with her ever again. And I don't think you should have anything more to do with Mrs. Parsons."

Joanna's eyes found Tanner's.

"I don't want my mother to have anything to do with Mr. Lund, either." Kristen spun around and glared at Tanner and Nicole.

"I think we'd best separate these two and find out what happened," Joanna suggested. She pointed toward Kristen's bedroom. "Come on, honey, let's talk."

Kristen averted her face. "I have nothing to say!" she declared melodramatically and stalked out of the room without a backward glance.

Joanna raised questioning eyes to Tanner, threw up her hands and followed her daughter.

CHAPTER TWELVE

"KRISTEN, WHAT'S WRONG?" Joanna sat on the end of her daughter's bed and patiently waited for the eleven-year-old to repeat the list of atrocities committed by Nicole Lund.

"Nothing."

Joanna had seen her daughter wear this affronted look often enough to recognize it readily, and she felt a weary sigh work its way through her. Hell hath no fury like a sixth-grader done wrong by her closest friend.

"I don't ever want to see Nicole again."

"But, sweetheart, she's your best friend."

"*Was* my best friend," Kristen announced theatrically. She crossed her arms over her chest with all the pomp of a queen who'd made her statement and expected unquestioning acquiescence.

With mounting frustration, Joanna folded her hands in her lap and waited, knowing better than to try to reason with Kristen when she was in this mood. Five minutes passed, but Kristen didn't utter another word. Joanna wasn't surprised.

"Does your argument have to do with something that happened at school?" she asked as nonchalantly as possible, examining the fingernails on her right hand.

Kristen shook her head. She pinched her lips as if to suggest that nothing Joanna could say would force the information out of her.

"Does it involve a boy?" Joanna persisted.

Kristen's gaze widened. "Of course not."

"What about another friend?"

"Nope."

At the rate they were going, Joanna would soon run out of questions. "Can't you just tell me what happened?"

Kristen cast her a look that seemed to question her mother's intelligence. "No!"

"Does that mean we're going to sit here all night while I try to guess?"

Kristen twisted her head and tilted it at a lofty angle, then pantomimed locking her lips.

"All right," Joanna said with an exaggerated sigh, "I'll simply have to ask Nicole, who will, no doubt, be more than ready to tell all. Her version should be highly interesting."

"Mr. Lund made you cry!" Kristen mumbled, her eyes lowered.

Joanna blinked back her astonishment. "You mean to say this whole thing has to do with Tanner and me?"

Kristen nodded once.

"But—"

"Nicole claims that whatever happened was obviously your fault, and as far as I'm concerned that did it. From here on out, Nicole is no longer my friend and I don't think you should have anything to do with...with that man, either."

"That man?"

Kristen sent her a sour look. "You know very well who I mean."

Joanna shifted farther onto the bed, brought up her knees and rested her chin on them. She paused to carefully measure her words. "What if I told you I was beginning to grow fond of 'that man'?"

"Mom, no!" Her daughter's eyes widened with horror, and she cast her mother a look of sheer panic. "That would be the worst possible thing to happen. You might marry him and then Nicole and I would end up being sisters!"

Joanna made no attempt to conceal her surprise. "But, Kristen, from the not-so-subtle hints you and Nicole have been giving me and Mr. Lund, I thought that was exactly what you both wanted. What you'd planned."

"That was before."

"Before what?"

"Before...tonight, when Nicole said those things she said. I can't forgive her, Mom, I just can't."

Joanna stayed in the room a few more silent minutes, then left. Tanner and Nicole were talking in the living room, and from the frustrated look he gave her, she knew he hadn't been any more successful with his daughter than Joanna had been with hers.

When he saw Joanna, Tanner got to his feet and nodded toward the kitchen, mutely suggesting they talk privately and compare stories.

"What did you find out?" she asked the minute they were alone.

Tanner shrugged, then gestured defeat with his hands. "I don't understand it. She keeps saying she never wants to see Kristen again."

"Kristen says the same thing. Adamantly. She seems to think she's defending my honour. It seems this all has to do with our misunderstanding earlier this afternoon."

"Nicole seems to think it started when you didn't order anything at McDonalds," Tanner said, his expression confused.

"What?" Joanna's question escaped on a short laugh.

"From what I can get out of Nicole, Kristen claims you didn't order a Big Mac, which is supposed to mean something. Then later, before I arrived, there was some mention of your emptying the garbage when it was only halffull?" He paused to wait for her to speak. When she simply nodded, he continued, "I understand that's unusual for you, as well?"

Once more Joanna nodded. She'd wanted to hide her tears from the girls, so taking out the garbage had been an excuse to escape for a couple of minutes while she composed herself.

Tanner wiped his hand across his brow in mock relief. "Whew! At least neither of them learned about the Oreos!"

Joanna ignored his joke and slumped against the kitchen counter with a long slow sigh of frustration. "Having the girls argue is a problem neither of us anticipated."

"Maybe I should talk to Kristen and you talk to Nicole?" Tanner suggested, all seriousness again.

Joanna shook her head. "Then we'd be guilty of interfering. We'd be doing the same thing they've done to us—and I don't think we'd be doing them any favours."

"What do you suggest then?" Tanner asked, looking more disgruntled by the minute.

Joanna shrugged. "I don't know."

"Come on, Joanna, we're intelligent adults. Surely we can come up with a way to handle a couple of preadolescent egos."

"Be my guest," Joanna said, and laughed aloud at the comical look that crossed Tanner's handsome face.

"Forget it."

Joanna brushed the hair away from her face. "I think our best bet is to let them work this matter out between themselves."

Tanner's forehead creased in concern, then he nodded, his look reluctant. "I hope this doesn't mean you and I can't be friends." His tender gaze held hers.

Joanna was forced to lower her eyes so he couldn't see just how important his friendship had become to her. "Of course we can."

"Good." He walked across the room and gently pulled her into his arms. He kissed her until she was weak and breathless. When he raised his head, he said in a husky murmur, "I'll take Nicole home now and do as you suggest. We'll give these two a week to settle their differences. After that, you and I are taking over."

"A week?" Joanna wasn't sure that would be long enough, considering Kristen's attitude.

"A week!" Tanner repeated emphatically, kissing her again.

By the time he'd finished, Joanna would have agreed to almost anything. "All right," she managed. "A week."

"HOW WAS SCHOOL TODAY?" Joanna asked Kristen on Monday evening while they sat at the dinner table. She'd waited as long as she could before asking. If either girl was inclined to make a move toward reconciliation, it would be now, she reasoned. They'd both had ample time to think about what had happened and to determine the value of their friendship.

Kristen shrugged. "School was fine, I guess."

Joanna took her time eating her salad, focusing her attention on it instead of her daughter. "How'd you do on the math paper I helped you with?"

Kristen rolled her eyes. "You showed me wrong."

"Wrong!"

"The answers were all right, but Mrs. Andrews told me they don't figure out equations that way anymore."

"Oh. Sorry about that."

"You weren't the only parent who messed up."

That was good to hear.

"A bunch of other kids did it wrong. Including Nicole."

Joanna slipped her hand around her water glass. Kristen sounded far too pleased that her ex-friend had messed up the assignment. That wasn't encouraging. "So you saw Nicole today?"

"I couldn't very well not see her. Her desk is across the aisle from mine. But if you're thinking what I think you're thinking, you can forget it. I don't need a friend like Nicole Lund."

Joanna didn't comment on that, although she practically had to bite her tongue. She wondered how Tanner was doing. Staying out of this argument between the two girls was far more difficult than she'd imagined. It was obvious to Joanna that Kristen was miserable without her best friend, but saying as much would hurt her case more than help it. Kristen needed to recognise the fact herself.

The phone rang while Joanna was finishing up the last of the dinner dishes. Kristen was in the bath, so Joanna grabbed the receiver, holding it between her hunched shoulder and her ear while she squirted detergent into the hot running water.

"Hello?"

"Joanna? Good Lord, you sounded just like Kristen there. I was prepared to have the phone slammed in my ear," Tanner said. "How's it going?"

Her heart swelled with emotion. She hadn't talked to him since Saturday, and it felt as though months had passed since she'd heard his voice. It wrapped itself around her now, warm and comforting. "Things aren't going too well. How are they at your end?"

"Not much better. Did you know Kristen had the nerve to eat lunch with Nora this afternoon? In case you weren't aware of this, Nora is Nicole's sworn enemy."

"Nora?" Joanna could hardly believe her ears. "Kristen doesn't even like the girl." If anything, this war between Kristen and Nicole was heating up.

"I hear you bungled the math assignment," Tanner said softly, amused.

"Apparently you did, too."

He chuckled. "Yeah, this new math is beyond me." He paused, and when he spoke, Joanna could hear the frustration in his voice. "I wish the girls would hurry and patch things up. Frankly, Joanna, I miss you like crazy."

"It's only been two days." She should talk—the last forty-eight hours had seemed like an eternity.

"It feels like two years."

"I know," she agreed softly, closing her eyes and savouring Tanner's words. "But we don't usually see each other during the week anyway." At least not during the past couple of weeks.

"I've been thinking things over and I may have come up with an idea that will put us all out of our misery."

"What?" By now, Joanna was game for anything.

"How about a movie?" he asked unexpectedly, his voice eager.

"But Tanner—"

"Tomorrow night. You can bring Kristen and I'll bring Nicole, and we could accidentally-on-purpose meet at the theatre. Naturally there'll be a bit of acting on our part and some huffing and puffing on theirs, but if things work out the way I think they will, we won't have to do a thing. Nature will take its course.''

Joanna wasn't convinced this scheme of his would work. The whole thing could blow up in their faces, but the thought of being with Tanner was too enticing to refuse. ''All right,'' she agreed. ''As long as you buy the popcorn and promise to hold my hand.''

''You've got yourself a deal.''

ON TUESDAY EVENING, Kristen was unusually quiet over dinner. Joanna had fixed one of her daughter's favourite meals—macaroni-and-cheese casserole—but Kristen barely touched it.

''Do you feel like going to a movie?'' Joanna asked, her heart in her throat. Normally Kristen would leap at the idea, but this evening Joanna couldn't predict anything.

''It's a school night, and I don't think I'm in the mood to see a movie.''

''But you said you didn't have any homework, and it sounds like a fun thing to do...and weren't you saying something about wanting to see Tom Cruise's latest film?'' Kristen's eyes momentarily brightened, then faded. ''And don't worry,'' Joanna added cheerfully, ''you won't have to sit with me.''

Kristen gave a huge sigh. ''I don't have anyone else to sit with,'' she said, as though Joanna had suggested a trip to the dentist.

It wasn't until they were in the parking lot at the theater that Kristen spoke. ''Nicole likes Tom Cruise, too.''

Joanna made a noncommittal reply, wondering how easily the girls would see through her and Tanner's scheme.

"Mom," Kristen cried. "I see Nicole. She's with her dad. Oh, no, it looks like they're going to the same movie."

"Oh, no," Joanna echoed, her heart acting like a Ping-Pong ball in her chest. "Does this mean you want to skip the whole thing and go home?"

"Of course not," Kristen answered smugly. She practically bounded out of the car once Joanna turned off the engine, glancing anxiously at Joanna when she didn't walk across the parking lot fast enough to suit her.

They joined the line, about eight people behind Tanner and Nicole. Joanna was undecided about what to do next. She wasn't completely sure that Tanner had even seen her. If he had, he was playing his part perfectly, acting as though this whole thing had happened by coincidence.

Kristen couldn't seem to stand still. She peeked around the couple ahead of them several times, loudly humming the song of Heart's that she and Nicole had performed in the talent show.

Nicole whirled around, standing on her tiptoes and staring into the crowd behind her. She jerked on Tanner's sleeve and, when he bent down, whispered something in his ear. Then Tanner turned around, too, and pretended to be shocked when he saw Joanna and Kristen.

By the time they were inside the theatre, Tanner and Nicole had disappeared. Kristen was craning her neck in every direction while Joanna stood at the refreshment counter.

"Do you want any popcorn?"

"No. Just some of those raisin things. Mom, you said I didn't have to sit with you. Did you really mean that?"

"Yes, honey, don't worry about it, I'll find a place by myself."

"You're sure?" Kristen looked only mildly concerned.

"No problem. You go sit by yourself."

"Okay." Kristen collected her candy and was gone before Joanna could say any more.

Since it was still several minutes before the movie was scheduled to start, the theatre auditorium was well lit. Joanna found a seat towards the back and noted that Kristen was two rows from the front. Nicole sat in the row behind her.

"Is this seat taken?"

Joanna smiled up at Tanner as he claimed the seat next to her, and had they been anyplace else she was sure he would have kissed her. He handed her a bag of popcorn and a cold drink.

"I sure hope this works," he muttered under his breath, "because if Nicole sees me sitting with you, I could be hung as a traitor." Mischief brightened his eyes. "But the risk is worth it. Did anyone ever tell you how kissable your mouth looks?"

"Tanner," she whispered frantically and pointed toward the girls. "Look."

Kristen sat twisted around and Nicole leaned forward. Kristen shook a handful of her chocolate-covered raisins into Nicole's outstretched hand. Nicole offered Kristen some popcorn. After several of these exchanges, both girls stood up, moved from their seats to a different row entirely, sitting next to each other.

"That looks promising," Joanna whispered.

"It certainly does," Tanner agreed, slipping his arm around her shoulder.

They both watched as Kristen and Nicole tilted their heads toward each other and smiled at the sound of their combined giggles drifting to the back of the theatre.

CHAPTER THIRTEEN

AFTER THEIR NIGHT at the movies, Joanna didn't give Tanner's invitation to the dinner party more than a passing thought until she read about the event on the society page of Wednesday's newspaper. The *Review* described the dinner, which was being sponsored by Spokane Aluminum, as the gala event of the year. Anyone who was anyone in the eastern half of Washington state would be attending. Until Joanna noticed the news article, she'd thought it was a small intimate party; that was the impression Tanner had given her.

From that moment on, Joanna started worrying, though she wasn't altogether sure why. As a loan officer, she'd attended her share of business-related social functions . . . but never anything of this scope. The problem, she decided, was one she'd been denying since the night of Nicole's slumber party. Tanner's social position and wealth far outdistanced her own. He was an important member of their community, and she was just a spoke in the wheel of everyday life.

Now, as she dressed for the event, her uneasiness grew, because she knew how important this evening was to Tanner—although he hadn't told her in so many words. The reception and dinner were all part of his becoming half owner of a major corporation and, according to the newspaper article, had been in the planning stages for several months after his arrival. All John Becky's way of introducing Tanner to the community leaders.

Within the first half hour of their arrival, Joanna recognised the mayor and a couple of members from the city council, plus several other people she didn't know, who nonetheless looked terribly important.

"Here," Tanner whispered, stepping to her side and handing her a glass of champagne.

Smiling up at him, she took the glass and held the dainty stem in a death grip, angry with herself for being so unnerved. It wasn't as though she'd never seen the mayor before—okay, only in pictures, but still… "I don't know if I dare have anything too potent," she admitted.

"Why not?"

"If you want the truth, I feel out of it at this affair. I'd prefer to fade into the background, mingle among the draperies, get acquainted with the wallpaper. That sort of thing."

Tanner's smile was encouraging. "No one would know it to look at you."

Joanna had trouble believing that. The smile she wore felt frozen on her lips, and her stomach protested the fact that she'd barely managed to eat all day. Tonight was important, and for Tanner's sake she'd do what she had to.

The man who owned the controlling interest in Columbia Basin Savings and Loan strolled past them and paused when he recognised her. Joanna nodded her recognition, and when he continued on she swallowed the entire glass of champagne in three giant gulps.

"I feel better," she announced.

"Good."

Tanner apparently hadn't noticed how quickly she'd downed the champagne, for which Joanna was grateful.

"Come over here. There are some people I want you to meet."

More people! Tanner had already introduced her to so many that the names were swimming around in her head like fish crowded in a small pond. She'd tried to keep them all straight, and it had been simple in the beginning when he'd started with his partner, John Becky, and John's wife, Jean, but from that point on her memory had deteriorated steadily.

Tanner pressed his hand to the middle of her spine and steered her across the room to where a small group had gathered.

Along the way, Joanna picked up another glass of champagne, just so she'd have something to do with her hands. The way she was feeling, she had no intention of drinking it.

The men and women paused in the middle of their conversation when Tanner approached. After a few words of greeting, introductions were made.

"Pleased to meet all of you," Joanna said, forcing some life into her fatigued smile. Everyone seemed to be looking at her, expecting something more. She nodded toward Tanner. "Our daughters are best friends."

The others smiled.

"I didn't know you had a daughter," a voluptuous blonde said, smiling sweetly up at Tanner.

"Nicole just turned twelve."

The blonde seemed fascinated with this information. "How very sweet. My niece is ten and I know she'd just love to meet Nicole. Perhaps we could get the two of them together. Soon."

"I'm sure Nicole would like that."

"It's a date then." She sidled as close to Tanner as she possibly could, practically draping her breast over his forearm.

Joanna narrowed her gaze and took a small sip of the champagne. The blonde, whose name was—she searched her mind—Blaise, couldn't have been any more obvious had she issued an invitation to her bed.

"Tanner, there's someone you must meet—that is, if I can drag you away from Joanna for just a little minute." The blonde cast a challenging look in Joanna's direction.

"Oh, sure." Joanna gestured with her hand as though to let Blaise know Tanner was free to do as he wished. She certainly didn't have any claims on him.

Tanner frowned. "Come with us," he suggested.

Joanna threw him what she hoped was a dazzling smile. "Go on. You'll only be gone a little minute," she said sweetly, purposely echoing Blaise's words.

The two left, Blaise clinging to Tanner's arm, and Joanna chatted with the others in the group for a few more minutes before fading into the background. Her stomach was twisted in knots. She didn't know why she'd sent Tanner off like that, when it so deeply upset her. Something in her refused to let him know that; it was difficult enough to admit even to herself.

Hoping she wasn't being obvious, her gaze followed Tanner and Blaise until she couldn't endure it any longer, and then she turned and made her way into the ladies' room. Joanna was grateful that the outer room was empty, and she slouched onto the sofa. Her heart was slamming painfully against her rib cage, and when she pressed her hands to her cheeks her face felt hot and feverish. Joanna would gladly have paid the entire three hundred and fifteen dollars in her savings account for a way to gracefully disappear.

It was then that she knew.

She was in love with Tanner Lund. Despite all the warnings she'd given herself. Despite the fact that they were worlds apart, financially and socially.

With the realisation that she loved Tanner came another. The night had only begun—they hadn't even eaten yet. The ordeal of a formal dinner still lay before her.

"Hello again," Jean Becky said, strolling into the ladies' room. She stopped for a moment, watching Joanna, then sat down beside her.

"Oh, hi." Joanna managed the semblance of a smile to greet the likeable older woman.

"I just saw Blaise Ferguson walk past clinging to Tanner. I hope you're not upset."

"Oh heavens, no," Joanna lied.

"Good. Blaise, er, has something of a reputation, and I didn't want you to worry. I'm sure Tanner's smart enough not to be taken in by someone that obvious."

"I'm sure he is, too."

"You're a sensible young woman," Jean said, looking pleased.

At the moment, Joanna didn't feel the least bit sensible. The one emotion she was experiencing was fear. She'd fallen in love again, and the first time had been so painful she had promised never to let it happen again. But it had. With Tanner Lund, yet. Why couldn't she have fallen for the mechanic who'd worked so hard repairing her car last winter, or someone at the office? Oh, no, she had to fall—and fall hard—for the most eligible man in town. The man every single woman in the party had her eye on this evening.

"It really has been a pleasure meeting you," Jean continued. "Tanner and Nicole talk about you and your daughter so often. We've been friends of Tanner's for several years now, and it gladdens our hearts to see him finally meet a good woman."

"Thank you." Joanna wasn't sure what to think about being classified as a "good woman." It made her wonder who Tanner had dated before he'd met her. She'd never asked him about his social life before he'd moved to Spokane—or even after. She wasn't sure she wanted to know. No doubt he'd made quite a splash when he came to town. Rich, handsome, available men were a rare commodity these days. It was a wonder he hadn't been snatched up long before now.

Five minutes later, Joanna had composed herself enough to rejoin the party. Tanner was at her side within a few seconds, noticeably irritable and short-tempered.

"I've been searching all over for you," he said, frowning heavily.

Joanna let that remark slide. "I thought you were otherwise occupied."

"Why'd you let that she-cat walk off with me like that?" His eyes were hot with fury. "Couldn't you tell I wanted out? Good Lord, woman, what do I have to do, flash flags?"

"No." A waiter walked past with a loaded tray, and Joanna deftly reached out and helped herself to another glass of champagne.

Just as smoothly, Tanner removed it from her fingers. "I think you've had enough."

Joanna took the glass back from him. She might not completely understand what was happening to her this evening, but she certainly didn't like his attitude. "Excuse me, Tanner, but I am perfectly capable of determining my own limit."

His frown darkened into a scowl. "It's taken me the last twenty minutes to extract myself from her claws. The least you could have done was stick around instead of doing a disappearing act."

"No way." Being married to Davey all those years had taught her more than one valuable lesson. If her ex-husband, Tanner, or any other man, for that matter, expected her to make a scene over another woman, it wouldn't work. Joanna was through with those kinds of destructive games.

"What do you mean by that?"

"I'm just not the jealous type. If you were to go home with Blaise, that'd be fine with me. In fact, you could leave with her right now. I'll grab a cab. I'm really not up to playing the role of a jealous girlfriend because another woman happens to show some interest in you. Nor am I willing to find a flimsy excuse to extract you from her clutches. You look more than capable of doing that yourself."

"You honestly want me to leave with Blaise?" His words were low and hard.

Joanna made a show of shrugging. "It's entirely up to you—you're free to do as you please. Actually you might be doing me a favour."

Joanna couldn't remember ever seeing a man more angry. His eyes seemed to spit fire at her. His jaws clamped together tightly, and he held himself with such an unnatural stiffness, it was surprising that something in his body didn't crack. She observed all this in some distant part of her mind, her concentration focused on preserving her facade of unconcern.

"I'm beginning to understand Davey," he said, his tone as cold as an arctic wind. "Has it ever occurred to you that your ex-husband turned to other women out of a desperate need to know you cared?"

Tanner's words hurt more than any physical blow could have. Joanna's breath caught in her throat, though she did her best to disguise the pain his remark had inflicted. When she was finally able to breathe, the words tumbled from her lips. "No. Funny, I never thought of that." She paused and searched the room. "Pick a woman then, any woman will do, and I'll slug it out with her."

"Joanna, stop it," Tanner hissed.

"You mean you don't want me to fight?"

He closed his eyes as if seeking patience. "No."

Dramatically, Joanna placed her hand over her heart. "Thank goodness. I don't know how I'd ever explain a black eye to Kristen."

Dinner was about to be served, and, tucking his hand under her elbow, Tanner led Joanna into the banquet room, which was quickly filling up.

"I'm sorry, I didn't mean that about Davey," Tanner whispered as they strolled toward the dining room. "I realise you're nervous, but no one would ever know it—except me. We'll discuss this Blaise thing later."

Joanna nodded, feeling subdued now, accepting his apology. She realized that she'd panicked earlier, and not because this was an important social event, either. She'd attended enough business dinners in her career to know she hadn't made a fool of herself. What disturbed her so much was the knowledge that she'd fallen in love with Tanner.

To add to Joanna's dismay, she discovered that she was expected to sit at the head table between Tanner and John Becky. She trembled at the thought, but she wasn't about to let anyone see her nervousness.

"Don't worry," Tanner said, stroking her hand after they were seated. "Everyone who's met you has been impressed."

His statement was meant to lend her courage; unfortunately it had the opposite effect. What had she said or done to impress anyone?

When the evening was finally over, Tanner appeared to be as eager to escape as she was. With a minimum of fuss, they made their farewells and were gone.

Once in the car, Tanner didn't speak. But when he parked in front of the house, he turned off the car engine and said quietly, "Invite me in for coffee."

It was on the tip of Joanna's tongue to tell him she had a headache, which was fast becoming the truth, but delaying the inevitable wouldn't help either of them.

"Okay," she mumbled.

The house was quiet, and Sally was asleep on the sofa. Joanna paid her and waited on the front porch while the teenager ran across the street to her own house. Gathering her courage, she walked into the kitchen. Tanner had put the water and ground coffee into the machine and taken two cups down from the cupboard.

"Okay," he said, turning around to face her, "I want to know what's wrong."

The bewilderment in his eyes made Joanna raise her chin an extra notch. Then she remembered Kristen doing the same thing when she'd questioned her about her argument with Nicole, and the recollection wasn't comforting.

Joanna was actually surprised Tanner had guessed anything was wrong. She thought she'd done a brilliant job of disguising her distress. She'd done her best to say and do all the right things. When Tanner had stood up, after the meal, to give his talk, she'd whispered encouragement and smiled at him. Throughout the rest of the evening, she'd chatted easily with both Tanner and John Becky.

Now she had to try to explain something she barely understood herself.

"I don't think I ever realised what an important man you are," she said, struggling to find her voice. "I've always seen you as Nicole's father, the man who was crazy enough to agree to a slumber party for his daughter's birthday. The man who called and disguised his voice so Kristen wouldn't recognise it. That's the man I know, not the one tonight who stood before a filled banquet room and promised growth and prosperity for our city. Not the man who charts the destiny of an entire community.''

Tanner glared at her. ''What has that got to do with anything?''

''You play in the big league. I'm in the minors.''

Tanner's gaze clouded with confusion. ''I'm talking about our relationship and you're discussing baseball!''

Pulling out a kitchen chair, Joanna sat in it and took a deep breath. The best place to start, she decided, was the beginning. ''You have to understand that I didn't come away from my marriage without a few quirks.''

Tanner started pacing, clearly not in the mood to sit still. ''Quirks? You call what happened with Blaise a quirk? I call it loony. Some woman I don't know from Adam comes up to me—''

''Eve,'' Joanna inserted, and when he stared at her, uncomprehending, she elaborated. ''Since Blaise Ferguson's a woman, you don't know her from Eve.''

''Whatever!''

''Well, it does make a difference.'' The coffee had finished filtering into the pot, so Joanna got up and poured them each a cup. Holding hers in both hands, she leaned against the counter and took a tentative sip.

''Some woman I don't know from Eve,'' Tanner tried again, ''comes up to me, and you act as if you can't wait to get me out of your hair.''

''*You* acted as if you expected me to come to your rescue. Honestly, Tanner, you're a big boy. I assumed you could take care of yourself.''

''You looked more than happy to see me go with her.''

''That's not true. I was content where I was.'' Joanna knew they were sidestepping the real issue, but this other business seemed to concern Tanner more.

''You were content to go into hiding.''

"If you're looking for someone to fly into a jealous rage every time another woman winks at you, you'll need to look elsewhere."

Tanner did some more pacing, his steps growing longer and heavier with each circuit of the kitchen. "Explain what you meant when you said you didn't come away from your marriage without a few quirks."

"It's simply really," she said, making light of it. "Davey used to get a kick out of introducing me to his women friends. Everyone in the room knew what he was doing, except me. I was so stupid, so blind, that I just didn't know any better. Once the scales fell from my eyes, I was astonished at what a complete fool I'd been. But when I became wise to his ways, it was much worse. Every time he introduced me to a woman, I'd be filled with suspicion. Was Davey involved with her, or wasn't he? The only thing left for me to do was hold my head high and smile." Her voice was growing tighter with every word, cracking just as she finished.

Tanner walked toward her and reached out his hands as though to comfort her. "Joanna, listen—"

"No." She set her coffee aside and wrapped her arms around her middle. "I feel honoured, Tanner, that you would ask me to attend this important dinner with you tonight. I think we both learned something valuable from the experience. At least, I know I did."

"Joanna—"

"No," she cut in again, "let me finish, please. Although it's difficult to say this, it needs to be said. We're not right for each other. We've been so caught up in everything we had in common and what good friends the girls are and how wonderful it felt to...be together, we didn't stop to notice that we live in different worlds." She paused and gathered her resolve before continuing.

"Knowing you and becoming your friend has been wonderful, but anything beyond that just isn't going to work."

"The only thing I got carried away with was you, Joanna. The girls have nothing to do with it."

"I feel good that you would say that, I really do, but we both lost sight of the fact that neither one of us wants to become involved. That had never been our intention. Something happened, and I'm not sure when or why, but suddenly everything is so intense between us. It's got to stop before we end up really hurting each other."

Tanner seemed to mull over her words. "You're so frightened of giving another man the power to hurt you that you can't see anything else, can you?" His brooding, confused look was back. "I told you this once, but it didn't seem to sink into that head of yours—I'm never going to do the things Davey did. We're two entirely different men, and it's time you realised that."

"What you say may very well be true, Tanner, but I don't see what difference it's going to make. Because I have no intention of involving myself in another relationship."

"In case you hadn't noticed, Joanna, we're already involved."

"Roller-skating in the couples round doesn't qualify as being involved to me," she said, in a futile attempt at humor. It fell flat.

Tanner was the first to break the heavy silence that followed. "You've obviously got some thinking to do," he said wearily. "For that matter, so do I. Call me, Joanna, when you're in the mood to be reasonable."

CHAPTER FOURTEEN

"HI, MOM," Kristen said, slumping down on the sofa beside Joanna. "I hope you know I'm bored out of my mind," she said, and sighed deeply.

Joanna was busy counting the stitches on her knitting needle and didn't pause to answer until she'd finished. "What about your homework?"

"Cute, Mom, real cute. It's spring break—I don't have any homework."

"Right. Phone Nicole then. I bet she'll commiserate with you." And she might even give Kristen some information about Tanner. He'd walked out of her house, and although she'd thought her heart would break she'd let him go. Since then, she'd reconsidered. She was dying to hear something from Tanner. Anything. But she hadn't—not since the party more than a week earlier, and each passing day seemed like a lifetime.

"Calling Nicole is a nothing idea."

"I could suggest you clean your room."

"Funny, Mom, real funny."

"Gee, I'm funny and cute all in one evening. How'd I get so lucky?"

Not bothering to answer, Kristen reached for a magazine and idly thumbed through the pages, not finding a single picture or article worth more than a fleeting glance. She set it aside and reached for another. By the time she'd gone through the four magazines resting on top of the coffee table, Joanna was losing her patience.

"Call Nicole."

"I can't."

"Why not?"

"Because I can't."

That didn't make much sense to Joanna. And suggesting that Kristen phone Nicole was another sign of her willingness to settle this rift between her and Tanner. It had been so long since she'd last seen or heard from him. Ten interminable days, and with each one that passed she missed him more. She'd debated long and hard about calling him, wavering with indecision, battling with her pride. What she'd told him that night had been the truth—they did live in different worlds. But she'd overreacted at the dinner party, and now she felt guilty about how the evening had gone. When he'd left the house, Tanner had suggested she call him when she was ready to be reasonable. Well, she'd been ready the following morning, ready to acknowledge her fault. And her need. But pride held her back. And with each passing day, it became more difficult to swallow that pride.

"You know I can't call Nicole," Kristen whined.

"Why not? Did you have another argument?" Joanna asked without looking at her daughter. Her mind was preoccupied with counting stitches. She always knitted when she was frustrated with herself; it was a form of self-punishment, she suspected wryly.

"We never fight. Not anymore. Nicole's in West Virginia."

Joanna paused and carefully set the knitting needles down on her lap. "Oh? What's she doing there?"

"I think she went to visit her mother."

"Her mother?" It took some effort to keep her heart from exploding in her throat. According to Tanner, Nicole hadn't seen or heard from Carmen in three years. His biggest worry, he'd told her, was that someday his ex-wife would develop an interest in their daughter and steal her away from him. "Nicole is with her mother?" Joanna repeated, to be certain she'd heard Kristen correctly.

"You knew that."

"No, I didn't."

"Yes, you did. I told you she was leaving last Sunday. Remember?"

Vaguely, Joanna recalled the conversation—she'd been peeling potatoes at the sink—but for the last week, every time Kristen mentioned either Tanner or Nicole, Joanna had made an effort to tune her daughter out. Now she was hungry for information, starving for every tidbit Kristen was willing to feed her.

The eleven-year-old straightened and stared at her mother. "Didn't Mr. Lund mention Nicole was leaving?"

"Er, no."

Kristen sighed and threw herself against the back of the sofa. "You haven't been seeing much of him lately, have you?"

"Er, no."

Kristen picked up Joanna's hand and patted it gently. "You two had a fight?"

"Not exactly."

Her daughter's hand continued its soothing action. "Okay, tell me all about it. Don't hold back a single thing—you need to talk this out. Bare your soul."

"Kristen!"

"Mom, you need this. Releasing your anger and frustration will help. You've got to work out all that inner agitation and responsive turbulence. It's disrupting your emotional poise. Seriously, Mom, have you ever considered Rolfing?"

"Emotional poise? Responsive turbulence? Where'd you hear about that? Where'd you hear about Rolfing?"

Kristen blinked and cocked her head to one side, doing her best to look concerned and sympathetic. "Oprah Winfrey."

"I see," Joanna muttered, and rolled her eyes.

"Are you or are you not going to tell me all about it?"

"No, I am not!"

Kristen released a deep sigh that expressed her keen disappointment. "I thought not. When it comes to Nicole's dad, you never want to talk about it. It's like a deep dark secret the two of you keep from Nicole and me. Well, that's all right—we're doing our best to understand. You don't want us to get our hopes up that you two might be interested in each other. I can accept that, although I consider it grossly unfair." She stood up and gazed at her mother with undisguised longing, then loudly slapped her hands against her sides. "I'm perfectly content to live the way we do...but it sure would be nice to have a baby sister to dress up. And you know how I've *always* wanted a brother."

"Kristen!"

"No, Mom." She held up her hand as though she were stopping a freight train. "Really, I do understand. You and I get along fine the way we are. I guess we don't need to complicate our lives with Nicole and her dad. That could even cause real problems."

For the first time, her daughter was making sense.

"Although heaven knows, I can't remember what it's like to be part of a *real* family."

"Kristen, that's enough," Joanna cried, shaking her head. Her daughter was invoking so much guilt that Joanna was beginning to hear violins in the background. "You and I *are* a real family."

"But, Mom, it could be so much better." Kristen sank down beside Joanna again and crossed her legs. Obviously her argument had long since been prepared, and without pausing to breathe between sentences, she proceeded to list the advantages of joining the two families.

"Kristen—"

Once more her daughter stopped her with an outstretched hand, as she started on her much shorter list of possible disadvantages. There was little Joanna could do to stem the rehearsed speech. Impatiently she waited for Kristen to finish.

"I don't want to talk about Tanner again," Joanna said in a no-nonsense tone of voice reserved for instances such as this. "Not a single word. Is that clearly understood?"

Kristen turned round sad eyes on her mother. The fun and laughter seemed to drain from her face as she glared back at Joanna. "Okay—if that's what you really want."

"It is, Kristen. Not a single word."

Banning his name from her daughter's lips and banning his name from her own mind were two entirely different things, Joanna decided an hour later. The fact that Nicole was visiting Carmen concerned her—not that she shared Tanner's worries. But knowing Tanner, he was probably beside himself worrying that Carmen would want their daughter to come and live with her.

It took another half hour for Joanna to build up enough courage to phone Tanner. He answered on the second ring.

"Hello, Tanner...it's Joanna." Even that was almost more than she could manage.

"Joanna." Just the way he said her name revealed his delight in hearing from her.

Joanna was grateful that he didn't immediately bring up the dinner party and the argument that had followed. "How have you been?"

"Good. How about you?"

"Just fine," she returned awkwardly. She leaned against the wall, crossing and uncrossing her ankles. "Listen, the reason I phoned is that Kristen told me Nicole was with her mother, and I thought you might be in need of a divorced-parent prep talk."

"What I really need is to see you. Lord, woman, it took you long enough. I thought you were going to make me wait forever. Ten days can be a very long time, Joanna. Ten whole days!"

"Tanner—"

"Can we meet someplace?"

"I'm not sure." Her mind struggled with a list of excuses, but she couldn't deny how lonely and miserable she'd been, how badly she wanted to feel his arms around her. "I'd have to find someone to sit with Kristen, and that could be difficult at the last minute like this."

"I'll come to you then."

It was part question, part statement, and again, she hesitated. "All right," she finally whispered.

The line went oddly silent. When Tanner spoke again there was a wealth of emotion in his words, although his voice was quiet. "I'm glad you phoned, Joanna."

She closed her eyes, feeling weak and shaky. "I am, too," she said softly.

"I'll be there within half an hour."

"I'll have coffee ready."

When she replaced the receiver, her hand was trembling, and it was as though she were twenty-one again. Her heart was pounding out of control just from the sound of his voice, her head swimming with the knowledge that she'd be seeing him in a few minutes. How wrong she'd been to assume that if she put him out of her sight and mind she could keep him out of her heart, too. How foolish she'd been to deny her feelings. She loved this man, and it wouldn't matter if he owned the company or swept the floors.

Joanna barely had time to refresh her makeup and drag a brush through her hair. Kristen had been in her room for the past hour without a sound; Joanna sincerely hoped she was asleep.

She'd just poured water into the coffee maker when the doorbell chimed.

The bedroom door flew open, and Kristen appeared in her pajamas, wide awake. "I'll get it," she yelled.

Joanna started to call after her, but it was too late. With a resigned sigh, she stood in the background and waited for her daughter to admit Tanner.

Kristen turned to face her mother, wearing a grin as wide as the Mississippi River. "It's that man whose name I'm not supposed to mention ever again."

"Yes, I know."

"You know?"

Joanna nodded.

"Good. Talk it out with him, Mom. Relieve yourself of all that inner stuff. Get rid of that turmoil before it eats you alive."

Joanna cast a weak smile in Tanner's direction, then turned her attention to Kristen. "Isn't it your bedtime, young lady?"

"No."

Joanna's eyes narrowed. "Yes, it is."

"But, Mom, it's spring break, so I can sleep in tomorrow—Oh, I get it, you want me out of here."

"In your room reading or listening to a cassette should do nicely."

Kristen beamed her mother a broad smile. "'Night, Mom. 'Night . . . Nicole's dad."

"'Night."

With her arms swinging at her sides, Kristen strolled out of the living room. Tanner waited until they heard her bedroom door shut, then he started across the carpet toward Joanna. He stopped suddenly, frowning. "She wasn't supposed to say my name?"

Joanna gave a weak half shrug, her gaze holding his. No man had ever looked better. His eyes seemed to caress her with a tenderness and aching hunger that did crazy things to her equilibrium.

"It's so good to see you," she said, her voice unsteady. She took two steps towards him.

When Tanner reached for her, a heavy sigh broke from his lips and the tension left his muscles. "Dear Lord, woman, ten days you left me dangling." He said more, but his words were muffled in the curve of her neck as he crushed her against his chest.

Joanna soaked up his warmth, and when his lips found hers she surrendered with a soft sigh of joy. Being in Tanner's arms was like coming home after a long journey and discovering the comfort in all that's familiar. It was like walking in sunshine after a bad storm, like holding the first rose of summer in her hand.

Again and again his mouth sought hers in a series of passionate kisses, as though he couldn't get enough of the taste of her.

The creaky sound of a bedroom door opening caused Joanna to break away from him. "It's Kristen," she murmured, her voice little more than a whisper.

"I know, but I don't care." Tanner kept her close for a moment longer. "Okay," he breathed, and slowly stroked the top of her head with his chin. "We need to settle a few things. Let's talk."

Joanna led him into the kitchen, since they were afforded the most privacy there. She automatically took down two cups and poured them each some coffee. They sat at the small table, directly across from each other, but even that seemed much too far.

"First, tell me about Nicole," she said, her eyes meeting his. "Are you worried now that she's with Carmen?"

A sad smile touched the edges of Tanner's mouth. "Not particularly. Carmen, who prefers to be called Rama Sheba now, contacted my parents at the end of last week. According to my mother, the reason we haven't heard from her in the past three years is that Carmen's been on a long journey in India and Nepal. Apparently Carmen went halfway around the world searching for herself. I guess she found what she was looking for, because she's back in the United States and enquiring about Nicole."

"Oh, dear. Do you think she wants Nicole to come live with her?"

"Not a chance. Carmen, er, Rama Sheba, doesn't want a child complicating her life. She never did. Nicole wanted to see her mother and that's understandable, so I sent her back to West Virginia for a visit with my parents. While she's there, Carmen will spend an afternoon with her."

"What happened to . . . Rama Sheba and the baseball player?"

"Who knows? He may have joined her in her wanderings, for all I know. Or care. Carmen plays such a minor role in my life now that I haven't the energy to second-guess her. She's free to do as she likes, and I prefer it that way. If she wants to visit Nicole, fine. She can see her daughter—she has the right."

"Do you love her?" The question sounded abrupt and tactless, but Joanna needed to know.

"No," he said quickly, then grinned. "I suppose I feel much the same way about her as you do about Davey."

"Then you don't hate her?" she asked next, not looking at him.

"No."

Joanna ran a fingertip along the rim of her cup and smiled. "Good."

"Why's that good?"

She lifted her eyes to meet his and smiled a little shyly. "Because if you did have strong feelings for her it would suggest some unresolved emotion."

Tanner nodded. "As illogical as it sounds, I don't feel anything for Carmen. Not love, not hate—nothing. If something bad were to happen to her, I suppose I'd feel sad, but I don't harbour any resentments toward her."

"That's what I was trying to explain to you the afternoon you dropped by when Davey was here. Other people have a hard time believing this, especially my parents, but I honestly wish him success in life. I want him to be happy, although I doubt he ever will be." Davey wasn't a man who would ever be content. He was always looking for something more, something better.

Tanner nodded.

Once more, Joanna dropped her gaze to the steaming coffee. "Calling you and asking about Nicole was only an excuse, you know."

"Yes. I just wish you'd come up with it a few days earlier. As far as I'm concerned, waiting for you to come to your senses took nine days too long."

"I—"

"I know, I know," Tanner said before she could list her excuses. "Okay, let's talk."

Joanna managed a smile. "Where do we start?"

"How about with what happened the night of the party?"

Instantly Joanna's stomach knotted. "Yes, well, I guess I should be honest and let you know I was intimidated by how important you are. It shook me, Tanner, really shook me. I'm not used to seeing you as chairman of the board. And then later, when you strolled off with Blaise, those old wounds from my marriage with Davey started to bleed.''

"I suppose I did all the wrong things. Maybe I should have insisted you come with me when Blaise dragged me away, but—''

"No, that wouldn't have worked, either.''

"I should have guessed how you'd feel after being married to Davey.''

"You had no way of knowing.'' Now came the hard part. "Tanner,'' she began, and was shocked at how thin and weak her voice sounded, "I was so consumed with jealousy that I just about went crazy when Blaise wrapped her arms around you. It frightened me to have to deal with those negative emotions again. I know I acted like an idiot, hiding like that, and I'd like to apologise.''

"Joanna, it isn't necessary.''

She shook her head. "I don't mean this as an excuse, but you need to understand why I was driven to behave the way I did. I'd thought I was beyond that—years beyond acting like a jealous fool. I promised myself I'd never allow a man to do it to me again.'' In her own way, Joanna was trying to tell him how much she loved him, but the words weren't coming out right.

He frowned at that. "Jealous? You were jealous? Good Lord, woman, you could have fooled me. You handed me over to Blaise without so much as a hint of regret. From the way you were behaving, I thought you *wanted* to be rid of me.''

The tightness in Joanna's throat made talking difficult. "I already explained why I did that.''

"I know. The way I acted when I saw your ex here was the other kind of jealous reaction—the raging-bull kind. I think I see now where *your* kind of reaction came from. I'm not sure which one is worse, but I think mine is.'' He smiled ruefully, and a silence fell between them.

"Could this mean you have some strong feelings for me, Joanna Parsons?"

A smile quirked at the corners of her mouth. "You're the only man I've ever eaten Oreos over."

The laughter in Tanner's eyes slowly faded. "We could have the start of something very important here, Joanna. What do you think?"

"I . . . I think you may be right."

"Good." Tanner looked exceedingly pleased with this turn of events. "That's exactly what I wanted to hear."

Joanna thought—no, hoped—that he intended to lean over and kiss her. Instead his brows drew together darkly over brooding blue eyes. "Okay, where do we go from here?"

"Go?" Joanna repeated, feeling uncomfortable all of a sudden. "Why do we have to go anywhere?"

Tanner looked surprised. "Joanna, for heaven's sake, when a man and a woman feel about each other the way we do, they generally make plans."

"What do you mean 'feel about each other the way we do'?"

Tanner's frown darkened even more. "You love me."

Only a few moments before, Joanna would have willingly admitted it, but silly as it sounded, she wanted to hear Tanner say the words first. "I . . . I . . ."

"If you have to think about it, then I'd say you obviously don't know."

"But I do know," she said, lifting her chin a notch higher. "I'm just not sure this is the time to do anything about it. You may think my success is insignificant compared to yours, but I've worked damn hard to get where I am. I've got the house I saved for years to buy, and my career is starting to swing along nicely, and Robin—he's my boss—let me know that I was up for promotion. My goal of becoming the first female senior loan officer at the branch is within sight.''

"And you don't want to complicate your life right now with a husband and second family?''

"I didn't say that.''

"It sure sounded like it to me.''

Joanna swallowed. The last thing in the world she wanted to do was argue with Tanner. Craziest of all, she wasn't even sure what they were arguing about. They were in love with each other and both just too damn proud. "I don't think we're getting anywhere with this conversation.''

Tanner braced his elbows on the table and folded his hands. "I'm beginning to agree with you. All week, I've been waiting for you to call me, convinced that once you did, everything between us would be settled. I wanted us to start building a life together, and all of a sudden you're Ms Career Woman, and about as independent as they come.''

"I haven't changed. You just didn't know me.''

His lips tightened. "I guess you're right. I don't know you at all, do I?''

"Mom, Mom, come quick!''

Joanna's warm cozy dream was interrupted by Kristen's shrieks. She rolled over and glared at the digital readout on her clock radio. Five. In the morning. "Kristen?'' She sat straight up in bed.

"Mom!''

The one word conveyed such panic that Joanna's heart rushed to her throat and she threw back her covers, running barefoot into the hallway. Almost immediately, her feet encountered ice-cold water.

"Something's wrong," Kristen cried, hopping up and down. "The water won't stop."

That was the understatement of the year. From the way the water was gushing out of the bathroom door and into the hallway, it looked as though a dam had burst.

"Grab some towels," Joanna cried, pointing toward the hallway linen closet. The hems of her long pajamas were already damp. She scooted around her daughter, who was standing in the doorway, still hopping up and down like a crazed kangaroo.

Further investigation showed that the water was escaping from the cabinet under the sink.

"Mom, Mom, here!" Dancing around, Kristen threw her a stack of towels that separated in midair and landed in every direction.

"Kristen!" Joanna snapped, squatting down in front of the sink. She opened the cabinet and was immediately hit by a wall of foaming bubbles. The force of the flowing water had knocked over her container of expensive bubble bath and spilled its contents. "You were in my bubble bath!" Joanna cried.

"I . . . How'd you know?"

"The cap's off, and now it's everywhere!"

"I just used a little bit."

Three bars of Ivory soap, still in their wrappers, floated past Joanna's feet. Heaven only knew what else had been stored under the sink or where it was headed now.

"I'm sorry about the bubble bath," Kristen said defensively. "I figured you'd get mad if you found out, but a kid needs to know what luxury feels like, too, you know."

"It's all right, we can't worry about that now." Joanna waved her hands back and forth trying to disperse the bubbles enough to assess the damage. It didn't take long to determine that a pipe had burst. With her forehead pressing against the edge of the sink, Joanna groped inside the cabinet for the knob to turn off the water supply. Once she found it, she twisted it furiously until the flowing water dwindled to a mere trickle.

"Kristen!" Joanna shouted, looking over her shoulder. Naturally, when she needed her, her daughter disappeared. "Get me some more towels. Hurry, honey!"

A couple of minutes later, Kristen reappeared, her arms loaded with every towel and washcloth in the house. "Yuck," she muttered, screwing her face into a mask of sheer disgust. "What a mess!"

"Did any water get into the living room?"

Kristen nodded furiously. "But only as far as the front door."

"Great." Joanna mumbled under her breath. Now she'd need to phone someone about coming in to dry out the carpet.

On her hands and knees, sopping up as much water as she could, Joanna was already soaked to the skin herself.

"You need help," her daughter announced.

The child was a master of observation. "Change out of those wet things first, Kristen, before you catch your death of cold."

"What about you?"

"I'll dry off as soon as I get some of this water cleaned up."

"Mom—"

"Honey, just do as I ask. I'm not in any mood to argue with you."

Joanna couldn't remember ever seeing a bigger mess in her life. Her pajamas were soaked; bubbles were popping around her head—how on earth had they got into her hair? She sneezed violently, and reached for a tissue that quickly dissolved in her wet hands.

"Here, use this."

The male voice coming from behind her surprised Joanna so much that when she twisted around, she lost her footing and slid down into a puddle of the coldest water she'd ever felt.

"Tanner!" she cried, leaping to her feet. "What are you doing here?"

CHAPTER FIFTEEN

DUMBFOUNDED, Joanna stared at Tanner, her mouth hanging open and her eyes wide.

"I got this frantic phone call from Kristen."

"Kristen?"

"The one and only. She suggested I hurry over here before something drastic happened." Tanner took one step toward her and lovingly brushed a wet tendril away from her face. "How's it going, Tugboat Annie?"

"A pipe under the sink broke. I've got it under control now—I think." Her pajamas hung limply at her ankles, dripping water onto her bare feet. Her hair fell in wet spongy curls around her face, and Joanna had never felt more like bursting into tears in her life.

"Kristen shouldn't have phoned you," she said, once she found her voice.

"I'm glad she did. It's nice to know I can be useful every now and again." Heedless of her wet state, he wrapped his arms around Joanna and brought her close, gently pressing her damp head to his chest.

A chill went through her and she shuddered. Tanner felt so warm and vital, so concerned and loving. She'd let him think she was this strong independent woman, and normally she was, but when it came to broken pipes and floods and things like that, she crumbled into bite-sized pieces. When it came to Tanner Lund, well . . .

"You're soaked to the skin," he whispered, close to her ear.

"I know."

"Go change. I'll take over here."

The tears started then, silly ones that sprang from somewhere deep inside her and refused to be stopped. "I can't get dry," she sobbed, wiping furiously at the moisture that rained down her face. "There aren't any dry towels left in this entire house."

Tanner jerked his water-blotched tan leather jacket off and placed it around her shoulders. "Honey, don't cry. Please. Everything's going to be all right. It's just a broken pipe, and I can have it fixed for you before noon—possibly sooner."

"I can't help it," she bellowed, and to her horror, hiccuped. She threw a hand over her mouth and leaned her forehead against his strong chest. "It's five o'clock in the morning, my expensive Giorgio bubblebath is ruined, and I'm so much in love I can't think straight."

Tanner's hands gripped her shoulders and eased her away so he could look her in the eye. "What did you just say?"

Joanna hung her head as low as it would go, bracing her weight against Tanner's arms. "My Giorgio bubblebath is ruined." The words wobbled out of her mouth like a rubber ball tumbling down stairs.

"Not that. I want to hear the other part, about being so much in love."

Joanna sniffled. "What about it?"

"What about it? Good Lord, woman, I was here not more than eight hours ago wearing my heart on my sleeve like a schoolboy. You were so casual about everything, I thought you were going to open a discussion on stock options."

"*You* were the one who was so calm and collected about everything, as if what happened between us didn't really matter to you." She rubbed her hand under her nose and sniffled loudly. "Then you made everything sound like a foregone conclusion and—"

"I was nervous. Now, shall we give it another try? I want to marry you, Joanna Parsons. I want you to share my life, maybe have my babies. I want to love you until we're both old and gray. I've even had fantasies about us traveling around the country in a mobile home to visit our grandchildren!"

"You want grandkids?" Timidly, she raised her eyes to his, almost afraid to believe what he was telling her.

"I'd prefer to take this one step at a time. The first thing I want to do is marry you. I couldn't have made that plainer than I did a few hours ago."

"But—"

"Stop right now, before we get sidetracked. First things first. Are you and Kristen going to marry me and Nicole?"

"I think we should," the eleven-year-old said excitedly from the hallway, looking smugly pleased with the way things were going. "I mean, it's been obvious to Nicole and me for ages that you two were meant to be together." Kristen sighed and slouched against the wall, crossing her arms over her chest with the sophistication that befitted someone of superior intelligence. "There's only one flaw in this plan."

"Flaw?" Joanna echoed.

"Yup," Kristen said, nodding with unquestionable confidence. "Nicole is going to be mad as hops when she finds out she missed this."

Tanner frowned, and then he chuckled. "Oh, boy. I think Kristen could be right. We're going to have to stage a second proposal."

Feeling slightly piqued, Joanna straightened. "Listen, you two, I never said I was going to marry anybody—yet."

"Of course you're going to marry Mr. Lund," Kristen inserted smoothly. "Honestly, Mom, now isn't the time to play hard to get."

"W-what?" Stunned, Joanna stood there staring at her daughter. Her gaze flew from Kristen to Tanner and then back to Kristen.

"She's right, you know," said Tanner.

"I can't believe I'm hearing this." Joanna was standing in a sea of wet towels, while her daughter and the man she loved discussed her fate as though she was to play only a minor role in it.

"We've got to think of a way to include Nicole," Tanner said thoughtfully.

"I am going to change my clothes," Joanna murmured, eager to escape.

"Good idea," Tanner answered, without looking at her.

Joana stomped off to her bedroom and slammed the door. She discarded her pajamas and, shivering, reached for a thick wool sweater and blue jeans.

Tanner and Kristen were still in the bathroom doorway, discussing details, when Joanna reappeared. She moved silently around them and into the kitchen, where she made a pot of coffee. Then she gathered up the wet towels, hauled them onto the back porch, threw them into the washer and started the machine. By the time she returned to the kitchen, Tanner had joined her there.

"Uh-oh. Trouble," he said, watching her abrupt angry movements. "Okay, tell me what's wrong now."

"I don't like the way you and my daughter are planning my life," she told him point-blank. "Honestly, Tanner, I haven't even agreed to marry you, and already you and Kristen have got the next ten years all figured out."

He stuck his hands in his pants pockets. "It's not that bad."

"Maybe not, but it's bad enough. I'm letting you know right now that I'm not about to let you stage a second proposal just so Nicole can hear it. To be honest, I'm not exactly thrilled about Kristen being part of this one. A marriage proposal is supposed to be private. And romantic, with flowers and music, not...not in front of a busted pipe with bath bubbles popping around my head and my family standing around applauding."

"Okay, what do you suggest?"

"I don't know yet."

Tanner looked disgruntled. "If you want the romance, Joanna, that's fine. I'd be more than happy to give it to you."

"Every woman wants romance."

Tanner walked toward her then and took her in his arms, and until that moment Joanna had no idea how much she did, indeed, want it.

Her eyes were drawn to his. Everything about Tanner Lund fascinated her, and she raised her hand to lightly caress the proud strong line of his jaw. She really did love this man. His eyes, blue and intense, met hers, and a tiny shiver of awareness went through her. His arms circled her waist, and then he lifted her off the ground so that her gaze was level with his own.

Joanna gasped a little at the unexpectedness of his action. Smiling, she looped her arms around his neck.

Tanner kissed her then, with a hunger that left her weak and clinging in its aftermath.

"How's that?" he asked, his voice husky.

"Better. Much better."

"I thought so." Once more his warm mouth made contact with hers. Joanna was startled and thrilled at the intensity of his touch. He kissed her again and again, until she thought that if he released her, she'd fall to the floor and melt at his feet. Every part of her body was heated to fever pitch.

"Joanna—"

She planted warm moist kisses across his face, not satisfied, wanting him until her heart felt as if it might explode. Tanner had awoken the sensual part of her nature, buried all the years since her divorce, and now that it had been stirred back to life, she felt starved for a man's love—this man's love.

"Yes," she breathed into his mouth. "Yes, yes, yes."

"Yes what?" he asked in a breathless murmur.

Joanna paused and smiled gently. "Yes, I'll marry you. Right now. Okay? This minute. We can fly somewhere . . . find a church . . . Oh, Tanner," she pleaded, "I want you so much."

"Joanna, we can't." His words came out in a groan, forced from deep inside him.

She heard him, but it didn't seem to matter. She kissed him and he kissed her. Their kiss continued as he lowered her to the floor, her body sliding intimately down his.

Suddenly Joanna realized what she'd just said, what she'd suggested. "We mustn't. Kristen—"

Tanner shushed her with another kiss, then said, "I know, love. This isn't the time or place, but I sure wish . . ."

Joanna straightened, and broke away. Shakily, she said, "So do I . . . and, uh, I think we should wait a while for the wedding. At least until Nicole gets back."

"Right."

"How long will that be?"

"The end of the week."

Joanna nodded and closed her eyes. It sounded like an eternity.

"What about your job?"

"I don't want to work forever, and when we decide to start a family I'll probably quit. But I want that promotion first." Joanna wasn't sure exactly why that was so important to her, but it was. She'd worked years for this achievement, and she had no intention of walking away until she'd become the first female senior loan officer.

Tanner kissed her again. "If it makes you happy keep your job as long as you want."

At that moment, however, all Joanna could think about were babies, family vacations and homemade cookies.

"THAT'S HER PLANE now," Tanner said to Kristen, pointing toward the Boeing jet that was approaching the long narrow landing strip at Spokane International.

"I get to tell her, okay?"

"I think Tanner should do it, sweetheart," Joanna suggested gently.

"But Nicole and I are best friends. You can't expect me to keep something like this from her, something we planned since that night we all went to the Pink Palace. If it weren't for us, you two wouldn't even know each other."

Kristen's eyes were round and pleading as she stared up at Tanner and Joanna.

"You two would have been cast adrift in a sea of loneliness if it hadn't been for me and Nicole," she added melodramatically.

"All right, all right," Tanner said with a sigh. "You can tell her."

Poised at the railing by the window of the terminal, Kristen eagerly studied each passenger who stepped inside. The minute Nicole appeared, Kristen flew into her friend's arms as though it had been years since they'd last seen each other instead of a week.

Joanna watched the unfolding scene with a quiet sense of happiness. Nicole let out a squeal of delight and gripped her friend around the shoulders, and the two jumped frantically up and down.

"From her reaction, I'd guess that she's happy about our decision," Tanner said to Joanna.

"Dad, Dad!" Nicole raced up to her father, and hugged him with all her might. "It's so good to be home. I missed you. I missed everyone," she said, looking at Joanna.

Tanner returned the hug. "It's good to have you home, cupcake."

"But everything exciting happened while I was away," she said, pouting a little. "Gee, if I'd known you were finally going to get rolling with Mrs. Parsons, I'd never have left."

Joanna smiled blandly at the group of people standing around them.

"Don't be mad," Kristen said. "It was a now-or-never situation, with Mom standing there in her pajamas and everything."

Now it was Tanner's turn to notice the interested group of onlookers.

"Yes, well, you needn't feel left out. I saved the best part for you," Tanner said, taking a beautiful solitaire diamond ring out of his pocket. "I wanted you to be here for this." He reached for Joanna's hand, looking into her eyes, as he slowly, reverently, slipped it onto her finger. "I love you, Joanna, and I'll be the happiest man alive if you marry me."

"I love you, Tanner," she said in a soft voice filled with joy.

"Does this mean we're going to be sisters from now on?" Kristen shrieked, clutching her best friend's hand.

"Yup," Nicole answered. "It's what we always wanted."

With their arms wrapped around one another's shoulders, the girls headed toward the baggage-claim area.

"Yours and mine," Joanna said, watching their two daughters.

Tanner slid his arm around her waist and smiled into her eyes.

Although born in England, **Sandra Field** has lived most of her life in Canada; she says the silence and emptiness of the north speaks to her particularly. While she enjoys travelling, and passing on her sense of a new place, she often chooses to write about the city which is now her home. Sandra says, 'I write out of my experience; I have learned that love with its joys and its pains is all-important. I hope this knowledge enriches my writing, and touches a chord in you, the reader.' She has been writing for Mills & Boon® for over 20 years and has written nearly 40 novels which have been published worldwide.

THE DATING GAME
by
SANDRA FIELD

─────────●◦●◦●─────────

CHAPTER ONE

HE WAS in a foul mood.

Teal Carruthers rolled down his car window. Several vehicles ahead of him, at the traffic lights, a delivery truck and a taxi had collided at the intersection; a tow truck and a police car were adding to the confusion without, as far as he could see, in any way ameliorating it. Behind him the cars were lined up as far as he could see. He looked at his watch. Five to five. He was going to be late home.

Today was Monday. On Mondays Mrs Inkpen came to clean the house and stayed with his son Scott until he, Teal, got home at five. Scott liked Mrs Inkpen, whose language was colorful and whose cooking bore no relation to the rules of good nutrition. Teal had gotten in the habit of taking Scott out for supper on Mondays, in theory to save Mrs Inkpen the trouble of preparing a meal, in actuality to protect himself from hot dogs adorned with anything from cream cheese to crunchy peanut butter. Even Scott, as he recalled, had not been too crazy about the peanut butter.

Mrs Inkpen didn't like him to be late.

The driver of the tow truck was sweeping up the broken glass on the road and the policeman was taking a statement from the truck driver. Teal ran his fingers through his hair and rested his elbow on the window-ledge. It was the first really hot day of the summer, the kind of day that made Scott, aged eight, complain loudly about having to go to school. Heat was shimmering off

5

the tarred surface of the road and the smell of exhaust
fumes was almost enough to make Teal close his window.

The policeman shoved his notebook in his back pocket
and began directing the traffic. Teal eased the BMW in
gear and inched forward. Bad enough that he was late.
Worse that he had had an interminable day in court.
Worst of all was the fact that he had enough work in
his briefcase to keep him up past midnight.

The traffic light turned red. He should never have
trusted Mike with the brief today; that had been a bad
mistake. A really bad mistake. Particularly with old
Mersey presiding. Mr Chief Justice Mersey had been
trying to trip Teal up for the last three years, and today
he had more than succeeded. And all because Teal had
left Mike, his brilliant but erratic assistant, to cross-
examine one of the prosecution's main witnesses.

Mike, Teal now suspected, had been suffering from a
hangover. In consequence he had been erratic rather than
brilliant, and had committed not one but two errors of
procedure. Mersey had had a field day chewing him out
and Teal had been left holding the bag. Which meant
he now had to rebuild their case from scratch. The only
good thing about the day was that court had recessed
until Wednesday. Tonight once Scott was in bed he'd
have to get a sitter and chase down his two main witnesses, and tomorrow he'd catch up with the rest of them.
Both nights he'd be burning the midnight oil to come
up with Wednesday's strategy.

Who was he kidding? The three a.m. oil was more
like it.

But Willie McNeill was innocent. Teal would stake his
life on it. And it was up to him to produce enough doubt
in the minds of the jurors so that they couldn't possibly
bring in a guilty verdict.

It wouldn't be easy. But he could do it.

The light turned green. The traffic began to move and the bus that was two cars ahead belched out a cloud of black smoke. The policeman was sweating under his helmet, while the cabbie and the truck driver were laughing uproariously at some private joke. Very funny, Teal thought morosely. It was now ten past five.

By the time he turned into his driveway it was twenty-five past and Mrs Inkpen was waiting for him on the back porch. She was clad in a full-length pink raincoat with a hat jammed on her brassy curls, her pose as militant as an Amazon. Before Teal had married Elizabeth, Mrs Inkpen had cleaned for Elizabeth's parents, and he sometimes thought she should have been included on the marriage license. Although she was now well over retiring age, his tactful suggestions that she might prefer to be home with her ageing husband were met with loud disclaimers; she was fanatically loyal.

Bracing himself, he climbed out of the car. Mrs Inkpen tapped her watch ostentatiously. 'This'll cost you overtime, Mr C,' she said. 'If I'd known you was goin' to be this late, I could've cooked you a nice supper.'

At least he had been spared that. 'There was an accident on the corner of Robie and Coburg.'

Her eyes brightened. 'Anyone hurt?'

He shook his head, almost hating to disappoint her. 'A lot of broken glass and a traffic tie-up, that's all.'

'Drugs,' she said, nodding her head sagely. 'That's what it is, all them drugs. I said to my Albert just the other day, what with crack and hash and pot you can't trust no one these days. Never know when someone's goin' to creep up behind you and bash you on the head.' She rolled her eyes theatrically. 'Course you know all about that, Mr C, you bein' a lawyer and all.'

Mrs Inkpen's vision of what he did all day was drawn from television, and bore little resemblance to reality.

He said hurriedly, before she could ask him about his day, 'Can I give you a drive home to apologize for being late?'

'No need for that, I got to keep the old bones movin',' she said, her good humor restored. 'Smell the lilac, Mr C; ain't it a treat?'

Elizabeth had planted the lilac the year Scott had been born. Its plumes of tiny blossoms were a deep purple, the scent as pungent as spice. She had planned to plant a white lilac for the daughter that was to have followed Scott...

Wincing away from all the old memories, for there had been no daughter and now Elizabeth was dead, Teal said evenly, 'Lovely, yes...we'll see you next week, then, Mrs Inkpen.'

She gave him a conspiratorial grin. 'That nice Mrs Thurston phoned, and so did Patsy Smythe. It must be great to be so popular, Mr C—you don't never have to worry about a date on a Saturday night, do you?' The yellow daisies on her hat bobbed up and down. 'It's because you're so handsome,' she pronounced. 'Like the men in the soaps, is what I tell Albert—the ones the girls are always falling for. If I was twenty years younger, my Albert might be in trouble.' Cackling with laughter, she set off down the driveway between the tangle of forsythias and rose bushes.

The bushes all needed pruning. Scowling, because when was he supposed to find the time to get out in the garden and besides, Mrs Inkpen couldn't be more wrong—it was a damned nuisance to be so popular— Teal grabbed his briefcase from the back seat and went into the house. 'Scott?' he called. 'I'm home.'

The kitchen, starkly decorated in white and grey, was abnormally tidy. Mrs Inkpen achieved this effect, so Teal had realized soon after Elizabeth died, by opening the nearest drawer or cupboard and shoving everything inside. Any normal man would have fired her months ago. But he was fond of her, and loyalty worked both ways.

The telephone sat on a built-in pine desk by the window; the green light on his answering machine was flashing twice. His scowl deepened. One of those flashes, he would be willing to bet, was Janine, wanting him to confirm their date this weekend. Janine was nothing if not persistent. He didn't want to know who the other one was. He sometimes felt as though every woman in Halifax under the age of fifty was after him, each one certain that all he needed was a wife, a mother for his son, or a lover. Or a combination of all three, he thought with a twist to his mouth.

They were all wrong. He was doing a fine job bringing up Scott on his own, so why would he need to remarry? As for the needs of his body, they were buried so deeply he sometimes thought he should apply to the nearest monastery.

The telephone rang, breaking into his thoughts. Warily he picked it up and said hello.

'Teal? This is Sheila McNab, do you remember me? We met at the board meeting last week. How are you?'

He did remember her. A well-packaged brunette whose laugh had grated on his nerves. They chatted a few minutes, then she said, 'I'm wondering if you'd be free on Saturday evening to go to a barbecue in Chester with me? A friend of mine is celebrating her birthday.'

'I'm afraid that's impossible, Sheila; I already have plans that night,' he said truthfully.

'Oh... well, perhaps another time.'

'Actually I'm very busy these days. My job's extremely demanding and I'm a single parent as well...but it was nice of you to think of me, and perhaps we'll meet again some time.'

He put down the phone, feeling trapped in his own kitchen. Maybe he should shave his head and put on thirty pounds. Would that make the women leave him alone?

He heard Scott's footsteps thump down the stairs, followed by a swish that meant his son had taken to the banisters. The boy landed with a thud on the hall floor and came rushing into the room, waving a sheet of paper in one hand. 'Guess what, Dad?' he cried. 'There's a home and school meeting on Thursday, and you'll get to meet Danny's mum because she's going, too.'

Teal's smile faded. The last thing he needed was one more woman to add to the list. Especially such a paragon as Danny's mother. 'I thought home and school was finished for the year,' he said temperately, rumpling his son's dark hair.

Scott ducked, sending out a quick punch at his father's midriff. Teal flicked one back, and a moment later the pair of them were rolling around the kitchen floor in a time-honored ritual. 'Is that your soccer shirt?' Teal grunted. 'It needs washing in the worst way.'

'It'll only get dirty again,' Scott said with unanswerable logic, bouncing up and down on his father's chest. 'The meeting's so you can see our art stuff and our scribblers before school gets out; you'll come, won't you, Dad? Maybe we could take Danny and his mum with us,' he added hopefully. 'She's real nice; you'd like her. She made chocolate-fudge cookies today, I brought a couple home for you; she said I could.'

Janine, who had marriage in mind, had sent Teal flowers last weekend, and Cindy Thurston, who wanted something more immediate and less permanent than marriage, had tried to present him with a bottle of the finest brandy. He didn't want Danny's mother's chocolate-fudge cookies. 'I'd rather we went on our own,' he said. 'And you must change your shirt before we go out for supper.'

Scott stuck out his jaw. 'She's beautiful—like a movie star.'

Teal blinked. What eight-year-old noticed that his best friend's mother was beautiful? Feeling his antipathy toward the unknown woman increase in leaps and bounds, he said, 'There are clean shirts in your drawer. Move it.'

'She's prettier than Janine,' Scott said stubbornly.

Janine was a ravishing redhead. Teal sighed. 'I'm sure we'll meet her at the school,' he said.

And I'll be polite if it kills me. But just because her son and mine are fast turning into best friends it doesn't mean she has to become part of my life. I've got problems enough as it is, he added silently.

'Her name's Julie.' Scott tugged on his father's silk tie. 'Can we go to Burger King to eat, Dad?'

'Sure,' said Teal. 'Providing you have milk and not pop.'

With a loud whoop Scott took off across the room. Teal followed at a more moderate pace, loosening the knot on his tie. A sweatshirt and jeans were going to feel good after the day he'd had. He'd better phone for a sitter and drink lots of coffee with his hamburger so he'd stay awake tonight.

He was going to ignore both his phone messages until tomorrow.

Julie Ferris turned her new CD player up another notch and raised the pitch of her own voice correspondingly. She was no match for John Denver or Placido Domingo, but that didn't bother her. At the top of her lungs she sang about the memories of love, deciding that if even one of the men currently pursuing her could sing like that she might be inclined to keep on dating him.

Not a chance. On the occasions when her dates came to pick her up at the house, she sometimes contrived to have this song playing, *fortissimo*. Most of them ignored it; a few said they liked it; the odd one complained of the noise. But none burst into ravishing song.

It was just as well, she thought. She really didn't want to get involved with anyone yet; it was too soon after the divorce. Anyway, if the men she'd met so far were anything to go by, the options weren't that great. She was better off single.

'...dreams come true...' she carolled, putting the finishing touches to the chicken casserole she was making for supper. The sun was streaming in the kitchen window and the birds were chirping in the back garden. The garden was so painfully and geometrically orderly that she was almost surprised any self-respecting bird would visit it. On Friday she was going to find a nursery and do her best to create some colour and confusion among the right-angled beds with their trimmed shrubs and military rows of late red tulips.

Technically, her landlady had not forbidden her to do so. She had merely made it clear that she expected the house and the garden to be maintained in apple-pie order. An odd phrase, apple-pie order, Julie mused. A phrase she intended to interpret liberally.

The phone rang. Wiping her hands on the dishcloth, she crossed the kitchen to answer it, chuckling as Einstein the cat swiped at the cord with one large paw. She and Danny had only lived here for six weeks and already she had acquired a stray cat, an unkempt gray male who for the first week had eaten voraciously and virtually ignored them. Now, however, he was intent on running the household. She had called him Einstein because, despite his mass, he could move with the speed of light. 'Hello?' she said.

'Julie? Wayne here.'

She had had a date with Wayne last Saturday night; he was an intern at the hospital where she worked. They had seen an entertaining film she had enjoyed, had had an entirely civilized conversation about it over drinks at a bar, and then Wayne had driven her home, parking his sports car in her driveway. Before she had realized his intention he had suddenly been all over her, as if she were a wrestler he was trying to subdue. His hands had touched her in places she considered strictly off-limits, and his mouth had attacked hers with a technical expertise she had found truly insulting. She had pulled free from a kiss whose intimacy he in no way had earned and had scrambled out of the car, her lipstick smeared and her clothes disheveled. She had not expected to hear from him again.

'Julie—you there? Want to take in a film Friday night?'

Julie had, unfortunately, she sometimes thought, been well brought up. 'No, thank you,' she said.

'That film we talked about last Saturday is playing in Dartmouth; you said you hadn't seen it.'

She could lie and say she had plans for Friday night. She said, 'Wayne, I don't like having to fight my dates off. I'd rather not go out with you again.'

There was an appreciable pause. Then he said, sounding aggrieved, 'Fight me off? What are you talking about?'

'*I* have some say in who kisses me, that's what I'm talking about.'

'Hey, don't be so uptight—it was no big deal.'

'You felt like a tidal wave,' she said shortly. Large and wet and overwhelming.

'Don't tell me you're one of those feminists who charges a guy with assault if he as much as looks at them.'

Refusing to pursue this undoubted red herring, she said, 'I can hear my son getting home from school; I've got to go, Wayne.'

'What about the movie?'

'No, thanks,' she said crisply, and replaced the receiver.

Wayne was not the first of her dates to exercise what she considered liberties with her person and what they plainly considered normal—even expected—behavior. Robert had always told her she was unsophisticated, she thought grimly. Maybe he was right.

There was a loud squeal of brakes and then twin rattles as two bikes were leaned against the fence. Julie smiled to herself. Danny was home, and by the sound of it Scott was with him. A nice boy, Scott Carruthers, she decided thoughtfully. How glad she was that Danny and he had become such fast friends; it had eased the move from the country to the city immeasurably.

'Hi, Mum,' Danny cried, almost tumbling in the door in his haste. 'Scott fell off his bike and he's bleeding; can you fix him up?'

As Scott limped into the kitchen, any lingering thoughts about the peculiarities of male dating behavior dropped from Julie's mind. She quickly washed her hands at the sink, assessing the ugly grazes on Scott's bare knees. 'Danny, would you get the first-aid kit from the bathroom cupboard?' she said. 'That must be hurting, Scott.'

'Kind of,' said Scott, sitting down heavily on the nearest chair and scowling at his knees.

No two boys could be more different than Danny and Scott. Even discounting a mother's natural love for her son, Julie knew Danny was an exceptionally handsome little boy, with his thick blond hair, so like her own, and his big blue eyes, the image of Robert's. He was shy, tending to be a loner, and she had worried a great deal about uprooting him from the country village that had been his home since he was born. Scott, on the other hand, was a wiry, dark-haired extrovert, passionately fond of soccer and baseball, who had drawn Danny very naturally into a whole circle of new friends and activities.

She knelt down beside Scott, using a sterile gauze pad to pick the dirt from his scraped knees. Although he was being very stoical, she could see the glint of tears in his eyes. She said matter-of-factly, 'How did you fall off?'

'He was teaching me how to do wheelies,' Danny announced. 'But the bike hit a bump.'

Wheelies involved driving the bicycle on the back wheel only. Julie said, 'Not on the street, I hope.'

'Nope,' Scott said. 'Ouch, that hurts...my Dad said he'd confiscate my bike if he ever caught me doing wheelies on the street. Confiscate means take away,' he added, bunching his fists against the pain. 'My dad's a lawyer, so he knows lots of big words.'

The lawyer she had consulted to safeguard her interests in the divorce had charged her a great deal of money to do very little; Julie made a non-committal sound and wished Scott had practised his wheelies on grass rather than gravel. 'We're nearly done,' she said. 'I'm sorry I'm hurting you.'

'Do nurses always hurt people?' Scott asked pugnaciously.

Julie looked up, startled. There was more behind that question than simple curiosity. But she had no idea what. She said cautiously, 'They try very hard not to hurt anyone. But sometimes they have to, I guess.'

His scowl was back in full force. 'You work in a hospital; Danny told me you do.'

'That's right.'

'My mum died in hospital.'

Julie sat back on her heels. Danny had talked a lot about Scott but very little about his parents, she now realized. While there had been mention of a housekeeper—a Mrs Inkpen—Julie had assumed that the mother worked as well as the father, necessitating someone to stay with Scott. 'I didn't know that, Scott,' she said softly. 'How long ago did it happen?'

Scott looked as though he was regretting his outburst. 'Two years ago,' he mumbled.

'I'm sorry she's dead; you must miss her.'

'Sometimes I do, yeah... but my dad always took me to the soccer games, so that's still okay.'

The scrape on Scott's other knee was not nearly as dirty. As gently as she could Julie cleaned it up, then applied antibiotic ointment and two new pads. 'Use this tape, Mum,' Danny suggested.

The roll of tape had Walt Disney characters printed on it in bright colors. Julie used lots of it and asked, 'How does that feel?'

As Scott stood up gingerly, Danny interposed, 'I bet a popsicle'd make him feel better.'

Julie laughed. 'I bet you're right. I still have a few chocolate-fudge cookies, too.'

'We could go over to your place and play in the tree house,' Danny added.

'The cookies could be emergency rations,' Scott said, brightening.

'As long as you're home by five-thirty, Danny,' Julie said, packing two brown paper bags with cookies and juice, then watching as the boys wobbled down the driveway on their bikes.

So Scott had no mother, and Danny no father; maybe that was another reason why the boys had become friends. Even if Scott's father was a lawyer, he was doing a good job with his son, she thought generously, and went inside to slice the carrots.

The first Saturday night she was free, she might just take herself to see that film Wayne had offered to take her to. Alone.

One thing was sure: she wouldn't go with Wayne.

Because Scott had a dentist appointment at four-thirty on Wednesday, Teal left work immediately after court recessed. He hadn't let Mike say a word all day, and he'd been able to cast more than a reasonable doubt on several of the prosecution's main points. Which, for a man who had had less than five hours' sleep, wasn't bad.

He glanced at his watch. He didn't have a whole lot of time; the most difficult thing about being a single parent was the inevitable conflict between his work and his son's needs.

He navigated the traffic with absent-minded skill, and, when he drew up next to the house, honked the horn. The last thing he'd told Scott this morning was to be ready and waiting.

Scott did not appear. Teal leaned on the horn. He and Danny might be in the tree house, in which case they would have to scan the neighborhood, lower the rope ladder that kept enemies at bay, and then slither to the ground, clutching to their chests forked twigs that doubled as guns and slingshots.

But there were no bicycles leaning against the back porch. Impatiently Teal got out of the car, a tall, commanding figure in a pin-striped suit, and scanned the garden himself. 'Scott?' he called. 'Hurry up, we're going to be late.'

When neither boy appeared, he took the back steps two at a time and let himself in the door, which was firmly locked. There was a note propped on the kitchen table. 'School got out erly, a pipe berst,' it said. 'Gone to Danny's.'

His son might be a hotshot soccer player. But he was a lousy speller, Teal thought, and rummaged for the scrap of paper bearing Danny's phone number. He finally located it at the very bottom of the pile and dialed it quickly. A busy signal burred in his ear. Grimacing, he glanced at his watch and dialed it again. Still busy.

It was probably Danny's mother talking. In which case the phone could be tied up for hours, he thought with total unfairness. He'd better go over there right now. And he'd better hurry.

Danny lived six houses down the street in a stucco bungalow with a painfully tidy garden, which Teal disliked on sight. He parked on the street and marched up the narrow concrete path to the front door. The brass knocker was tarnished; Danny's mother wasn't quite the perfectionist that the garden would suggest. He pressed the doorbell and waited.

No one came. Through the open living-room window he could hear music, very loud music that was undoubtedly drowning out the sound of the bell. Feeling his temper rise, he pressed it again.

This time when no one came he pulled the screen door open and was about to pound on the door when the breeze wafted it open. Didn't she know this was the city, and that she should keep her doors locked? Stupid woman, he fumed. He went inside, wincing at the sheer volume of sound coming from the stereo equipment. Diana Ross, unless he was mistaken, singing something sultry and bluesy accompanied by a muted trumpet. It was not music calculated to improve his mood; he didn't want to hear a sensual, husky voice or the evocative slide of a trumpet over melancholy notes in a minor key. He had closed off that part of himself a long time ago.

Noises from the kitchen overrode the music. Teal strode down the hall and stopped in the doorway.

The four occupants of the kitchen all had their backs turned to him. Danny was leaning against the counter holding an imaginary trumpet, wailing tunelessly. Scott was perched on a stool licking cookie dough from his fingers. A scruffy gray cat was sitting on the counter next to him, washing its oversized paws much too close to the bowl of dough for Teal's liking. And, finally, a woman with a sheaf of streaked blonde hair held back by a ragged piece of purple ribbon was standing near the stove. She was singing along with Diana Ross, belting out the words with clear enjoyment.

Teal opened his mouth to say something. But before he could the buzzer on the stove went off, adding to the racket. The woman switched it off, swathed her hands in a pair of large mitts and bent to open the oven door.

She was wearing an old pair of denim shorts with a frayed hem, and a blue top that bared her arms and a wide strip of skin above her waist. The shorts must once have been jeans, which had been cut off. Cut off too high, Teal thought with a dry mouth, his eyes glued to the delectable, lightly tanned curves of her thighs, and the taut pull of the fabric as she leaned over to lift a cookie sheet out of the oven. He was suddenly angry beyond belief, irrationally, ridiculously angry, with no idea why.

'Perfect,' she said, and turned round to put the cookies on the rack on the counter.

She saw him instantly, gave a shriek of alarm and dropped the metal pan on the counter with a loud clatter. The cat leaped to the floor, taking a glass of juice with it. The glass, not surprisingly, smashed to pieces. The boys swerved in unison, gaping at him with open mouths. And the woman said furiously, 'Just who do you think you are, walking into my house without even so much as ringing the doorbell?'

Scott was right, Teal thought blankly. Danny's mother was beautiful. Quite incredibly beautiful, considering that she had a blob of flour on her nose, no make-up, and clothes that could have been bought at a rummage sale. He searched for something to say, he who was rarely at a loss for words, struggling to keep his gaze above the level of her cleavage.

'Hi, Dad,' Scott said. 'Boy, you sure scared the cat.'

'His name's Einstein,' Danny chimed in. 'Mum says that's 'cause he bends time and space.'

Teal took a deep breath and said with a calmness that would have impressed Mr Chief Justice Mersey, 'He certainly bent the glass—sorry about that. I'm Scott's father, Mrs Ferris . . . Teal Carruthers.'

'Julie Ferris,' Julie corrected automatically. Ever since Robert had walked out on her that last time, she had disliked the title Mrs. '*Did* you ring the doorbell?' she asked, more to give herself time to think than because she was interested in the answer.

'I did. But it couldn't compete with Diana Ross.' He added, wondering if her eyes were gray or blue, 'You should keep the door locked, you know.'

'I forget,' she said shortly. 'I'm used to living in the country.'

Why hadn't Danny warned her that Scott's father was so outrageously attractive? The most attractive man she'd ever met. Teal Carruthers wasn't as classically handsome as Robert, and looked as though he would be more at home in sports clothes than a pin-striped suit; but his eyes were the clear gray of a rain-washed lake, set under smudged lashes as dark and thick as his hair, and his body, carried with a kind of unconscious grace that made her hackles rise, was beautifully proportioned.

'Do you always let the cat sit on the counter?' he added. 'I thought nurses believed in hygiene.'

'Are you always so critical?' she snapped back, and with faint dismay realised that the two boys were, of course, listening to every word.

'If my son's to spend time in your house, I'd much prefer you to keep the doors locked,' he replied with an air of formal restraint that added to her irritation. What was the matter with her? She normally liked meeting new people, and certainly she had no desire to alienate the father of her son's best friend.

'That makes sense,' she said grudgingly, straightening the cookie sheet on the rack. Then she reached for some paper towel and knelt to pick up the shards of glass. Luckily they hadn't pierced the floor covering; she didn't think that would fall in the category of apple-pie order.

'I'll help,' Scott said.

As she stooped, Teal was presented with a view of delicate shoulderbones and the shadowed valley between full breasts. Her fingers were long and tapered, and the afternoon sunlight was tangled in her hair. He said flatly, 'We're late for your dentist appointment, Scott. I tried to phone you here, but the number was busy.'

'Darn,' said Julie. 'I bet Einstein knocked the phone off the hook again.'

Scott's face fell. 'I forgot about the dentist.'

'We'd better go,' Teal said, adding punctiliously, 'Thank you for looking after Scott this afternoon, Mrs Ferris. And for bandaging his knees yesterday—a very professional job.'

'The bill's in the mail,' she said flippantly, getting to her feet. Teal Carruthers didn't look the slightest bit grateful. And he had yet to crack a smile. 'I prefer to be called Julie,' she added, and gave him the dazzling smile she employed only rarely, and which tended to reduce strong men to a stuttering silence.

He didn't even blink an eyelash. 'Good afternoon,' he said, not calling her anything. He then nodded at Danny and left the room, Scott in tow. Julie trailed after him into the living-room, turning down the volume on the stereo as she watched a sleek black BMW pull away from the curb. It would be black, she thought. Black went with the man's rigidly held mouth, his immaculately tailored suit, his air of cold censure. Amazing that he had such an outgoing son as Scott. Truly amazing.

Her bare feet padding on the hardwood floor, she went to lock the front door.

CHAPTER TWO

THE home and school meeting was between six-thirty and eight on Thursday evening. Julie dressed with care in a plain blue linen tunic over a short matching skirt, her hair loose on her shoulders, and went promptly at six-thirty, partly because she had worked the last of her three overnight shifts the night before and needed to go to bed early, partly with a subconscious hope that she would thereby miss Teal Carruthers. Because of the connection between Danny and Scott it was inevitable that she would meet him sometimes. But there was no need to put herself in his path unnecessarily.

There was no sign of him when she got there. After Danny had shown her all his lively and inaccurate renditions of jet planes and African mammals, she chatted with his homeroom teacher—a pleasant young man she had met once before. The principal came over, a rather officious gentleman by the name of Bidwell, then the gym teacher and two school board representatives. It's happening again, Julie thought with a quiver of inner amusement. I seem to be gathering every man in the room around me.

The gym teacher, with all the subtlety of a ten-ton truck, had just revealed that he was newly divorced, when Julie glanced past his shoulder and saw Teal Carruthers. With another spurt of inner laughter she saw that if she was gathering the men he was like a magnet to the women. He was winning, though; he had six women to her five men.

23

'I wonder if I might give you a tour of our new computer-room, Mrs Ferris?' Mr Bidwell asked, bridling with old-fashioned chivalry.

'I'm sure Mrs Ferris would be more interested in the soccer facilities,' the gym teacher interrupted, giving his boss a baleful look.

'Actually,' Julie said, 'I'd like to meet Danny's music teacher—she's over there talking to Mr Carruthers. If you'll excuse me, please?'

Giving them all an impartial smile, she crossed the room to the cluster of women around Teal Carruthers. He was openly watching her approach, his expression unreadable. His lightweight trousers and stylish striped shirt were casual clothes in which he should have looked relaxed; he looked, she thought, about as relaxed as a tiger in a cage.

It was an odd image to use of a man so outwardly civilized. She gave him a cool smile, said, 'Good evening, Mr Carruthers,' and waited to see how he would respond.

With uncanny precision he echoed her own words. 'If you'll excuse me, please?' he said, flicking a glance around him. Then he took Julie by the elbow and walked her over to a display of books. 'I see you have the same problem as I do,' he said.

'You were one up on me,' she answered limpidly.

'But then you've only lived here just over a month.'

'You mean it's going to get worse?' Julie said with faint dismay.

Deliberately he looked her up and down, from the smooth, shining fall of her hair to her fine-boned feet in their pretty shoes. 'Very definitely, I'd say,' he drawled.

She was quite astute enough to realize he did not mean the words as a compliment. His fingers were still gripping her elbow, digging into her bare skin with unnecessary strength. 'I'm not going to run away,' Julie said, and saw with a primitive thrill of triumph that she had finally managed to disrupt his composure.

With a muttered word of apology Teal dropped his hand to his side, furious with himself for that small betrayal: he hadn't even realized he was still holding on to her. Standing as close to her as he was, it was no trouble to see why any red-blooded male under the age of ninety would be drawn to her, for besides being beautiful she exuded sensuality from every pore.

Her lips were soft and voluptuous, holding an unspoken promise that the imperious tilt of her cheekbones belied, a contrast that could be seen as both challenge and snare. Her body, curved and graceful, bore the same paradoxical blend of untouchability and beckoning. Although her height and slenderness made her as modern-looking as any model, her smile was both mysterious and ageless.

In the kitchen of her house he had wondered what color her eyes were. He now saw that they were neither gray nor blue, but shifting like smoke from one to the other. Chameleon eyes. Fickle eyes, he thought cynically.

'You don't like me very much, do you?' Julie said levelly.

He raised his brow. 'You believe in speaking your mind.'

'Life's short—it saves time.'

The women who pursued him always seemed to be smiling. Julie Ferris was not smiling. Suddenly exhilarated, Teal said, 'No—actually, I don't like you.'

Not wanting him to know that his opinion of her had the power to hurt, Julie chose her words with care. 'I was worried about Danny adjusting to the city and to a new school when we moved here, and I'm very happy that he and Scott are friends. It's really immaterial whether you and I like each other—but I wouldn't want our feelings to get in the way of the boys' friendship.'

'I'm quite sure we can keep meetings between us at a minimum, Mrs Ferris,' Teal said, and watched anger spark her eyes with blue.

'I certainly have no desire to do otherwise.'

'Then we understand each other,' he said. 'Ah, there's Scott's homeroom teacher; I must have a word with her about my son's appalling spelling. Good evening, Mrs Ferris.'

Julie watched him walk away from her. He was not a stupid man; he knew she didn't like being called Mrs Ferris. He had been needling her on purpose.

He really didn't like her.

Her thoughts marched on. In her kitchen she had labeled him as the most attractive man she had ever met. Attractive now seemed a flimsy word to describe him, and civilized a totally meretricious word. Sexy would have been more accurate, she thought shakily. Close up, the man projected raw magnetism simply by breathing; he was dynamite. As clearly as if he were still standing in front of her she could see the narrow, strongly boned features, the unfathomable gray eyes and cleanly carved lips. He had a cleft in his chin. His lashes were as black as soot. Not to mention his body...

Julie wriggled her shoulders under her tunic, trying to relax, and began searching the room for the music teacher. Dynamite has a tendency to blow up in your face, she chided herself. Dynamite is deadly. Besides, you were married to a man with charisma and you know darn well where that got you.

Learn from your mistakes, Julie Ferris. Which means, as Mr Teal Carruthers so succinctly phrased it, that you should keep meetings between you and him to a minimum.

An absolute minimum. Like none.

She caught the music teacher's eye and, smiling, walked across to meet her. Half an hour later, having assiduously avoided the gym teacher, she left the school with Danny and went home. She went to bed early, and woke up the next morning to the delightful knowledge that she had the next two days off. The sun was shining and the birds were singing... wonderful.

After Danny had gone to school, Julie took her coffee on to the porch and sat in the sun with her feet up. She felt very content. She had done the right thing by moving to the city, she knew that now. It had seemed an immensely difficult decision at the time, to leave the old country house where she had lived throughout her marriage; yet increasingly she had wanted more opportunities for Danny than the tiny local school could offer, and her own job at the county hospital had been in jeopardy because of cut-backs.

But there had been more to it than that. Inwardly she had longed to leave the house where she had been so unhappy, a house that had come to represent Robert's abandonment and betrayal; and she had craved more life, more people, more excitement than weekly bingo games and church socials.

She loved living in the city. On all counts except for the men she was meeting she had more than succeeded in her aims. Although she supposed there were those who would call her date with Wayne exciting.

She finished her coffee and went to two nurseries, loading her little car with flats of pansies and petunias and snapdragons. Home again, she changed into her oldest clothes and got the tools out of the little shed at the back of the garden. The spades and trowels were so clean she almost felt guilty about getting dirt on them. Almost, she thought happily, loosening the soil in one of the geometric beds and randomly starting to dig holes for the transplants. She disliked formal gardens. Too much control.

An hour later the hose was sprawled on the grass in untidy coils, the snapdragons were haphazardly planted among the box-wood, and a fair bit of mud had transferred itself from the beds to Julie's person. Singing to herself, she began scattering nasturtium seeds along the edges of the bed.

A man's voice said over the fence, 'Good morning, Mrs Ferris.'

The only person other than Teal Carruthers to call her Mrs Ferris was her next-door neighbor, a retired brigadier general called Basil Mellanby who lived alone and would not, she was sure, ever make the slightest attempt to date her. 'Good morning,' Julie called cheerily. 'Isn't it a beautiful day?'

'Indeed it is.' He cleared his throat, rather dubiously surveying the results of her labors. 'I have a measuring stick if you should want to borrow it—just the thing to keep the rows straight.'

His garden was a replica of her landlady's. 'I like things messy,' Julie said apologetically. 'You don't think Mrs LeMarchant will mind, do you?' Mrs LeMarchant was her landlady.

'I'm sure she won't,' the general replied, with more gallantry, Julie suspected, than truth. 'I had a letter from her today; she's doing very well in Vermont with her sister.'

And you miss her, thought Julie. 'How's her sister getting along since her heart attack?'

The general chatted away for half an hour, then Julie did her best to relieve the rigid straightness of the concrete path to the front door with masses of petunias, watched by Einstein, who also liked digging haphazardly in the garden. Danny came home from school. She made supper and cleaned up the dishes, and when Scott joined them got the two boys to help her wind the hose and hang it on the shed wall. Then she went back in the house to get a drink of juice.

Einstein was crouched on the kitchen floor with a rat under his paws. The rat, she saw with a gasp of pure horror, was not dead.

She backed up slowly, fumbled for the screen door and edged through it. Her hands were shaking so badly she could hardly close the door.

Danny clattered up the steps. 'We're going to play cowboys,' he said and reached for the door.

'Don't go in there,' Julie faltered. 'Einstein's caught a rat.'

'A rat—wow!'

'It's not dead,' she added, wringing her hands. 'What will I *do*?'

If she called the general, he'd probably want to blow the rat's head off with a shotgun; the general had an immoderate fondness for guns. Or else, she thought numbly, remembering the network of tiny veins in his ruddy cheeks, he might have a heart attack like Mrs LeMarchant's sister. No, she couldn't ask the general.

'Aren't you going to get your holsters, Danny?' Scott cried, bouncing up the steps.

'There's a rat in the house,' Danny said with evident relish. 'Mum says it's not dead. Einstein caught it.'

'Jeepers . . . a real rat?'

'I can't go in there,' Julie muttered. 'I'm being a lousy role model but I'm terrified of rats.'

Scott let out a war-whoop. 'I'll get my dad,' he said; 'he'll fix it.'

'No, you mustn't——'

'Let's go!' Danny cried, and the two boys took off down the street. The rest of Julie's protest died on her lips because there was no one there to hear it. The general would have been better than Teal Carruthers, she thought grimly, and looked down at herself. Her sneakers had holes in them, her knees were coated with mud, and her T-shirt had 'Handel With Care' emblazoned across her chest under a portrait of the composer. As for her shorts, they should have been thrown out when she moved.

Inside the house Einstein meowed, a long, piercing howl that almost made her feel sorry for the rat. She shuddered. A half-dead rat on the white kitchen tiles could not by any stretch of the imagination be called apple-pie order.

A black car turned into her driveway, pulling up behind her small green Chevette. The boys erupted from it, and in a more leisurely fashion Teal Carruthers climbed out. He too was wearing shorts, designer shorts with brand-new deck shoes and a T-shirt so close-fitting that her stomach, already unsettled, did an uneasy swoop.

'What seems to be the problem?' he drawled.

'There's a rat in the kitchen,' she said, and through the open screen heard Einstein howl again.

'Sure it's not a mouse?'

In a flash of insight Julie realized what he was implying. The rat, in his view, was nothing but a trumped-up excuse for her to see him again. She was chasing him. Just like all those other women. In a voice tight with rage she said, 'I once accidentally locked myself in the basement with two live rats. Trust me, Mr Carruthers—this is no mouse.'

Teal picked up a pair of heavy gloves from the back seat and closed the car door. 'Two meetings in less than twenty-four hours hardly qualifies as minimal,' he said, climbing the back steps.

'I didn't ask you to come here!' Julie spat. 'Our two sons did that. As far as I'm concerned you can go straight home and stay there—I'll ask the brigadier general to come over; I'm sure he'd be delighted to blast his way through my house with a shotgun.'

'I'm here now; I might as well have a look,' Teal said. With a twinge of remorse he saw that she was genuinely pale, her hands shaking with the lightest of tremors. Mouse or rat, she'd had a fright.

She was wearing those goddamned shorts again.

'Can we come, Dad?' Scott begged.

'No, you stay out here...I won't be long.'

The two boys glued themselves to the screen door, peering through to see what was happening. Julie leaned back against the railing, taking a couple of deep breaths to calm herself, every nerve on edge. She jumped as Einstein emitted an uncouth shriek expressive of extreme displeasure. Two minutes later Teal pushed open the door, the rat dangling from one gloved hand. 'Have you got a shovel?' he said. 'I'll bury it for you.'

'I'll get it,' Danny said eagerly. 'Can we have a proper funeral?'

Teal took one look at Julie's face; she was backed up against the railing as far as she could go, cringing from the dead animal in his hand. 'I don't think so,' he said drily, and started down the steps.

Julie stayed where she was. Her knees were trembling and she had no desire to go inside and face Einstein's wrath. The last time she and Robert had been together, two rats had gotten in the basement of their house. Robert had laughed at her fears, neglected to set traps and announced that he was divorcing her for another woman. Two days after he had gone back to New York the latch at the top of the basement stairs—which she had twice asked him to mend—had trapped her in the basement. She had been there for four hours, along with the rats, until Danny had come home from school and released her. Even thinking about it made her feel sick.

When Teal came back, she was still standing there. He said tersely, 'Have you got any brandy?' She shook her head. 'Get in the car and we'll go over to my place— you could do with a good stiff drink.'

He was scarcely bothering to disguise the reluctance in his voice. 'Oh, no—no, thanks,' Julie said. 'I'll be fine now that I know the rat's not in the house any more.'

Teal gave an impatient sigh. If he had the slightest sense he'd leave right now. She was a grown woman, and definitely not his responsibility. He heard himself saying, 'Scott, go over to the house and bring back the brandy, will you? The dark green bottle with the black label. Put it in a paper bag and don't forget to lock the door again.'

'C'mon, Danny,' Scott yelled, throwing his leg over the seat of his bicycle. 'Let's pretend we're ambulance drivers.'

Wailing like banshees, the two boys disappeared from sight. 'I wish you'd go, too,' Julie said raggedly. 'You don't want to be here any more than I want you here.'

A lot of Teal's work dealt with the shady areas of half-truths and outright lies; he found Julie Ferris's honesty oddly refreshing. 'You look as though you're either going to faint or be sick,' he said. 'Or both. And I have to clean up your kitchen floor. Let's go inside.' Hoping it was not obvious how little he wanted to touch her, he took her by the arm. She was trembling very lightly and her skin was cold, and he felt a swift, unexpected surge of compassion. More gently he said, 'You need to sit down, Julie.'

Tears suddenly flooded her eyes, tears she was too proud to show him. She ducked her head, fighting them back, and made for the door. As she stumbled into the kitchen Einstein pushed between her legs in his haste to get outside. Teal grabbed her arm again. 'Careful—where in hell's teeth did you get that cat? It's got worse manners than an eight-year-old boy.'

'He got us—he was a stray,' she said with a watery grin directed at the vicinity of his chest, and sat down hard in the nearest chair. She averted her eyes while Teal wiped the floor with wet paper towel, by which time Scott had returned with a brown paper bag which he plunked on the counter. The brandy was exceedingly expensive. She gulped some down and began to feel better.

Teal topped up her glass and stood up to go. 'Call me if there's a replay,' he said wryly. 'It makes a change from legal briefs.'

The boys had gone outside. Julie stood up as well, and perhaps it was the brandy that loosened her tongue. 'Do you think I faked all this just to get you over here?' she asked. 'One more woman who's hot in pursuit?'

'You don't miss much, do you?'

'As a lawyer you deal with people under one kind of stress—as a nurse I deal with them under another. Either way, after a while you get so you can read people.'

Teal looked at her in silence. There was a little color back in her cheeks, and the tears that she had tried to hide from him were gone. He said slowly, 'It would be very egotistical of me to assume that you're pursuing me.'

'Indeed it would,' she said agreeably.

'You really are scared of rats.'

'Terrified.'

'Tell me why.'

'Oh, I don't think so,' she said. 'That's personal stuff.'

He felt a tiny, illogical flicker of anger. 'No, I don't think you're pursuing me,' he said. 'Despite the message on your T-shirt.'

Julie had forgotten about 'Handel with Care'. She flushed scarlet, the mere thought of Teal Carruthers touching her breasts filling her with confusion. 'It's the only dark-colored shirt I've got,' she babbled. 'I always seem to cover myself in mud when I garden.'

'I noticed that... I'm going to round Scott up; I've got a couple of hours' work to do tonight. Goodnight, Julie Ferris.'

She said awkwardly but with undoubted sincerity, 'Thank you very much for killing the rat.'

He suddenly smiled, a smile that brought his whole face to life so that it crackled with vitality. It was as though a different man stood in front of her, a much younger man, unguarded and free. A very sexual man, Julie thought uneasily, and took a step back.

'Just call me St George,' he said. 'Take care.'

Julie was still rooted to the floor when Danny came in a few minutes later. 'Einstein's sulking,' he said cheerfully. 'He growled at me when I tried to pat him.'

'I think we'll leave him outside for now,' she said with a reminiscent shiver. 'Shower night, Danny,' she added, and braced herself for the usual protests; Danny had an aversion to hot water and soap. Her best friend in the country had teenage sons who she claimed almost lived in the shower. Some days Julie could hardly wait.

On Saturday Julie turned down a date with the gym teacher, was extremely short with Wayne when he phoned, and went out for dinner with Morse MacLeod, one of the anaesthetists on staff. His wife had left him five months ago, a situation which could only fill Julie with sympathy. But Morse was so immersed in misery that he had no interest in hearing her own rather similar story; all he wanted was large doses of commiseration along with complete agreement that his wife's behavior had been unfair, inhuman and castrating. By the time he took her home Julie's store of sympathy was long gone. She was a dinner-date, not a therapist, she thought, closing the door behind Morse with a sigh of relief. But at least he hadn't jumped on her.

School ended. Danny and Scott added a new room to the tree house and Julie had to increase the hours of her sitter. The surgeon who had invited her to go sailing on his yacht at Mahone Bay, an expedition she had looked forward to, turned out to be married; his protestations about his open marriage and about her old-fashioned values did not impress her.

Her next date was with a male nurse from Oncology, a single parent like herself. His idea of a night out was to take her home to meet his three young children, involve her in preparing supper and getting them to bed, and, once they were asleep, regale her with pitiful stories of how badly they needed a mother. Then as Julie sat on the couch innocently drinking lukewarm coffee he suddenly threw himself on her to demonstrate how badly he needed a wife. Julie fled.

Driving home, her blouse pulled out of her waistband, her lipstick smeared, she made herself a promise. She was on night duty the following Saturday. But if that film she'd yet to see was still playing the week after that, she was going to see it all by herself. No more dates. No more men who saw her as a potential mother or an instant mistress. One bed partner, made to order, she thought vengefully. Just add water and stir. Did men honestly think women were flattered to be mauled on the very first date?

A traffic light turned red and she pulled to a halt. Not one of the men she had dated since she had moved to Halifax had been at all interested in her as a person, she realized with painful truth. They never got beyond her face and her body. Was the fault hers? Was she giving off the wrong signals? Picking the wrong men? Or was she, as the surgeon had implied, simply hopelessly old-fashioned?

The light turned green. She shifted gears, suddenly aching to be in her own house, Danny asleep upstairs, Einstein curled up on the chesterfield. She knew who she was there. Liked who she was. And if she was retreating from reality, so be it. She was thoroughly disenchanted with the dating game.

The Saturday after the rat episode Teal had dinner with Janine. He had met her at a cocktail party at the law school, and had then made the mistake of inviting her to the annual dinner and dance given by his firm of solicitors. It was considered bad form to go to the dinner without a partner, and he had rather liked her. Unfortunately she had fallen head over heels in love with him.

He was not the slightest bit in love with her, had never made a move to take her to bed, and once he had realized how she felt had actively discouraged her. All to no avail. Bad enough that she was phoning him at home with distressing frequency. She had now taken to bothering him at work. So tonight he was going to end it, once and for all. It was the kindest thing to do.

Great way to spend a Saturday night, he thought, knotting his tie in the mirror. But she was young. She'd get over it. She'd come to realize, as everyone did sooner or later, that love wasn't always what it cracked up to be.

Would he ever forget—or forgive himself—that on the very day Elizabeth had died they'd had an argument? Something to do with Scott, something silly and trivial. But the hasty words he'd thrown at her could never be retracted.

Irritably he shrugged into his summerweight jacket. He should pin a button to his lapel: 'Not Available'. 'Once Burned, Twice Shy'. Would that discourage all these women who seemed to think he was fair game?

This evening Janine had offered to cook dinner for him. He kept the conversation firmly on impersonal matters throughout the meal, told her as gently as he could that he didn't want to hear from her again, and patiently dealt with her tears and arguments. He was home by ten. Thoroughly out of sorts, he paid the sitter and poured himself a glass of brandy.

Swishing it around the glass, absently watching the seventh inning of a baseball game on television, he found himself remembering Julie Ferris. Her fear of rats had reduced her to tears. But she had hated crying in front of him, and would be, he was almost sure, totally averse to using tears as a weapon. Unlike Janine. But then, unlike Janine, Julie Ferris wasn't in love with him. She didn't even like him.

He hadn't been strictly truthful when he had said he didn't like her. He did like her honesty.

His hands clenched around the glass as he remembered other things: the sunlight glinting in the shining weight of her hair; the way she had trembled at the sight of the rat; her incredibly long legs and the fullness of her breasts under the mud-stained T-shirt that said 'Handel with Care'.

His body stirred to life. With an exclamation of disgust he changed the channel to a rerun of *Platoon* and immersed himself in its claustrophobic tale of war and death.

He was going to stay away from Julie Ferris.

And for two weeks he did just that. But he wasn't always as successful at keeping her out of his thoughts. At a barbecue in Mike's back yard a young woman called Carole attached herself to him, agreeing with everything he said, laughing sycophantically at all his jokes; Julie's level gaze and caustic tongue were never far from Teal's mind. Then Marylee and Bruce, two of his oldest and most cherished friends, invited him to spend the day at their summer cottage on the Northumberland Strait.

'Can I ask Danny?' Scott said immediately. 'We could go swimming and play tennis, hey, Dad?'

'No,' Teal said, the reply out of his mouth before he even had time to think about it.

'Why not?' Scott wailed.

Teal didn't know why. Because he didn't want to explain to Bruce and Marylee who Danny was? Because he didn't want to phone Julie and tell her about the outing? Because he didn't want to feel that he should ask her as well?

Knowing he was prevaricating and not liking himself very much for doing it, Teal said, 'We can't go everywhere with Danny, son. And his mother might not like us driving all that distance and being late home. Maybe another time.'

Scott stuck his lower lip out and ran up the stairs, slamming the door to his room. Teal raked his fingers through his hair. He should discipline Scott for his behavior. But somehow he didn't have the heart to do so.

Logically, Julie Ferris was exactly the woman he should be taking with him to the cottage. She wasn't interested in him. She wouldn't be phoning him all the time or trying to give him presents he didn't want. She wouldn't be doing her best to entice him into her bed.

Restlessly he prowled around the room, picking up the scattered pages of the newspaper and a dirty coffee-mug. So why wasn't he phoning her and suggesting that she and Danny accompany them? It would be a foursome. Quite safe.

Like a family, he thought, standing stock-still on the carpet. A husband and a wife and their two children.

No wonder he wasn't picking up the telephone—the picture he had conjured up hit much too close to home. But there was no way he could explain to Scott the real reason why Danny and Julie Ferris couldn't go with them.

The cottage on a sunny afternoon in July was an extremely pleasant place to be. Scott was playing in the swimming-pool with Sara and Jane, Bruce and Marylee's two daughters, while the adults lay on the deck over-looking the blue waters of the strait, drinking rum fizzes and gossiping lazily about some of their colleagues, one of whom was having a torrid affair with a female member of parliament. Marylee, a brunette with big green eyes, said casually, 'Are you involved with anyone, Teal?' As he shook his head she tilted her sunhat back the better to see his face. 'It's two years since Elizabeth died...isn't it time?'

Glad that his dark glasses were hiding his eyes, Teal said flippy, 'Nope.'

Reflectively she extracted a slice of orange from her glass and chewed on it. 'Even if you don't want to get involved, that's no reason to eschew female company.'

'I don't,' he said, stung. 'Next Friday I'm going to a medical convention dance with a surgeon who's defi-nitely female.' He had wondered if Julie Ferris might also be going. But he wasn't going to share that with Marylee.

Wrinkling her tip-tilted nose, Marylee said, 'And I bet you five dollars that'll be your first and last date with the surgeon.'

'I'm not interested in another relationship,' Teal said tightly.

'You must have lots of offers.'

'Too many.'

'Well, you're a very sexy man,' she said seriously. Bruce, stretched out beside her, gave a snort of laughter. Ignoring him, she added, 'Plus you're a good father and a fine lawyer—you have integrity.'

Embarrassed, Teal said comically, 'I don't think the women are chasing me because of my integrity.'

'It's your body and your bank account—in that order,' Bruce put in.

'Stop joking, you two,' Marylee said severely. 'Grief is all very well, Teal, but Scott needs a mother. And it's not natural for you to live like a monk.'

Grief Teal could handle. It was the rest he couldn't. 'I'm not ready for any kind of commitment, Marylee,' he said, getting up from his chair and stretching the tension from his body. 'Who's going for a swim?'

'Men,' Marylee sniffed. 'I'll never understand them if I live to be a hundred.'

Bruce pulled her to her feet. 'You shouldn't bother your pretty little head over us, baby doll,' he leered. 'Barefoot and pregnant, that's your role in life.'

'Men have been divorced for less than that,' Marylee said darkly, then giggled as Bruce swept her off her feet with a passionate kiss.

Teal looked away, conscious of a peculiar ache in his belly. Although Bruce and Marylee had been through some struggles in their marriage, he would stake his life that the marriage was sound. Yet it hurt something deep within him to witness the love they shared.

Love... that most enigmatic and elusive of emotions.

No wonder he didn't want to get involved, he thought, and headed for the pool.

CHAPTER THREE

JULIE FERRIS was on Teal's mind again the following Friday when he and Dr Deirdre Reid entered the banquet hall in the hotel. He found himself searching the crowd for a crown of gleaming blonde hair, and didn't know whether he was disappointed or relieved when he couldn't find the tall, strikingly beautiful woman who was the mother of his son's best friend. His companion said something to him, then tugged at the sleeve of his tuxedo. 'Who are you looking for?'

'It's always interesting to see how many people I know at affairs like this,' he said vaguely. 'Do you have any idea where we're sitting?'

'At the head table—I told you I'm the president of the local association,' Deirdre said briskly, and began threading her way through the throng of people.

Grinning to himself, not at all surprised that they were at the head table, Teal followed. One reason he'd accepted Deirdre's invitation was because he didn't think there was any danger she'd fall in love with him; Deirdre Reid's emotions were very much under control. If indeed she had any. There were times when her acerbic sense of humor made him wonder. But she was good company, intelligent and well-informed politically.

He was introduced to a great many medical pundits on the way to the head table, where the meal was interjected with speeches, all fortunately brief, some very witty. But it was not until the dancing began in the next room that he saw the woman he had subconsciously been searching for all evening.

Julie Ferris. She was jiving with a tall, strikingly good-looking young man. She danced as if there were no tomorrow, every movement imbued with grace, joyous in a way that made his throat close. Her unselfconscious pleasure seemed to embody something he had lost—if indeed he had ever had it. He said, without having thought out the question at all, 'Who's the tall guy with the red hair?'

Deirdre followed his gaze. With a malicious smile she said, 'The youngest and most brilliant specialist on staff—neurosurgery—and the worst womanizer. Why do you ask?'

'I know the woman he's with.'

Deirdre said dismissively, 'He'll be bedding her before the night's out, I'm sure. She's rather pretty, isn't she? Shall we dance?'

So Julie Ferris liked sex. As much as the women who chased him. She just had a different man in mind; he, Teal, had not turned her on. Turning his back on her, he whirled Deirdre in a circle and began to dance.

The band was excellent and the wine had flowed freely during the meal. The crowd ebbed and flowed, the laughter ever louder, the colors of the women's dresses as bright as summer flowers, but not, Teal thought sardonically, as innocent. Smoothly he traversed the dance-floor, Deirdre following his every move with a clockwork precision. The waltz ended. Julie and her partner were standing not ten feet away from them, the neurosurgeon's hand placed familiarly low on her hip. Teal said clearly, 'Hello, Julie.'

Her head swung round. 'Teal...I noticed you were here,' she said, and removed the doctor's hand.

'I'd like you to meet Dr Deirdre Reid,' Teal said. 'Julie Ferris, Deirdre...her son and mine are friends.'

'Dr Reid and I have already met,' Julie said coolly, her smile perfunctory.

'Ferris?' Deirdre repeated with equal coolness. 'Oh, of course, Men's Surgical. I didn't recognize you out of uniform; all nurses look alike to me.' She smiled up at Julie's partner. 'Hello, Nick, how are you? Teal Carruthers...Dr Nicholas Lytton.'

The young neurosurgeon had very pale blue eyes, and Teal disliked him on sight. As the band struck up a slow foxtrot, he said, 'Dance with me, Julie?'

The twin patches of scarlet in her cheeks matched her outfit—a silk dinner-suit with a flounced neckline and glittering buttons; her hair was upswept on her crown, elaborate gold earrings swaying from her lobes. 'Thank you,' she said, and moved into his arms.

While the color in her cheeks could have stemmed from Deirdre's rudeness, Teal thought that more probably it was in anticipation of ending the night in the neurosurgeon's bed. She felt very different from Deirdre in his embrace, her body lissome, utterly in tune with the languorous, sensual music. He led her through a complicated turn and said, 'You know you're dating the worst womanizer in the entire hospital?'

Her head jerked up. Her eyes, he saw, were sparked blue with temper. 'Who told you that?'

'Deirdre.'

'Is she speaking from personal experience?'

Teal gave a choked laugh. 'It's not like you to be bitchy.'

'You have no idea what I'm like.'

The question forced itself past his lips. 'Are you going to bed with him, Julie?'

'Really, Teal, what kind of a question is that?'

'A fairly straightforward one, I would have thought.'

'You're not in court—this is no place for a cross-examination,' she said, and her lips—very kissable lips—compressed in a way that made his hands tighten their hold. 'Don't grab me,' she added crossly.

'Why not? Because I'm not a brilliant neurosurgeon, just a lawyer, and they're a dime a dozen?'

'Boy, you're sure spoiling for a fight, aren't you? Not that I'm surprised. Three hours of Dr Reid would put a saint in a bad mood.'

'She's an intelligent and attractive woman.'

'So are you going to bed with her, Teal?' she parried nastily.

'No,' he announced. 'Why was she so rude to you?'

'On my last shift she yelled at me in front of several interns and two other doctors for a mistake I hadn't made. When I pointed out her error, she declined to apologize.' Julie sniffed. 'She treats patients like collections of removable organs and nurses like dirt.'

Somehow Teal had no trouble believing every word Julie had just said. 'Then we agree about something,' he remarked.

'What's that?' she asked suspiciously.

'Neither of us likes the other's choice of a date.'

'You have no reason to dislike Nick,' she flashed.

He remembered the hand sliding down her hip and said curtly, 'Danny deserves better of you than someone like Nick.'

'Danny's got nothing to do with it!'

'So you don't take your men home when you go to bed with them? How discreet of you,' he sneered, recognizing with a distant part of his brain that he was behaving reprehensibly.

'What have you got against me, Teal?' Julie demanded. 'You've disliked me from the minute we met.'

You're beautiful and full of life and you're driving me crazy...

For a horrible moment Teal thought he had spoken the words out loud. 'Just don't expose my son to your love life—that's an order,' he said coldly. 'He likes you and I wouldn't want him thinking promiscuity is acceptable adult behavior.'

'I promise that when I stand on a street corner soliciting it won't be your street,' she snapped. 'It's beyond me how you have such a nice son! Since—like most men—you're totally wrapped up in your job, I can only presume that your wife brought Scott up.'

She felt Teal's instant response through her fingers: a tightening of his shoulder muscles, a rigidity in his spine. 'Leave my wife out of this,' he grated. 'She's none of your business and never will be. And now I'd better hand you back to Nick, hadn't I? I wouldn't want the two of you to waste any time.'

As the saxophone whispered its last chords and the dancers clapped he led her toward the other couple. 'Yours, I believe,' he said to Nick, and smiled rather more warmly than he had intended at Deirdre. 'Why don't we take a break and get a drink?' he suggested, and without a backward look threaded his way off the dance-floor.

There were two other couples that Teal knew at the bar, and they got into a ribald discussion on senate reform. An hour later when he and Deirdre went back to the ballroom, there was no sign of Nick and Julie.

They've gone to his place, Teal thought viciously, and wondered why in God's name it mattered to him. Almost as though she'd read his mind Deirdre said, 'Why don't we go to my apartment for a nightcap, Teal? I've just about had enough of this.' So he wouldn't mistake her meaning, she traced his lower lip with her finger, her eyes a mingling of mockery and seduction.

He removed her hand. 'I'm not into casual sex, Deirdre.'

'It's the only kind worth having.'

'Not for me . . . sorry.'

'I could change your mind.'

He gave her a smile every bit as mocking as her own. 'Haven't you heard that no means no?'

'What a liberated man you are, Teal,' she responded, with no intent to flatter. 'Tell the truth—if I were Julie Ferris, no would mean yes. Because you'd rather be standing in Nick's shoes than your own right now. Not that I can imagine Nick's still wearing his shoes.'

Teal felt a surge of pure fury. Battling it down, he said, 'I'll take you home.' And I won't go out with you again, he thought. Thank you very much.

Fifteen minutes later, having left Deirdre in the lobby of her apartment building, he drove past Julie's bungalow. There was a light on in the living-room and her car was the only one parked in the driveway. So he was right. She wouldn't risk Danny waking up. She'd conduct her affairs elsewhere, with discretion.

He sent the sitter home in a cab, poured himself a brandy and scowled at the antics of the Harlem Globetrotters on the television. Maybe Deirdre was right. Casual sex was the only kind worth having.

It would beat sitting here trying not to think about Julie Ferris.

A week later Julie finally took herself over to Dartmouth to see the film she'd refused to go and see with Wayne. She'd been shopping with Danny earlier in the day, had arranged a sitter for eight-fifteen, and got to the mall with twenty minutes to spare. The theater was inside the mall. There was a line-up for tickets, because several movies were playing at the same time. She got behind two young men in neon-tinted T-shirts and fumbled for her money, rather pleased with herself that she had come on her own.

Someone jostled her arm. As she looked up, surprised, the boy in the fluorescent green shirt, who had close-set eyes of an indeterminate shade of gray, said, 'Hey, babe, where's your date?'

'I don't have one,' she said shortly, and closed her purse.

The second one, whose T-shirt logo should have been banned for obscenity, laughed coarsely. 'There's two of us; we'll look after you,' he said, and added something that in crudity far surpassed the message on his shirt.

Neither of them was a day over seventeen. But they were taller than she, seething with unfocussed energy and smelling strongly of beer; Julie smothered her temper and turned her head away.

'Sure,' said the first one, 'we'll sit with you, won't we, Hank? Keep you company. Who wants to be alone on a Saturday night?'

'I do,' said Julie.

'Which movie you going to?' Hank asked, and grabbed for her elbow, his knuckles brushing her breast.

He had done it on purpose. Utterly furious, because the last thing she wanted was to be ogled by two young men in the combined thrall of alcohol and hormones, Julie said, 'Let me alone—or I'll have you thrown out of the theater.'

Hank straightened. 'You and who else?' he sneered.

'How about me?' said a voice behind Julie.

She whirled, knowing exactly who she was going to see. Teal Carruthers was standing on the fringe of the queue dressed in a faded denim shirt and jeans. He wasn't looking at her; his gaze was trained on Hank, and something in his stance kept Hank silent. Teal's energy was both contained and focussed, Julie thought uncertainly, and he looked ten times more dangerous than Hank.

Teal said evenly, 'You can shut up and leave her alone. Or you can leave the line-up—which is it to be?'

'Man, we were only kidding,' Hank's companion said uneasily. 'We weren't——'

'It didn't look that way to me,' Teal interrupted. 'Make your minds up.'

Hank, like most bullies, had finely tuned antennae for those stronger than himself. 'We weren't really planning to sit with her; we were only having a little fun.'

'I'd suggest you keep your sense of humor to yourself from now on,' Teal said.

'We'll leave her alone,' Hank answered sulkily.

As the two boys turned their backs, the line inched forward, and Julie said with a noticeable lack of sincerity, 'Thank you. Now you'd better go back to your date.'

'Haven't got one.'

So he wasn't here with Deirdre Reid. 'Goodness,' Julie said sweetly, 'is your phone out of order?'

'Not that I'm aware of. Has Einstein knocked yours off the hook?'

'*I* was endeavouring to have a quiet Saturday night without being hassled by anyone. Which includes you.'

'Rescuing you is getting to be a habit,' Teal responded. 'You're a walking trouble zone.'

'Are you insinuating I'm responsible for what just happened?' Julie blazed.

Unwisely Teal spoke the exact truth. 'You're very beautiful when you're in a rage,' he said.

'Oh!' she exclaimed between gritted teeth. 'I can't *stand* men! In particular I can't stand you. Go away!'

Discovering that he was thoroughly enjoying himself, and that it was going to have to be an exceedingly good movie to beat the pre-movie entertainment, Teal said, 'I've lost my place in the line by now.'

'You think you're pretty clever, don't you?'

'I came here to be on my own, too,' he said mildly, and watched her assess that piece of information.

'Don't tell me you can't stand women—I won't believe you.'

'But I'm supposed to believe you when you say you can't stand men? I'd hate to find you guilty of sexism, Julie.'

'You're a fine one to talk about sexism—accusing me of promiscuity just because I was dancing with Nick!' Not until she actually spoke did Julie realize how much that remark had rankled.

Ahead of her Hank and his cohort were buying their tickets; they were going to the latest horror film. Julie bought her own ticket and with a strange sense of fatalism heard Teal ask for the same movie. As they walked past the usher and into the lobby, she said, glaring at him, 'I suggest we sit at opposite ends of the theater.'

Teal thrust his hands in his pockets. 'I have no real evidence that you're promiscuous. I shouldn't have said that—I'm sorry.'

It was, in Julie's opinion, a fairly minimal apology. 'So why did you?' she demanded.

'I've said I'm sorry, Julie.'

She bit her lip. 'All right,' she said grudgingly. 'Just don't do it again.'

'So do you really want us to sit at opposite ends of the theater?'

If she was smart she'd say yes. She looked straight into his guarded gray eyes and said, knowing this was important, 'You haven't answered my question—whether

I'm responsible for the behavior of those two louts. I don't like being called a trouble zone, Teal. *I'm* not the cause of the trouble. Look at me—you can't say I'm dressed as if I'm looking for trouble.'

Her jeans, while slim-fitting, were not tight; her white shirt was tailored, her hair pulled back with a plain velvet ribbon. Teal looked at the full curve of her lip and the push of her breasts against the white cotton and said, 'It wouldn't matter what you wore, Julie—you've got that indefinable something called sex appeal. You're loaded with it. Any man who doesn't have one foot in the coffin and the other on a banana peel is going to react.'

She frowned at him. 'So it *is* my fault.'

'Of course it's not—I'm explaining, not excusing. I've handled enough rape cases not to buy the line that says the woman asked for it and the man's not responsible for his actions. It stinks.'

'I see,' said Julie, looking at him through narrowed eyes. 'If you really believe what you just said, I'm delighted—the justice system needs more like you. But if not, then I've caught you out. Because—to use your own logic—Nick's being a womanizer doesn't automatically make me promiscuous.'

'I should never have said that, okay? And that's the last apology you're getting!'

The turbulence in his eyes was having a most peculiar effect on her. 'If I've got sex appeal,' she said recklessly, 'so have you. Tons of it. Truckloads of it. And don't pretend I'm the first woman to tell you so.'

Marylee had used the word sexy; but she'd meant the same thing. Teal said smoothly, 'Then maybe we should sit together for our mutual protection,' and watched the first hint of laughter glint in Julie's face. Like a tiny explosion in his brain he felt an idea spring to life.

'Only if you like popcorn,' she replied.

'You mean I have to admit to all my addictions in order to sit with you?'

This time she laughed outright. 'Two large buttered popcorn coming up,' she said and led the way to the counter.

Her bottom swung entrancingly in the jeans. It's a lousy idea, Teal told himself, and pulled his wallet out. She paid for the popcorn and he for two Cokes; they found their seats in the theater and almost immediately the lights dimmed. The film absorbed Julie instantly and she gave herself over to its intriguing tale. Fortunately Teal, like she, liked to sit through the credits at the end.

As they left the theater, she said inadequately, 'Well...I really need to talk about that. Want to go for a coffee?'

Her face was bemused, and her thoughts obviously not on him. 'Sure,' said Teal, and led the way to a little restaurant further down the mall.

Her observations were acute and more emotional than his; but she listened carefully to what he had to say, sometimes arguing, sometimes agreeing. He found himself liking her, and pushing the feeling down. He didn't want to like her; it would complicate his idea. While it was a very interesting idea, if he were sensible he'd go home and think about it before suggesting it to her.

As the waitress refilled their cups, he said abruptly, 'Julie, I've got a proposition for you.'

She glanced up, her smoke-blue eyes suddenly hostile. 'No, thanks. I get too many propositions—that's why I was going to the movies on my own.'

So much for liking her. 'I'm not Nick,' he rapped.

'Then don't behave like him!'

Teal wrapped his hands around his coffee-mug, trying to calm down. Why did he let her get under his skin so easily? Normally he thought of himself as an even-tempered man. 'I was using "proposition" in the legal sense,' he said. 'A plan, a project, a business undertaking. No sexual innuendoes. I hadn't realized how sensitive you were—I should have said I've got an idea.'

'I'm quite able to cope with words over two syllables, thank you! And I would have thought after what happened in the line-up that you might have understood my so-called sensitivity,' Julie rejoined, and watched his hand tighten around his mug.

Teal gulped down some coffee to give himself time to think. He hadn't even said what his idea was and already she was in a temper. Oh, well, he might as well go the whole hog. 'There's something I need to know first,' he said. 'Whether you're having an affair with Nick.'

'The worst womanizer in the hospital? You sure know how to pour on the flattery.'

'Yes or no will do,' Teal said, and something in his eyes caused hers to drop.

'No,' she said. 'I'm not into affairs. With Wayne or with Morse or with Nick.' Or with you, she added silently.

Teal wanted very badly to believe her. 'You mean you didn't go to bed with him after the dance?'

'Teal, what is this? You don't have the right to pry into my private life. I'm not asking if you've ever gone to bed with Deirdre Reid.'

'I haven't. She's into casual sex and I'm not.'

Somehow Teal's honesty seemed to call up an answering honesty in Julie—part of which was admitting to herself how glad she was that Teal wasn't involved with Dr Deirdre Reid. 'I did not go to bed with Nick the night of the dance,' she declaimed, 'I have never gone to bed with him, and I see no reason why I should ever want to.'

This time Teal believed her—and felt a strange lightness in his chest. Making a valiant effort to get back on track, he said, 'I'm not into affairs either, Julie, and I know I'm not explaining myself well. But I'm getting the impression that a lot of men are chasing you and you're not exactly delighted by that...am I right?'

'You couldn't be more right.'

'I spend a hell of a lot of energy keeping a bunch of women at bay who think I need a wife, a mother for Scott or a mistress on the side. You know what we should do?'

'No,' she said warily.

'We should join forces—start going out together. Get the word out that we're a couple. Then the men would leave you alone and the women would quit chasing me.'

He was smiling at her as though he'd solved all the world's problems. 'You're crazy,' she said.

'Think about it for a minute. Some guy puts the make on you...Sorry buddy, you can say, I'm already taken. A woman calls me up... No can do; I have a committed relationship with someone else.'

He was serious, she thought incredulously. 'I couldn't even begin to think of doing that.'

'Why not? And make it good.'

'Well, to start with, we scarcely know each other.'

'A couple of dates will fix that.'

'Oh, sure...in the most superficial way.'

'Superficial is what I'm talking about, Julie,' Warming to his idea, he added, 'Another thing each of us could do is write up a brief autobiography. Age, place of birth, names of sisters and brothers, that kind of thing. Just so we wouldn't disgrace ourselves when we're with other people.'

'We're not talking about applying for a passport,' Julie said, exasperated. 'This is about being a couple. About having a relationship.'

'Only in the outward sense. Only so that people will leave us alone.'

She was beginning to get his drift—and was not at all sure that she cared for it. 'We can't do it—we don't like each other,' she said triumphantly.

'All the better—this is a business arrangement. Sensible. Rational. The last thing we need is for feelings to get in the way.'

She remembered her first sight of him, standing in her kitchen in his pin-striped suit, unsmiling, critical, crushingly formal. Her nerves on edge, she said, 'I'm not sure you have any feelings.'

A muscle clenched in Teal's jaw. 'My feelings—or lack of them—are not what this is about. This is for convenience. So we can get on with the rest of our lives.' As the waitress brought the bill, he picked it up. 'I can see you don't like the idea. Let's just drop it, then. Do you need a drive home?'

He had given her a perfect opening to say goodnight and be on her way. She said curiously, 'How long would you propose this—this arrangement would last?'

'Until you decide you want another husband. Or I decide I want a wife.'

'For me, that could be a very long time,' Julie said; she heard the raw hurt underlying her words and could have bitten off her tongue.

'For me, too,' Teal said.

His lips were tight-held, his gaze turned inward. Impulsively she rested her hand on his. 'I shouldn't have said that about feelings—you've been hurt too, haven't you?'

He snatched his hand back. 'Let's get something straight. This game-plan of mine is just that—a game. On the surface, for appearances only. I don't want you prying into my life any more than you want me prying into yours.'

Her voice rising, she demanded, 'So what will we talk about when we're together? The weather? The day's headlines?'

Creasing the bill between his fingers, feeling his own temper rise that she could be so obdurate, Teal said, 'We wouldn't have to be together that much. Halifax is a small city where everyone's somebody else's cousin—it wouldn't take long to get the word around. We'd have to go to a few public places together and tell our friends and acquaintances that we're a couple. After that, we could relax. The occasional date would do it.'

Why was she even considering an arrangement so cold-blooded, so essentially deceitful? 'We couldn't possibly do this—what about the boys? They'd probably think we were going to get married.'

'Oh, we'd have to tell them the truth. Or a version of the truth. That we're friends and we're trying to make life a little easier for each other. They'd be fine with that. Scott hates it when my dates try and mother him.'

Danny had disliked Wayne on sight. 'What if either of us does meet someone else? Someone we do want to get involved with?'

'We'll end it. Simple.'

'It sounds so calculated,' she muttered. 'Utilitarian. Like we're a couple of robots.'

'It is calculated and utilitarian—that's the whole point. We're using each other to simplify our respective lives.'

She looked at him moodily. 'And what would the house rules be?'

'No prying into each other's past. No dating anyone else for the duration of the agreement.'

'What about sex?' she said bluntly.

Her fingernails were rhythmically tapping the plastic table and she looked about as friendly as Einstein the cat. Letting his anger show, Teal replied, 'This isn't just an elaborate ruse to get you into my bed.'

'You're the one who said I was loaded with sex appeal...how do I know I can trust you?'

Something approaching a smile lessened the tension in his face. 'You said the same of me.'

But for Julie this had gone beyond joking. 'Men take one look at me and think I'm up for grabs. Literally. But I'm not, Teal. I got so I hated sex in my marriage. The best thing it gave me was Danny, and the last thing I want is an affair. Is that clear?'

Her honesty, as always, exhilarated him. But he could in no way match it; the pain was too deep and he was too unused to speaking about his feelings. 'You'll be in no danger from me,' he said shortly.

The cold-eyed lawyer was very much in evidence. Julie said thoughtfully, 'Because you don't like me?'

'That's one reason,' Teal said, and was glad he wasn't under oath. 'The rest's none of your business.'

She should, perhaps, feel angry with him; she did not. 'I've got another rule,' she rejoined. 'Freedom to re-negotiate or end the arrangement at any time.'

'I think we should commit ourselves to at least three months,' he argued. 'Just to give it time to work.'

'That's the whole summer!'

The dismay on her face annoyed Teal immoderately. 'It's not a life sentence,' he said.

'It sounds like one—because we'd be acting the whole time. Pretending to be something we're not. I loathe falsity!' The words came out more vehemently than Julie had intended. But she couldn't retract them because they were true.

'Are your other dates any less false than our agreement would be?' As she winced, remembering the surgeon with the yacht, Teal said shrewdly, 'I thought not.'

She looked at him in silence. If she really hated falsity, why hadn't she left five minutes ago? Perhaps, under the skin, she was like all the other women: intrigued by Teal's paradoxical blend of magnetism and control.

'There's one more rule,' Teal said solemnly. 'No more than one container of buttered popcorn per day.'

'Each?' she quipped.

'Of course,' he said, and watched as a reluctant smile tilted her lips. 'Are we on, Julie?' he added, and held out his hand across the table.

'I must be crazy even to be considering it,' she said, keeping her hands in her lap.

'Am I that repugnant?'

'Don't fish for compliments,' she said trenchantly. 'You can get those from all your other women.'

'If you agree to this, I won't have any other women.'

Nor would she be dating men who seemed to think that the price of a meal was an invitation to maul her. Brightening, she said, 'I suppose we could look on it as a vacation.'

He was still holding out his hand. 'My arm's getting tired,' he said.

'I'm out of my mind,' Julie said, and shook his hand.

Her fingers were warm, with unexpected strength; he disliked weak handshakes. 'Good,' he said. 'I'll get a couple of tickets to the symphony benefit that's coming up next weekend—if you're free?' Julie nodded. 'That'll be a good start. Anything going on at the hospital?'

'There's a nurses' reunion at the end of the month; all the staff are invited,' she said faintly.

'Good. I'm adding another rule—you can't dance with Nick.'

'And I'm adding another one—that you can't keep adding to them.' She pushed back her chair. 'Come on, Teal—admit that we're crazy to be doing this.'

A smooth blonde curl had fallen free of its ribbon and was lying on the lightly tanned skin bared by the neckline of her shirt. He was quite sure she was oblivious of it. He said drily, 'A plea of temporary insanity? No way.'

'Huh,' she said, then looked down at her watch and yelped, 'Lord, is that the time? I told the sitter I'd be home ten minutes ago.'

'I'll take you to your car.'

'There's no need——'

'Someone got mugged in this parking lot last April. Don't argue.'

There was something in the set of his jaw that made Julie decide that arguing would be a definite waste of time. She hurried out of the mall, Teal at her side. When they got to her car, she unlocked the door, slid into her seat and said demurely, 'You're going to have your work cut out to make our first proper date as interesting as this one. Goodnight.'

'I'll do my best,' he said. 'And I'll call you tomorrow about the symphony. 'Night, Julie.'

His fingers were hooked in his belt, which was at eye level. 'I go to work at seven-thirty in the evening,' she mumbled, and backed her car out. One of the rules of this ridiculous game they'd agreed to play was no sex, and she had told the truth about her and Robert; why then were her palms damp and her mouth dry? And why was the thought of a symphony benefit filling her with such a complicated and unsettling mixture of excitement and dread?

Crazy. Insane. Deranged.

She was all three. She had to be to have agreed to Teal Carruthers' proposition.

CHAPTER FOUR

AFTER lunch on Monday Scott went to join Danny at the playground across the street. Teal had brought papers home from the office because Mrs Inkpen was on holiday, and headed for his study to work on his next case. He had phoned Julie yesterday to tell her he had two tickets to the symphony benefit. She had sounded very formal on the telephone; he had purposely not asked how she felt about their arrangement now that she'd had the chance to sleep on it. He'd have to remember to take his tuxedo to the drycleaners tomorrow.

He was absorbed in the complexities of the DNA evidence the police were presenting when he heard his son yell his name, a note in his voice that made Teal drop the sheaf of papers on the desk and take the stairs two at a time.

There were three people standing in his kitchen: Scott, Danny and a girl he had never seen before. Scott had dirt all over his face and a scrape on his chin, Danny had a black eye, a bloody nose and a cut lip, and the girl, who looked about fifteen, was crying. 'What happened?' Teal said economically.

'We were at the playground,' Scott burst out, 'and these kids from grade six were there; they picked a fight with us, and by the time Sally got there Danny had a black eye.'

'I'm Danny's sitter,' Sally sniffled. 'I was talking to my boyfriend and I didn't realize the boys were fighting. Mrs Ferris is going to be some mad at me.'

Teal knelt in front of Danny, assessing the damage. 'What was the fight about?'

'They said I was pretty,' Danny said, scowling ferociously and looking as far from tears as it was possible to look. 'They called me "pretty boy" and "mama's boy" and other stuff I didn't understand. They said stuff about Mum, too. So I punched one of them and then there was a big fight.'

'They were being very ignorant,' Teal said matter-of-factly, well able to imagine what the boys might have said and thinking it was just as well Danny hadn't understood it. 'I'll put some ice on your eye and your lip and wash your face, and you'll feel a whole lot better.'

'You gotta teach Danny how to fight,' Scott said excitedly. 'He doesn't know how.'

'I do so!' Danny said.

'I was fighting too, and I'm not all beat up like you,' Scott said unarguably.

'I punched the big guy real hard.'

'Okay, okay,' Teal interposed, hiding a smile as he tipped the contents of an ice tray on a clean towel. 'No point in starting another fight here in the kitchen. I could show you some useful defensive moves, Danny, that can keep you from being hurt, that's what Scott means . . . hold still now; this might sting.'

The damage was not as bad as it looked. But Teal made the boys sit down with milk and cookies after they were cleaned up, and directed Sally to the bathroom to wash her face. 'Where's your mother, Danny?' he said.

'Asleep. She worked last night and she goes to work again tonight. That's why Sally took me to the playground.'

As Sally came back in the room Teal said, 'I'll look after the boys for the rest of the day if you want to go home, Sally.'

But Sally had passed from tearfulness to a sense of duty. 'Mrs Ferris said I was to wake her up if anything happened,' she said righteously. 'So I'll have to take Danny home right now and tell her about the fight.'

'I'll go with you,' Teal said.

'Why, Dad?' Scott asked, big-eyed.

'To see if she wants me to give Danny some lessons in self-defense,' Teal answered promptly, and wondered if that was the only reason.

The stucco bungalow drowsed in the heat. But something was different, Teal thought, puzzled. The flowers, that was it. The garden was a patchwork of color, pinks and purples and reds and yellows in sprawling confusion. He found himself grinning without being sure why as he followed Sally in the back door.

Einstein, who was lying on the windowsill in the sun, gave him a dirty look. Same to you, thought Teal, still grinning, and realized he was intensely curious to see Julie again.

Sally disappeared. Then there was a flurry of footsteps on the stairs and Julie rushed in the kitchen. Her eyes flew to her son's battered face. 'Oh, Danny...sweetheart,' she said in a voice Teal had not heard her use before, and dropped to her knees in front of him.

Her hair was a glorious tangle around her face, and the silk floral robe she had wrapped around her body was already slipping, revealing a thin-strapped chemise in palest blue that clung to her breasts. 'What were you fighting for?' she gasped. 'You know I told you you mustn't fight. There's blood all over your shirt, Danny.'

'I got a real good punch in,' Danny said, speaking lop-sidedly because of his cut lip.

'I *hate* fighting,' his mother pronounced.

Teal cleared his throat. As Julie looked up he watched her eyes widen with shock. 'What are *you* doing here?' she demanded, scrambling to her feet with less than her usual grace and hastily tightening the belt of her robe.

'They came to my house first,' Teal said. 'It's closer to the playground. I put ice on his eye and his lip.'

'Oh,' said Julie. She felt fogged with tiredness, her lids heavy, her body craving sleep. She added belatedly, 'Thanks.'

'I also suggested he needs lessons in the art of self-defense.'

'That's the last thing he needs,' Julie said fractiously.

'You're not hearing me,' Teal replied with a blandness that irritated her out of all proportion. 'I said defense, not offense.'

'It's all fighting!'

'Scott was in the same fight and didn't get a black eye or a cut lip.' Teal quirked his brow. 'I rest my case.'

Why did she always feel at such a disadvantage with Teal? Julie wondered. Right now she was acutely aware that her gown barely skimmed her knees and that her first instinctive emotion on seeing him had been pure pleasure. Furious with herself as much as with him, she snapped, 'Why do men always think that a short course in violence will fix everything?'

Teal's mouth tightened. 'I'm not *men*—don't stereotype me. And I'm a lawyer, not a boxer. There's violence out there in the world, Julie Ferris; you know that as well as I do. I've never taught Scott to instigate it. But as a responsible parent I think it's my duty to equip him to deal with it. To protect himself when the need arises.'

Glancing down, he saw that their two sons were following every word. He said calmly, 'Sally, why don't you take the boys outside for a few minutes? Mrs Ferris and I need to discuss this in private.'

Sally gave him a bedazzled smile. 'Sure,' she said.

No sooner had the screen shut behind them than Julie fumed, 'You've got a nerve, giving my sitter orders in my own kitchen.'

Her cheeks were pale and her eyes blue-shadowed. Teal said, 'You look tired out.'

'Don't change the subject!'

She wasn't weeping, like Janine, and she certainly wasn't agreeing with every word he said, like Carole. She looked, if anything, ready to throttle him. He said casually, 'I'd like to take the boys home with me. I'm going to barbecue hamburgers around five—you could join us after you've slept again, and I'll show you what I've taught Scott. How about it, Julie?'

She looked him straight in the eye. 'What were they fighting about, do you know?'

It never occurred to him to fob her off with half-truths: this was a woman who wanted the whole truth and nothing but the truth. 'They called Danny a pretty boy and some other things that fortunately passed over his head... but I gather he didn't wade in with both fists flying until they insulted you.'

She ran her fingers through her hair, her shoulders slumped. 'Oh, damn,' she said.

Deliberately probing, Teal said, 'Maybe you'd rather Danny's father took him in hand as far as fighting's concerned?'

'He almost never sees him,' she said absently. She had withdrawn into herself, picking at a nick in the edge of the counter with her fingernail, her pose entirely un-provocative. But under the shiny pink roses on her robe he could see the agitated rise and fall of her breast and the curve of her hip; he was all too aware that they were alone in the house.

'Go back to bed,' he said harshly. 'I'll look after Danny, and you can come for supper at five.'

'I can't watch him all day,' she blurted with a touch of desperation. 'When I work nights, I have to get some sleep.'

'When I'm at the office or in court, I'm not with Scott—same thing, Julie.'

'You're telling me I shouldn't feel guilty, aren't you?' She sighed, crossing her arms over her breasts. 'I shouldn't, you're right. But I do. Anyway, there's no need for you to invite me and Danny for supper.'

'I already have.'

She gave him a hostile look. He was wearing navy sweatpants and a loose T-shirt, ordinary clothes that made her acutely conscious of the body beneath them. 'It's not in the agreement that we have meals together,' she announced. 'What's the point, after all? There's no one there to see us—unless the women who've been chasing you spy on your back garden with binoculars.'

Teal leaned against the counter, realizing that once again he was enjoying himself. 'You've got a mean tongue on you.'

'All the more reason for me to stay home.'

'The invitation has nothing to do with our agreement. I can show Danny a few moves and then we'll demonstrate what he's learned. I'm sure he'd love you to be there. After all, you are his mother.'

'A moment ago you said I shouldn't feel guilty and now you're trying to motivate me by guilt—do lawyers always play dirty?'

'Do I detect a certain prejudice against my profession?'

'Not prejudice. Outright dislike.'

He laughed and walked over to her. Julie held her ground, every nerve tense. Lifting her chin with one finger, he gave her a crooked smile. 'Go back to bed and set your alarm for quarter to five...I'll see you at five. I don't do desserts.'

'So it's my chocolate-fudge cookies you want, not me.'

'You got it.'

Teal dropped his hand to his side. Her skin was as silky as her robe, and she smelled faintly of flowers. But he didn't want her. Of course he didn't. That would be totally counter to their agreement. 'See you later—and lock the door behind me.'

Grimacing, Julie did as she was told. Crazy was exactly the word to describe her behavior as far as Teal Carruthers and his famous agreement were concerned.

Sharp at five Julie walked up the driveway of Teal's house. By following the delicious smell of roasting chicken, she located the gas barbecue on the back deck. The garden was a wild tangle of shrubbery and over-grown perennials that made her efforts in Mrs LeMarchant's garden look like those of a rank amateur. There was no one in sight.

She pushed open the patio doors and stepped inside, calling Teal's name. The room was large and airy, with off-white walls and a pale gray chesterfield set. The only pictures were black and white photographs, and the sole notes of color a couple of magazines lying on a glass coffee-table. Next time she came—if there was a next time—she'd bring a big bunch of petunias, she decided, standing near the hall door and stroking the un-doubtedly expensive fabric on one of the wing chairs. Even a few nasturtiums would help.

From upstairs Danny gave a shriek of laughter, Scott yelled a warning, and footsteps hurtled down the stairs.

Before she could move, the door was thrust open and a body ran headlong into her. She was flung against the arm of the chair. The chair slid sideways across the carpet, dumping her flat on her back on the soft gray pile. A weight was crushing her chest, a weight that was warm and hard and smelled faintly of sweat. She looked up.

Teal's face was only inches from hers. He was naked to the waist, his body hair rough against her arm, the breadth of his shoulders blocking out the rest of the room. One of his knees had jammed itself between her thighs. The heat of his skin seeped through her cotton dress and burned into her palms, which were trapped against the corded muscles of his belly.

For a brief, searing moment she was thrown backwards in time to the early days of her marriage to Robert, when he had seemed to want her as much as she had wanted him, and when she had been happy. Deep within her, like an animal that had been long asleep, desire uncurled itself and stirred to life.

Teal lifted himself on his elbows and said flatly, 'God, Julie—did I hurt you?'

Making as much noise as a dozen small boys, Scott and Danny burst into the room, swinging on the door. 'What're you doing on the floor, Dad?' Scott asked with interest.

'Why's my mum underneath?' Danny added.

Hot color flooded Julie's cheeks. Bad enough that for a wild moment she had wanted to wrap her arms around Teal's neck and pull him back down to kiss her. Worse that their two sons should find them gazing into each other's eyes on the living-room carpet.

'I knocked her down,' Teal said in the same flat voice. 'By accident—I didn't know she was there. Are you okay, Julie?'

'I'm fine,' she muttered. It was a good thing she wasn't hooked to a lie detector; she was about as far from fine as she could be.

Then Teal got to his feet, taking her by the hands and pulling her up with him, so that she found herself standing entirely too close to a very impressive set of chest muscles. He was wearing the same navy sweatpants and nothing else. She yanked her hands free and said in a rush, 'I called your name but I guess you didn't hear me.'

A muscle was twitching in his jaw, and his gray eyes were as opaque as storm clouds. 'I'm sorry,' he said, 'really sorry...Scott, will you and Danny wipe off the picnic table while I check the barbecue?'

As the boys raced across the carpet and disappeared, Teal headed after them. His hair was tousled, his spine a long indentation from his nape to the elastic on his sweatpants, and he moved with a lithe grace. This time Julie's desire was not the gradual uncurling of an animal from its winter den, cautious and slow, but rather a great leap, like a tiger springing from its cage. A wild and unruly tiger, roaming free in search of its mate.

Shaken to the roots of her being, she stood still. And in her brain a small voice screamed, over and over again, No, no, no...

Dimly she heard the clatter of the barbecue tools as Teal turned the chicken on the rack. I've got to calm down, she thought frantically. I can't afford to feel like this. Not with Teal. Especially not with Teal.

Then the patio door slid open and he was standing in front of her again. Say something, Julie, she told herself. Act normally, as though nothing's happened.

He took her by the arm, his gray eyes full of concern. 'I hurt you, didn't I? You'd better sit down; you don't look so hot.'

His choice of words brought a bubble of hysterical laughter to Julie's lips. She choked it back. There was a dusting of dark hair over his breastbone, and a small white scar notched the curve of his topmost rib: intimate details that made her shiver with awareness. 'I'm all right,' she mumbled. 'You took me by surprise, that's all.'

And that's the truth, she thought, with another uprising of laughter.

Teal steered her over to the chesterfield and pushed her down on it. 'I'll pour you a drink. Stay put.'

She pulled the hem of her dress down over her knees. It was a pretty dress, with little flowers scattered over a thin cotton that molded her breasts and fell loosely to mid-calf. She should have worn something in heavy linen with long sleeves and a high collar, she thought, leaning her head back and closing her eyes. Like a nun's habit. Then a small body jumped on the chesterfield beside her, and Danny said, 'You all right, Mum?'

She smiled at him, rubbing her chin on the top of his head. 'Fine...how did you like your lessons?'

'Neat!' he crowed. 'Hey, Scott, come show my mum what we were doing.'

As the two boys started sparring in front of her, Teal came back in the room. After putting her drink on the coffee-table, he adjusted the set of Danny's shoulders, then demonstrated some fast footwork. Scott yelled encouragement. Teal jabbed a fist at him, Scott dodged with the ease of long practice, and suddenly all three of them were rolling around on the floor at her feet, Teal laughing breathlessly as the boys tried to tickle his ribs.

Julie clutched the glass to her chest, where a pain had lodged itself, sharp as a knife. Robert had never lost his dignity enough to fool around on the floor with his son. Never. As Danny butted his blond curls into Teal's armpit and Teal automatically put a protective arm around him, the pain spread. Danny needed what Teal was giving him. Needed it as much as he needed food and a roof over his head and his mother's love.

But this is only an arrangement between Teal and me, she thought numbly. An arrangement that might not last beyond three months. And then what?

She took a big gulp of rum and Coke, and followed it with another. Teal hauled himself upright, a boy clinging to each arm. His sweatpants had been dragged low over one hip; dark hair curled to his navel. Julie looked the other way and took another hefty swallow.

'The chicken must be ready by now,' Teal gasped. 'If you guys want to eat, you'd better treat the cook with more respect. Do you want to get the salad, Scott? And you could bring in the rolls, Danny.'

Danny gave him a gap-toothed grin. 'Sure,' he said, and raced after Scott.

'Bring your drink out on the deck, Julie,' Teal suggested, hitching at his waistband and trying to comb his hair into order. Then his gaze sharpened. 'What's wrong?'

'Nothing!'

He looked at her soberly, his gray eyes as clear as rainwater. 'I guess I've already come to count on your honesty—and that's not an honest answer.'

She stood up, tilting her chin. 'Our arrangement, you said, was to be superficial and convenient. Honesty and superficiality make strange bedfellows...you can't always have both.'

His lips compressed; he didn't like her reply one bit. 'Are you calling me a fool?'

'Myself, more likely,' she said, and deliberately changed the subject. 'How's the chicken? I'm starving.'

Although if I'm to be honest it's not for food, she thought, and strove to keep from blushing.

While he was sure something was wrong, Teal had no idea what it was. And it was pretty clear that Julie had no intention of telling him. He turned away, going out on the deck to check the barbecue one more time, sensing through every nerve-ending when she followed him. 'It's ready,' he said briefly. 'Pass me those plates, would you, Julie?'

They ate on a wooden picnic table on the deck, in the shade of an old maple tree that housed a family of chickadees. On the surface it was a light-hearted picnic. But all through the meal Julie was aware of Teal watching her, his expression inscrutable. She had no idea what he was thinking, and could only hope that he, equally, could not read her thoughts.

After they had eaten, the boys went inside to watch their favorite cartoon show on television. Julie sipped her coffee and said casually, 'Great flavour.'

'Java blend—I get it at the local delicatessen. We'll have to go there sometime; the owner's always trying to match me up with one of his four daughters.' He lifted his head. 'Now what are the boys squabbling about?'

Julie got up. 'I'll have to take Danny home soon anyway.'

She went inside, Teal close on her heels. The television was in a smaller room leading off the living-room. Even as she crossed the all too familiar gray carpet, she heard Danny say shrilly, 'He *is* my father!'

'Sure thing,' Scott replied with heavy sarcasm. 'Every kid on the block's got a father who's on TV.'

'He's an actor; that's why he's on TV!'

She pushed the door open, knowing what she was going to see, already hearing Robert's deep, beautifully modulated voice scrape across her nerves. A man and woman were sharing the screen, a tall, handsome man and a black-haired beauty; she stopped dead in her tracks. It was Robert. Robert and Melissa. Striving to sound natural, she said, 'That is Danny's father, Scott. His father and his stepmother.'

Danny, she saw, was on the verge of tears. She pulled him to her. 'I watched that play one night after you were in bed, Danny. Your dad won an award for it.'

'Robert Ferris,' Teal said quietly. 'I never made the connection.'

'No reason why you should,' Julie said coldly, rubbing at the tension in her son's shoulders.

'He's a fine actor.'

'Oh, yes,' she said, fighting to keep the irony from her voice, 'he's a very fine actor.'

Scott muttered, 'You're lucky, Danny—you got a famous father.'

Julie said steadily, 'There's a cost to being famous, Scott. You don't have a lot of time to spend at home, for instance. You don't have time for barbecues and teaching your son how to fight—because you're always off doing the things that make you famous.'

She could see Scott struggling to digest this, and from the corner of her eye saw Robert take Melissa in his arms and kiss her. Danny said, his voice quivering, 'Let's watch cartoons, Scott.'

'Okay,' said Scott. 'You can have my cars to play with while we watch.'

As Danny pulled free of his mother, Teal took her by the elbow. 'They'll be all right now,' he said. 'I'll pour you a fresh coffee.'

Julie didn't want coffee. She wanted to put her head down on the table and cry her eyes out. She shook her arm free and went back outside, the shadows from the leaves criss-crossing her face as she sat down.

'Teal,' she said abruptly, 'I can't go on with this arrangement of ours. I was silly even to consider it. I want to end it now before it really begins. Before we tell the boys.'

When he sat down across from her, the same shadows drifted lazily over his bare shoulders. She averted her eyes. He said evenly, 'Tell me what's going on.'

Oh, no, she thought, I'm not going to do that. 'I can't operate at a superficial level,' she said. 'We're not a lawyer and a witness in a courtroom, communicating in questions and answers. We're people, dammit! Living, breathing people. Or at least I am. Danny is. Scott is.' In a rush she finished, 'And I'm afraid Danny will get too fond of you if we keep on seeing each other.'

'This all started because Danny and Scott were friends,' Teal rejoined in a hard voice. 'If they're friends, Danny's going to be around me and Scott around you. That's got nothing to do with the two of us going out on a few dates, and you know it.'

'It's selfish and irresponsible.' She glared at him across the table. 'Only someone totally out of touch with his feelings could have come up with such a hare-brained scheme.'

'You seem to be forgetting that you agreed to it.'

'I've changed my mind.'

'A divorce before there's even been a wedding? So you're a quitter.'

'I'm not! I——'

'You're hyperventilating,' he said. 'Calm down.'

Her hiss of indrawn breath overrode the whispering of the leaves over their heads. Spacing her words, she said, 'I want out.'

'We said we'd give it a minimum of three months. This is less than forty-eight hours. We shook hands on it—it was a contract between us.'

'I didn't sign on the dotted line!'

His eyes narrowed. 'Why don't you tell me the truth about what's going on here?'

'I *am* afraid Danny will get too attached to you.'

'You can't legislate that,' Teal said forcibly. 'The same could be true of Scott—he already really likes you. Anyway, I know there's more to this than Scott and Danny. Come clean, Julie.'

'If I tell the truth, you'll think I'm just like the rest of them—all those women who are chasing you,' she said.

Then her eyes widened involuntarily. If she told the truth, he'd run a mile. Of course he would. He'd change his mind faster then Einstein could catch a rat. The beginnings of a smile on her lips, she said, 'All right— you asked for it. It's about sex.'

She had taken Teal by surprise, she could tell. 'You're too much man for me,' she went on crisply. 'When you were lying on top of me half naked, I wanted you to stay there.'

The wind moved softly through the trees and the birds chattered overhead. Teal sat still, his coffee untouched in front of him. Whatever he had expected, it had not been this. 'I don't believe you,' he said.

'You're overwhelming, you're gorgeous, you're sexy,' she answered with an impudent grin, feeling much better now that she had the problem out in the open. 'If you don't want me chasing you, you'd better end the agreement right now.'

He reached out and grasped her wrist with a strength that frightened her. 'Don't play games with me—I don't like it.'

Refusing to back down, she said, 'Some men might see the fact that I desire them as a compliment.'

'I'm not "some men"—I keep telling you that.'

Exasperated, she said, 'The rules specified no sex. So the agreement's over.'

'You're confusing the thought with the deed——'

'Oh, do stop talking like a lawyer!'

'I am a lawyer, and I'm damned if I'm going to spend half my time apologizing for that fact! You and I are not going to bed together, believe me. So there's no reason to end the agreement.'

Frowning, Julie said indelicately, 'Do you prefer men?'

'I do not. And I have a clean bill of health, in case that's what you're worrying about.'

'So you really don't have feelings.'

'Don't see me as a challenge, Julie—I won't put up with that.'

'Trying to get you to act like an ordinary man is not a challenge that interests me,' she seethed, and looked down at her watch. 'I've got to go. My shift starts at eight and I like to get there early.'

'Fine. I'm glad we had this discussion; it cleared the air—I now know you find me attractive and we both know we're not going to do anything about it. I'll see you Saturday at the symphony benefit. It's formal, by the way. And maybe one evening this week—say Thursday—we could exchange the autobiographies... that would probably save a lot of trouble.'

His face was expressionless and clearly he took her acquiescence for granted. As Julie felt her adrenaline level rise, she knew she hadn't been overly truthful a moment ago. She did see him as a challenge. Had done since he had first proposed the agreement. It would be exceedingly interesting to get beneath the surface of the man called Teal Carruthers and find out what made him tick.

She remembered his laughter as he'd rolled around on the floor with the boys. She remembered the bite of his fingers in her wrist and the cold anger in his voice. She remembered the heat of his body pressing her into the carpet.

Teal had feelings. She'd be willing to bet on it. What they were, and why he had buried them so deeply, was a mystery she might very easily want to solve.

Which could, of course, just be a different form of craziness.

CHAPTER FIVE

JULIE worked four straight night shifts that week, getting home from the last one on Thursday morning while Danny was still asleep. Because she now had four days off, she stayed up most of the day to get her sleeping patterns back on schedule.

Danny and Scott had both been invited to the same birthday party; when her son had gone, clutching his gift, Julie went out into the garden to do some weeding. The brigadier general was mowing his lawn ruthlessly short, a knotted handkerchief perched on his head. When he saw Julie, he turned off the mower and walked over to the fence. 'Your garden looks very nice,' he puffed, wiping his face. 'Ethelda will be pleased to see so many flowers.'

Ethelda was Mrs LeMarchant. 'Is she coming for a visit?'

'In two weeks,' he beamed. 'I'll be happy to see her, m'dear, I might as well tell you.' Checking that no one was in the vicinity, he leaned further over the fence and lowered his voice confidentially. 'You know, I once proposed to Ethelda—wasn't easy; I'd rather face an enemy battalion than ask a gel to marry me. She turned me down, though.' He gave a philosophical sigh. 'Just as well, I suppose. She never did approve of me going to the legion for a few beers—very strait-laced, Ethelda.'

Julie looked over the fence at his lawn, which was most certainly in apple-pie order. 'That's too bad,' she said. 'I would have thought you were soulmates.'

'We lived next door for nearly twenty years,' he answered wistfully. Then he straightened, tucking in his chin and clicking his heels together as best he could in his disgraceful old Oxfords. 'It's all for the best, no doubt. She didn't like me smoking a pipe, either—kept emptying the ashtray before I had the chance to fill it...ah, you have a guest, m'dear.'

Julie glanced over her shoulder. Teal was striding across the grass toward them. The autobiography, she thought in dismay. They'd agreed to get together tonight, and she'd forgotten all about it. Probably because she didn't want to do it. She smiled at him and quickly made the introductions. Teal put an arm around her shoulders, kissed her on the cheek and said, 'I missed you—seems like a long time since Monday.'

She gaped at him, wondering if he was out of his mind. His lips had been warm on her cheek and the weight of his arm felt altogether wonderful. Then, in peculiar mingling of relief and disappointment, she realized what he was doing. He was giving the general the message that she was taken: the agreement put into action. In swift mischief she laced her arms around his waist and batted her lashes at him. 'I missed you too,' she said.

'Hrrumph,' said the general. 'Must get back to my lawn, m'dear. Good evening to you, Mr Carruthers.'

Under the roar of the mower Teal said, 'Took you a while to catch on.'

'Give me a break—I've been on my feet for twenty-eight hours. And no, I don't have my autobiography done; I forgot all about it.'

Looping his arm around her waist, Teal steered her back to the house. 'Let's go inside; I can't hear myself think with that noise.'

His hip moved against hers as they walked, and she could feel the heat of his arm through her thin cotton shirt. The tiger called desire ripped at her composure and, irritably, as soon as they were out of sight of the general, she pulled free. 'I don't know if I'm up for this; I'm really tired.'

'It won't take long,' Teal said implacably. 'Just a few facts.'

The kitchen was cool, Einstein sprawled belly up on the tiled floor. Julie poured two glasses of iced tea, added slices of lemon and took the sheet of paper Teal was holding out to her. It was a computer printout, which for some reason incensed her. She plunked herself down on one of the stools and tossed the paper on the counter. 'Why don't you just tell me what's in it?'

Teal sat down as well, crunching a piece of ice between his teeth. Her legs—those impossibly long legs—were tanned a light golden colour; she had shucked off her sandals when she had come in the door, and the mud between her toes filled him when an emotion he could not possibly have categorized.

He said, 'I'm thirty-four years old, born in Ontario, an only child. My parents divorced when I was six and had joint custody. I left home—or I suppose I should say homes—when I was seventeen and graduated from law school when I was twenty-four. I was asked to join a top Toronto firm, where I discovered I hated corporate law, and shortly afterwards met Elizabeth. We married, moved to Halifax, and had Scott.' He paused. 'She died two years ago. The rest you know.'

Julie poked at the ice cubes in her glass. They bobbed on the surface with most of their volume hidden, rather like Teal's recital of facts. 'Joint custody was unusual thirty years ago, wasn't it?'

'My parents had never been able to agree on anything. No reason why they should agree on who had custody.'

She licked her finger, then flicked a glance at Teal. 'They both wanted you that much.'

In spite of himself his mouth tightened. 'Yeah,' he said.

'You're lying, Teal.'

He forced himself to calmness. 'Those facts should be all you'll need. I have a couple of cousins in Ontario whom I see occasionally, and I was a champion sculler and chess player at university.'

Both solitary pursuits, she thought, unsurprised. Although the sculling would explain his chest muscles. She said, trusting her intuition, 'Neither of your parents wanted you, did they?'

With brutal force Teal answered, 'Lay off, Julie. This agreement isn't about mutual psychoanalysis and I'll thank you to keep——'

'Everything superficial,' she flashed. 'It's not your fault if your parents didn't want you.'

'—your nose out of my business,' Teal finished with deadly precision. 'Now it's your turn. How old are you? Where were your born?'

'I'll tell you one fact,' Julie said tightly. 'In all my twenty-eight years I have never met a man who makes me as angry as you do.'

His smile was full of mockery. 'That's two facts.'

She got up from her stool, her arms crossed over her chest, and prowled up and down the kitchen, clipping off her words. 'Born on a farm in New Brunswick, parents still living, two older sisters, met Robert while doing my nurses' training in Halifax, married at nineteen, lived on the south shore, had Danny, divorced seven months ago and moved to Halifax. I hope you took notes because I'm not going through it again.'

'And you hated sex.'

'That's not the kind of fact you need. You've got what you need. Goodbye, Teal,' she snapped.

She looked as though she would take considerable pleasure in pouring the jug of iced tea over his head. Mingled with his anger, laughter bubbled in his chest. Knowing that if he were wise he'd head for the door, Teal asked with genuine interest, 'Monday night you said you wanted to go to bed with me—how can you desire someone you don't even like?'

'At the moment my one desire is for you to leave my house!'

He stood up, his muscles uncoiling with easy strength, and for an exhilarating moment forgot logic and caution. One thing was crystal-clear to him: he was not about to obey her. Paraphrasing what she had told him, he said, 'In all my thirty-four years I have never met a woman as beautiful as you.'

He had expected her to blush, or at least look confused. Instead she looked around the kitchen, her brows raised, and remarked, 'Apart from Einstein—who is manifestly uninterested in us—we're quite alone. So if I were you, Teal, I'd save the compliments for the symphony benefit, when we'll have an audience who'll appreciate your winning way with words.'

How long was it since a woman had made him laugh? Too long, Teal thought, and walked closer to her, watching unease dart across her face. 'I need practice,' he drawled.

'Sing my praises in the shower,' she retorted. 'Proclaim my virtues to the mirror when you're shaving. But right now go home.'

Suddenly for Teal the game changed into something very different. Different and far more dangerous. He said, 'That isn't what I need to practise. And I don't like being told what to do.'

'Of course not—because you're into control,' she rejoined. 'Controlling everyone, including yourself. Yourself worst of all.'

'When I want your diagnosis I'll ask for it,' Teal snarled, taking her by the elbows and pulling her toward him. She was taller than Elizabeth and fitted into his arms as if she had been made for him, her breasts brushing his chest with tantalizing softness. Before she had time to react, he took her chin in one hand, lowered his head and kissed her full on the mouth.

He had begun this from some primitive need to assert himself, to let Julie know she couldn't get away with telling him what to do—and found that the warmth of her mouth and the startled rigidity of her body made him instantly lose the very control she had accused him of. His senses swimming, he buried one hand in the silken weight of her hair, caressed the long curve of her waist and hip with the other, and deepened the pressure of his lips on hers.

He wanted her to respond. With every cell in his body he wanted to know that he had that power over her, the most basic power in the world.

And suddenly, to his infinite gratification, she yielded to him, her arms looping around his neck, her lips parting. Dizzy with the sweetness of her mouth and the pliancy of her body, he thrust with his tongue, cupping her face in his palms and kissing her as if there were no tomorrow. Only now. A man and a woman meeting as though for the first time, in that place where nothing else mattered but the beat of blood and the imperious heat of desire.

He wanted her. Wanted her now. Wanted her in——
And here Teal's thoughts stopped short and with agonizing swiftness he plummeted into that cold place of despair where Elizabeth's death had left him. Fool, he

thought savagely. You fool...are you going to let yourself be caught again? Is that what you want?

He pushed Julie away, hearing his breathing rasp in his throat, seeing blank shock obliterate the blur of passion in her smoke-blue irises. 'I shouldn't have done that,' he grated. 'It won't happen again, I swear it won't.'

She staggered a little, grabbing at the counter for support, and even in the midst of a turmoil that was tearing him apart Teal was aware of admiration as he watched her struggle to find words. 'That wasn't practice,' she managed finally. 'That was the real thing.'

She was wrong. Utterly and completely wrong. 'No, it wasn't,' he said offensively. 'It's what happens when I don't take the Deirdre Reids of this world to bed.'

Julie flinched visibly. Her hand made a tiny, telling gesture of distress as she said, 'It's me, isn't it? It happens all the time. There's something about me—my looks, my body—that drives men crazy. But it's nothing to do with the real me. The person under the face, the woman under the skin. None of you is the slightest bit interested in her.'

To Teal's horror her lip was trembling. She turned away, pulled a tissue from the box on the counter and noisily blew her nose. In a cracked voice he said, 'I haven't gone to bed with anyone since Elizabeth died.'

Julie spun round, her eyes awash with unshed tears. '*What* did you say?'

Wishing the words unsaid, Teal muttered, 'You heard—and now I'm getting the hell out of here. I'll pick you up at seven-thirty on Saturday.'

'You must have loved her very much.'

He couldn't take any more of this. 'I'll see you Saturday,' he repeated, brushed past her and took the back steps two at a time in his haste to be gone. As he jogged down the street towards his house, finding relief in physical action, he knew he'd learned one thing in the last ten minutes. He wouldn't ever kiss Julie Ferris again.

Not for a thousand agreements would he do that.

Saturday night found Julie in a horrible state of nerves. On Thursday in the kitchen she had decided that Teal was just like all the other men who had passed through her life in the last few weeks, interested only in her appearance and her body, kissing her out of lust and that deadly male drive for power. But then, like a knife in her heart, she would remember the anguish in his gray eyes as he had confessed to her that his bed had been empty for two long years.

He hadn't meant to tell her that, she would swear to it.

Why had he been celibate since Elizabeth's death?

The obvious answer was the one she had instinctively spoken: that he had loved his wife so much he couldn't bear to replace her with anyone else. But Julie wasn't sure that was the real—or the only—answer. Somehow, she mused, smoothing on pink lipstick with absent-minded care, it all came down to that word control. Teal had his emotions so deeply buried it would take an earthquake to free them.

Or a kiss, she thought wryly. A kiss that for her had been the equivalent of an earthquake.

And, of course, it was her ambivalence toward Teal that had caused her yesterday to commit herself to being with him for the next three months, accepting the challenge of a man who excited, infuriated and mystified her.

Last night she had taken Danny aside and explained what she privately called The Agreement to him, knowing it was a fateful step yet finding to her chagrin that he

was only a touch more interested than Einstein would
have been. 'That's neat—can I go out and play for
another half an hour, Mum?' he had said, and all her
carefully rehearsed justifications had remained unsaid.

Ten minutes before Teal was to pick her up, Julie was
ready. In silence she looked at herself in the mirror in
her bedroom. She had had two dresses to choose from
for her début as Teal's partner—a pretty full-length dress
with a swirling skirt of many colors, and the one she
was now wearing.

My minimalist period, she thought, dry-mouthed,
tossing her head so that her earrings caught the light and
admitted to herself that she was using the most basic of
weapons to attack Teal's control. The dress was covered
in glossy pearl-white sequins; it bared her throat, her
cleavage, her shoulders and arms, most of her back and,
from mid-thigh, her legs. Pearlized pantihose and thin-
heeled pumps completed her outfit.

She would be noticed, that was for sure.

The outer woman was firmly in place, she thought,
staring at her reflection. The surface woman, beautiful
and assured, whom men wanted to bed and whom a lot
of women disliked.

Panic-stricken, she ran for her closet and pulled out
the other dress, fumbling for the zipper on the back of
the one she was wearing. Downstairs the doorbell pealed.
Her hands stilled. Teal was early. She would have to keep
on the dress she had chosen.

She shot herself a hunted glance in the mirror. This
was all about acting, wasn't it? And after all, what was
she complaining about? The dress was a knockout, she
loved to dance and she was dating the sexiest man in the
city. If not the entire province.

She ran downstairs and pulled the front door open,
standing back so Teal could come in, her eyes lowered

in sudden shyness. The evening sun shone full on her, glinting among the sequins and shimmering in the loose fall of her hair. Teal stood stock-still on the step. 'My God,' he said.

Her strategy had worked. So far at least.

Her lashes flickered upward. He looked magnificent in a tuxedo, his pleated shirt-front a crisp white, his height and breadth of shoulder subtly emphasized by the formality of his attire. She managed a weak smile. 'I echo your sentiments exactly.'

Fighting to recover his composure, Teal said brusquely, 'Are you ready?'

'My shawl's in the kitchen.'

She led the way down the hall, achingly conscious of him following her. As she reached for the lacy shawl hanging on the back of one of the stools, he passed her a small white florist's box. 'I'm not sure there's enough dress to pin them on,' he said drily.

She took the box with noticeable reluctance, opening it slowly. Nestled in tissue paper was a corsage of two exquisite pale pink orchids. She blurted, 'Why did you do that? You didn't have to,' and winced at her own lack of finesse.

'Don't you like orchids?'

'They're beautiful,' she said truthfully. 'But...'

'But what, Julie?'

She raised her chin. 'Robert didn't believe in giving gifts. But just about every man I've dated in the last three months has given me a gift of some kind. A gift with a price attached that's supposed to make me feel grateful and indebted so later on I'll come across.'

'Sexually.'

'Well, of course.'

His gray eyes were opaque with anger. 'I said on Thursday I wouldn't touch you like that again and I meant it.'

She could feel tears pricking at the backs of her eyes. 'So why are you giving me orchids, Teal?'

'They're a gift. Unentailed. Freely given. If you can't accept them in that spirit, you can throw them on the compost heap for all I care!'

She said carefully, 'I don't understand . . . you just felt like giving them to me?'

His fury vanished as quickly as it had arisen. 'This is a big deal for you, isn't it?'

'Pretty big, yes.'

'If I say they were so beautiful that they reminded me of you, you'll jump on me,' he said with a twist of his mouth. 'But that was one reason.'

'What were the others?'

He jammed his hands deep in his trouser pockets. 'I suppose because I admire your honesty and courage.'

The waxen petals of the orchids blurred in Julie's vision. 'If I start to cry,' she said shakily, 'it'll ruin my mascara and then we'll be late.'

Unable to prevent himself, Teal stepped closer. 'Didn't your husband love you?'

She shook her head. 'He only loved himself. I was a useful ornament, a tribute to his good taste, to be trotted out on appropriate occasions. The terrible thing is that I don't think he ever loved Danny, either.'

'The man's a fool. You know that?'

She gave a helpless shrug. 'We'd better go.'

Very gently Teal rested his hands on her bare shoulders. 'So what's to be the fate of the orchids? Your dress or the compost pile?'

She looked up, aware of the slight roughness of his palms in every nerve in her body, and said without artifice, 'I'd be proud to wear them.' Her mouth quirked. 'But I think you'll have to pin them in my hair; there's no room on the dress.'

His eyes ranging her face, Teal said roughly, 'Every time I go near you, things go awry. I figured you'd be pleased to be given orchids, you'd thank me, and that would be that. In my experience most women accept gifts as their due, one of the pleasantries that go with dating.'

She tossed her head. 'You didn't give me orchids because I'm superficial.'

'Are you ever at a loss for an answer?'

'With you, I'm not sure I even know the question.'

He gave an impatient sigh. 'The orchids, Julie.'

She pulled a comb that was glittering with rhinestones out of her hair. 'Can we attach them to that?' she asked, and watched as he did so with deft fingers. Then he reached over and pushed the comb back into the thick waves of her hair.

His voice taut with repressed feeling, he said, 'You could have stepped out of a Gauguin painting. You look exotic...pagan.'

With no idea where the words came from Julie whispered, 'Please don't hate me, Teal.'

'I have no more intention of hating you than I have of loving you,' he said levelly. 'This arrangement is for our mutual convenience, and if we don't leave soon we'll be late for dinner.'

He had withdrawn to a place she couldn't follow; nor was it the first time he had done that. Feeling her insides churn with nervousness, Julie said, 'Wait here a minute.' Then she took a pair of scissors out of the drawer and hurried outside. Within two minutes she was back, carrying a pale pink rosebud from the garden, the petals smooth as silk and delicately scented. Rummaging in the same drawer, she came up with a safety-pin. 'Hold still,' she ordered, and took the lapel of his jacket in her fingers.

Teal, who hated being controlled, stood still. In his nostrils Julie's scent mingled with that of the rose as she wrestled with the safety-pin and the thorns on the stem, her tongue caught between her teeth as she concentrated on her task. Her skin, he was sure, would be as smooth as the petals of the rose, and her beauty was every bit as complex. What would it be like to watch her unfold to him, open like a rosebud to the sun?

His heart was hammering in his chest so loudly that he wondered if she could hear it. She gave a tiny exclamation of pain as she stabbed herself on a thorn, then finally managed to secure the rose at the angle she wanted. 'There,' she said with immense satisfaction, stepping back and smiling at him.

She wasn't flirting with him, and he knew that what she had done was somehow very important to her. 'Did you give gifts to Robert?' he asked.

With painful accuracy she said, 'I used to at first. But then I'd discover them lying around broken or uncared for, and realized he didn't want them or value them. So I stopped.' She bit her lip. 'He didn't even notice that I'd stopped—I think that was what hurt the most.'

He remembered how she had stood in front of the television set in his house, holding her son to her body as she watched her ex-husband and his second wife kiss each other on the screen; and how all her normal vitality and joy of life had drained out of her, leaving her looking depleted and tired, older than her years. The words wrenched from him, he said, 'Do you still love him?'

She shook her head. 'No... the day he told me he was divorcing me for Melissa I realized that I'd stopped loving him quite a while ago. It was humiliating and horrible to be told there was another woman, and I was furious at the way he'd deceived me. But even though my self-esteem was at an all-time low, my heart wasn't broken.' She sighed. 'Yet when we got married I was crazy about him.'

Teal had been in love with Elizabeth on his wedding-day. But why was he even thinking about Elizabeth? And why was he asking Julie about her husband when he would refuse outright to answer similar questions about his wife? He said, feeling gauche and off balance and masking it with a surface politeness, 'Thank you for the rose, Julie... and now we'd really better go.'

Politeness could be deadly, Julie thought, already regretting her confidences. Rather than thanking her, Teal might just as well have slammed a metal fence between them plastered with 'No Trespassing' signs: it would have been more honest.

But then the agreement wasn't about honesty. It was about superficiality.

She picked up her shawl, draping it round her shoulders, and walked out to the car with him.

CHAPTER SIX

JULIE had cheered up by the time she and Teal arrived at the hotel, and was wickedly amused that almost the first couple they met when they entered the big ballroom was Nick accompanied by Deirdre. You two deserve each other, she thought. And this is where I get some fun out of The Agreement. She tucked her hand in the crook of Teal's elbow and said demurely, 'Good evening, Nick...Dr Reid.'

Nick raised one brow in a way she was sure most women found irresistible. 'I didn't know you two were dating each other.'

'Come on, Nick,' she teased. 'Teal and I were made for each other—or so we've discovered, haven't we, darling?' And she laughed up at her companion, leaning her cheek intimately against his black-clad shoulder.

Only she felt the steel-hard tension in his arm and the tightness in his shoulder muscles as Teal said with a perfect blend of warmth and conviction, 'Absolutely...a match made in heaven.'

'A match that must have happened very fast,' Nick said quizzically.

'Just like lightning,' Julie rejoined. 'That's how we knew it was so right for us.'

'So I don't even get one dance?' Nick queried.

'Oh, maybe one,' Julie said.

'Only one,' Teal announced with an unarguable ring of authority.

Deirdre said sweetly, 'Really, Teal, you're the last man I would have expected to fall for a pretty face.'

'Life is full of surprises, Deirdre,' Teal said with a blandness that amused Julie mightily. 'Although "pretty" is a gross understatement.'

As he looked down at Julie, even she, knowing he was acting, was disarmed by the glow in his eyes. He added, 'We'd better go in search of Bruce and Marylee, Julie; they're holding a place for us.'

Julie gave the other couple a dazzling smile that she hoped was untinged with malice, and allowed Teal to steer her among the circular dinner-tables, which were decorated with flowers and sparkling silverware. Teal growled in her ear, 'One of our rules was that you couldn't dance with Nick.'

She said with impeccable logic, 'We need Nick to get the message you and I are a number—he knows so many women that that should ensure your safety.'

'You have a point. Just don't let his hands go any lower than your waistline.'

Tucking in the back of her mind the knowledge that Teal had noticed Nick's roaming fingers, Julie replied with exaggerated complaisance, 'Your every wish is my command.'

Teal gave a reluctant chuckle. 'Spare me, Julie—I know you better than that.'

She widened her eyes and pouted her lips. 'But this is about acting, Teal, not about reality.'

Once again, Teal thought, she had gotten under his skin. 'I hadn't forgotten,' he said smoothly. 'You can trust me to impress upon your favorite female surgeon that you and I are meant for each other—which should get the word around the hospital. Now come and meet my best friends.'

Julie liked Marylee and Bruce immediately, and did her best to act like a woman smitten. It was uphill work, partly because she felt she was being deceptive with a couple who clearly cared for Teal, partly because Teal all of a sudden was giving her very little help. With his innate good manners he made sure she was included in every conversation, filling her in on private and long-held jokes among the other three. But if he was trying to give the impression of a man madly in love he was out to lunch. Or, more appropriately, out to dinner.

The remains of an excellent lobster cocktail were removed, and the band was playing a waltz. Julie rested her fingers on Teal's wrist. 'Dance with me, darling? I love to waltz.'

Teal didn't know which he hated most: his body's instant response to her touch, or the fraudulence behind her endearment. 'Sure,' he said, getting to his feet and taking her by the hand.

The dance-floor was parquet, large and dimly lit. As Teal took Julie in his arms, holding her an impersonal distance from his body, she said in a furious whisper, 'You're not behaving at all like a man in love...what's wrong with you? I feel like an idiot, lacing my conversation with "darling"s and "honey"s—I never realized how much I dislike that word honey—and falling all over you while you sit there like a stick talking to Bruce about the scarcity of brook trout.'

Teal missed a step. 'Sorry,' he muttered. 'Did I forget to tell you? I warned Bruce and Marylee what was going on—so there's no need to pretend in front of them.'

'You mean I've been acting my fool head off for nothing?' Julie squeaked.

'They're my best friends; I couldn't deceive them. I told them about our agreement a couple of days ago.'

'Thanks a lot,' she said bitterly. 'I only hope Nick isn't watching us have our first fight—that man's got eyes in the back of his head. Teal, we can't turn it on and off like a tap. Either we're in love or we're not.'

Angry with himself, he said shortly, 'I should have told you—I'm sorry.'

'I feel like I've made a fool of myself!'

'Look on it as practice for when you dance with Nick.'

'To hell with Nick—this is about us.'

He said in a measured voice. 'Nick and Deirdre have just joined us on the dance-floor—smile, Julie.'

She directed a ferocious smile at him and said through gritted teeth, 'Is there such a thing in your law books as justifiable homicide? If so, it might be wise of you to check your soup for arsenic.'

Laughing, Teal led her through an intricate *chassé*. 'They've delivered the salad to our table; we could sit down now...and I think you should drop calling me honey; I don't like it, either.'

'What I feel like calling you at this precise moment is unprintable,' Julie said, waving in a sprightly fashion at Nick and Deirdre, and then wending her way back through the tables to the one they were sharing with Bruce and Marylee.

It was a Caesar salad, which Julie adored, followed by Chateaubriand and strawberry cheesecake; throughout the rest of the meal Julie did not once touch Teal and called him neither darling nor honey. Then, as liqueurs and coffee were poured, the band struck up again. Bruce swung Marylee up on the dance-floor, and more sedately Teal followed suit.

While Julie also danced with Bruce and a couple of Teal's colleagues as the evening went on, she mostly danced with Teal. She could not fault his technique, for he knew steps she had never even thought of and guided her through them with a skill she had to admire. But, although he held her close enough to satisfy the impression they were trying to give of two newly met lovers, his body was taut with an underlying resistance, and he danced as if the music never once touched his soul.

Julie had loved to dance for as long as she could remember; losing herself in music's rhythms and surrendering to its melodies had always freed her from the cares of every day. But Teal was surrendering nothing. At midnight, as she circled the floor with him, she found herself thinking, I hate this. It's all an act, and I hate it. I can't stand the way he's so controlled.

While she was getting dressed earlier this evening she had worried that she'd be ravaged by desire for Teal in the middle of the dance-floor. She needn't have worried, she thought grimly. Dancing with Teal was more of an ordeal than an incentive to lovemaking.

Not stopping to think, she said, 'You know how bananas get when they're overripe—sort of mottled and squishy? Do you like them like that?'

Puzzled, Teal said, 'Can't say that I do.'

'That's the way you're holding me. As if I were an overripe banana.' Warming to her theme, she added, 'Or something rather disgusting that's been tucked at the back of your refrigerator, all green and slimy and long overdue for the garbage can. You know the kind of thing I mean? You pick it up in the very tips of your fingers.'

As the waltz ended, Teal whirled her in a complicated turn. 'You don't like the way I dance?' he said coldly.

Over her shoulder she saw Nick leading Deirdre in their direction. She smiled provocatively at Teal, running her fingernail down the nape of his neck, and said, just as the band launched into some raucous rock and roll, 'You're extremely competent—and here comes Nick.'

'Dance, Julie?' Nick asked.

'Love to,' she said promptly.

The beat of the bass pulsed through her veins, and in a surge of rebellion Julie forgot that she was supposed to be the love of Teal's life and for the first time that night danced her heart out, a lithe, sexy figure in her spangled dress. Nick caught the wildness of her energy, and when the song came to an end there was a brief smatter of applause. In faint dismay Julie looked around for Teal. He was standing at the edge of the floor talking to Deirdre. 'I promised Teal this one, Nick,' she lied valiantly.

As Teal watched her walk back toward him, he was so overwhelmed by primitive aggression that part of him—but only a very small part—was horrified. By a huge effort of will he managed to wait until Deirdre and Nick had joined another couple before seizing Julie by the elbow and marching her to a secluded corner behind some large, anemic-looking potted palms. Pulling her round to face him, he blazed, 'You did sleep with him, didn't you?'

'I did not!'

'Don't lie to me—I watched the two of you on the dance-floor and I know basic chemistry when I see it.'

It had been a very long evening, and Julie was tired of pretending to be something she was not with someone who couldn't stand even to hold her in his arms.

'I'm not sexually attracted to Nick and never have been,' she flared. 'I told you that the night we began this ridiculous agreement. Your problem is that you don't recognize basic chemistry when it's standing right under your nose!'

'And what's that supposed to mean?'

A palm branch was gently waving over his head, but she had no inclination to laugh; he looked far too angry for that. Nor had she meant to speak her mind quite so forthrightly. Equivocating, she said, 'You already know that I find you attractive.'

'That is not what you meant!'

'All right, it's not! When you kissed me in the kitchen the other evening I felt as though the sun, the moon and the stars had all come out at once. But did you recognize that? Oh, no—you pushed me away as though you'd been embracing a piece of poison ivy and then you apologized all over the place. That's what I mean.'

Spacing his words, Teal said, 'I don't want to get sexually involved with anyone, Julie Ferris, and that includes you. Have you got that straight?'

'So why should you care whether I slept with Nick?'

'The guy's a lush.'

'Whereas you're a monk.'

He said unpleasantly, 'If this were one of your husband's plays, I'd now haul you off to bed to prove my manhood. You've got the wrong plot—and the wrong man. You can't provoke me into doing something I don't want to do.'

'So what's so awful about sex, Teal?'

She had asked the one question he couldn't possibly answer.

'Why would I want to have sex with a woman who hates it?' he said meanly, and watched her flinch.

'I'll never in a million years dance with Nick again,' she said bitterly. 'But if you want this agreement to succeed, you and I have got to stop dancing like a couple of strangers—or no one's going to believe that we're in love.'

'Bruce has already told me more or less the same thing.'

Bruce, in less colorful language than Julie's, had claimed that Teal was holding Julie like a maiden aunt.

Julie sighed, suddenly feeling extraordinarily tired. 'I don't understand you at all,' she muttered. 'I've never met anyone who kept his emotions and his sexuality so much under wraps.'

'You don't have to understand me! This is an arrange-ment for our mutual convenience—and that's all it is.'

Her shoulders slumped. 'I don't think it'll work. Because it's a toss-up which of us is the worse actor.'

Teal raked his fingers through his hair and said with raw honesty, 'Certainly superficiality flies out of the window whenever we come within ten feet of each other.'

She grinned ruefully. 'You've noticed that?'

'Yeah, I've noticed it...I'm not that much out of touch.' He hesitated. 'You look wiped—why don't we have one more dance and then leave?'

'It's hard work, pretending to be in love. Maybe we should have put an announcement in the paper and skipped the public performances.'

Through the potted palms 'Lara's Theme' drifted to Teal's ears; it was one of his favorite songs. 'I love that music,' he said. Suddenly sick to death of play-acting, he lifted her hand to his lips. 'Dance with me, Julie?'

There was no one else in sight; his gesture had been for her alone. Her heart playing its own melody in her breast, a wild and happy little melody, Julie said, 'Thank you, I'd like that.'

Teal took her hand in his, cradling it, and led her back to the dance-floor. This time when he took her in his arms he didn't send out any mixed messages; his arms strong around her, he drew her close and left out all his fancy steps, his cheek resting on her hair as he swayed to the music. Julie dropped her head to his shoulder, closed her eyes and let the hauntingly sad tune envelop her. For the first time in several hours she felt happy— as though she was where she wanted to be.

Slowly and lazily the tiger uncoiled itself, stretching its sleek limbs in indolent pleasure. Julie watched it in her mind's eye, held Teal a little closer and let her senses take over. His body was hard and fit, his strength understated, while his skin smelled of soap and shaving lotion and something both more individual and more elusive that was the very essence of the man. She let one hand drift to the back of his neck and moved a little closer to him, so that her breasts were pressed to his chest.

Then, with a thrill of sheer pleasure, she felt his hand slide across the bare expanse of her back, pulling her closer still. They were dancing hip to hip; there was no mistaking his arousal. No mistaking, either, the fact that he hadn't tried to hide it from her.

She wanted Teal; wanted him so badly she was almost faint with longing. She wanted to be intimate with him in ways she could barely imagine, ways that made her heartbeat race and the blood sing in her veins. What she had learned in the last few minutes was that he wanted her, too.

As Lara's song came to an end, Teal muttered, 'I can recognize body chemistry when it's under my nose.'

She said contentedly, 'So can I.'

With a little edge to his voice he said, 'I didn't want you thinking I was in any way defective.'

She suddenly reared her head, as alert as a wild animal at the first scent of danger. 'That wasn't just a game for you, Teal?' she said, appalled.

He countered that with another question. 'Do you still have complaints about my dancing?'

'No. Answer me!'

He couldn't; he didn't know what to tell her. He said coolly, 'Then let's say goodbye to Marylee and Bruce and I'll take you home.'

Julie didn't want to go home; she wanted to stay in an embrace that had filled her with a dizzying mixture of security and desire. Openly pleading with him, she said, 'The way we danced—that was real! For me it was real. Wasn't it for you?'

'You know what the agreement said—no sex.'

He was easing her away from his body. In true anguish she said, 'I have to know when we're acting and when we're not—I have to!'

He said hoarsely, 'I might live like a monk. That doesn't mean I don't have the normal urges of a man. I'd have to be two years old or a hundred and two not to want you, Julie—but that doesn't mean I'm going to do anything about it.'

It was not the answer she had hoped for, but it was all the answer she was going to get. He hadn't had a woman in two years; and she, Julie, had thrust herself at him, flaunting her body in a dress that left little to the imagination, constantly needling him. Of course he was aroused. A stone statue would have been aroused.

And once again she had exposed her feelings to him, her vulnerabilities. She was as transparent as a piece of glass, she thought wretchedly. Whereas he was like a mirror, reflecting the enigma of the man himself and nothing more.

With a sudden need to revenge herself, she curved her lips in a seductive smile, brushed her breasts lightly against the front of his jacket and said, 'You've never made love on a dance-floor?'

'Never. Have you?'

'Never. I like new experiences.'

Some of his frustration escaping in spite of himself, Teal said, 'Do you? I'm not so sure. I'm a new experience for you, aren't I—a man who's not falling all over you on the first date? And frankly I think it's irritating the hell out of you.'

She felt as though he had slapped her. Stepping back, her smile congealed on her face like a clown's mask, Julie said in a thin voice, 'Enough's enough. I want to go home.'

'Don't forget the eyes in the back of Nick's head,' he taunted, and led her off the dance-floor.

Somehow Julie got through saying goodbye to Bruce and Marylee without telling them precisely what she thought of their best friend; she stalked out to Teal's car and sat in a frigid silence all the way home. He pulled up by the curb and said, 'I'll walk you to the door.'

Not deigning to argue, she preceded him up the path between the velvet-petalled petunias. Putting her key in the door, she said, 'We have just had our first and our last date. Goodnight, Teal.'

To her fury he looked not the slightest bit put out. 'I rather doubt that,' he said. 'Goodnight.'

She opened the door, composing her features for the sitter, and closed it behind her. Ten minutes late, the sitter having departed in a taxi, Julie was stripping off her make-up in front of the bathroom mirror.

The trouble was, she thought, scouring her cheeks with cleansing cream, there had been an element of truth in what Teal had said. Despite his warning her to the contrary, she had seen him as a challenge. She had wanted to penetrate his armour and find the real man within.

Tonight she had found out that there was no real man. Just a consummate actor who had manipulated her feelings from beginning to end. A lawyer on duty twenty-four hours a day and always one step ahead of her, who lusted after her but cared not one whit for her feelings.

She had lived with an actor for nearly nine years; she didn't need another one; and she thoroughly disliked lawyers. Whereas if it was lust she wanted she need go no further than Nick.

As far as she was concerned, any agreements between her and Teal were dead in the water.

* * *

A week passed, during which Teal did not get in touch with Julie. She told herself she was glad he'd taken the hint, and jumped every time the telephone rang.

It wasn't ringing as much as it had. Apparently the symphony benefit had accomplished something.

She worked four day shifts, slept badly most nights and devoted her free time to the garden and her son. The trouble was that Scott came along with Danny. And Scott, with his dark hair and gray eyes, reminded her acutely of his father.

On a Tuesday evening, as restless as Einstein watching a flock of birds, she decided to take Danny to the Dairy Queen for an ice-cream. He'd enjoy the outing and it would get her out of range of the telephone.

Danny was playing with Scott in the tree house in Teal's back garden. So she had two choices. She could phone Teal and ask him to send Danny home. Or she could walk over there and get Danny herself. The latter seemed a much preferable course of action because she wouldn't have to speak to Teal at all.

She put on a long skirt made of turquoise crinkled cotton and a matching top with a round neckline and cap sleeves, so that she looked very different from the dancer in the spangled dress, and set off down the street.

It was a beautiful summer evening. Lawn sprinklers hissed in the front gardens, the drops of water catching the sun's rays; the bright colors of the flowers lightened her step. She needed to cultivate a sense of perspective, she told herself, admiring a particularly elegant Turkish lily in the garden next to Teal's. The agreement, brief though it had been, had done its work and she could live very well without a man. Particularly one as complicated and inaccessible as Teal.

Jauntily she walked up his driveway. The black BMW was parked under the shade of a giant old oak tree. She passed it, pushed her way through a tangle of shrubbery into the back garden and called Danny's name.

The garden was deserted except for a flock of sparrows scratching in the undergrowth. The boys must be inside.

She almost turned around to go home. But Teal had given her orchids because of her courage, and she couldn't avoid him forever. Why not see him now and get it over with?

Feeling as though she was on her way to the dentist with a mouth full of cavities, she marched up the steps and knocked on the back door, which was ajar. From inside she heard Teal yell, 'Would you get that, Scott?' and her heart gave an uncomfortable lurch. Please answer the door, Scott, she thought, rubbing her palms down the sides of her skirt.

However, neither Scott nor Danny came running through the kitchen to find out who was there. Chewing on her lip, Julie knocked again, and was rewarded by the slap of bare feet taking the stairs two at a time. They were a man's footsteps, not a boy's. Adjusting her face muscles into a smile that was a nicely judged mixture of politeness and disdain, Julie waited.

Teal swung the door open. 'Julie!' he exclaimed, and his heart jolted in his chest as if he'd touched a live wire.

He was wearing the navy sweatpants she remembered so well, and was bare-chested. Smothering any pretensions the tiger might have to rearing its head, trying to ignore that Teal looked exhausted, Julie quoted nastily, '"If my son's to spend time in your house, I'd much prefer you to keep the doors locked." Would you get him for me, please?'

'You're a woman alone in the house—there's a difference.'

She bit back a number of replies ranging from the merely catty to the obscene, and repeated, 'I'd like to speak to Danny.'

'Come in—he must be up in the attic; I'll get him.'

'Perhaps you could just send him home for me.'

'Oh, come in, Julie,' Teal said impatiently. 'I don't bite.'

As meekly as a feudal maiden, she did as she was told. The kitchen was a mess. Teal said defensively, 'Mrs Inkpen couldn't come yesterday, and I've been working night and day on a case.'

'The perfect lawyer,' she said ironically.

'You really don't like lawyers, do you?'

Realizing she was itching for a fight, she said concisely, 'I don't. I paid a lawyer a lot of money to arrange the financial side of the divorce, Robert moved back to New York and isn't paying support, and in order to do anything I'll have to get two more lawyers, one here and one there—all at my expense, you understand.'

'We're not all like that.'

She raised her brows in delicate disbelief. 'No?'

'No!' His hands gripped the edge of the kitchen table, which was littered with dirty dishes, he leaned forward and said with passionate intensity, 'This case I'm working on . . . I'm representing a fourteen-year-old boy who shot and wounded his father on the back steps of his house. In cold blood, supposedly.

'I don't think it was in cold blood; I think the kid—and his mother—have been abused since he was born and he finally got big enough to turn on the man who did it. So it's up to me to get the boy's story out of him, and to tell that story in court and make sure he gets a fair deal, including the best counseling on family violence that's available, so we can break the pattern and he won't end up abusing his own children.

'Sure, the system goes wrong, and sure, rehabilitation can be the worst joke there is—but it's all we've got and for the kid's sake I'll raise heaven and earth and work night and day if I have to.'

Julie said dazedly, 'So you do have feelings.'

'Oh, go to hell.'

'You keep them all for your work, that's all.'

Wishing he hadn't revealed a part of himself he preferred to keep private, Teal rapped, 'I happen to have feelings for my son, too—in case you hadn't noticed.'

'You're a very good father,' Julie said and gave him her most generous smile. 'The only person you're not looking after is yourself.' She glanced around her. 'I'll help you clean up the dishes if you like.'

'You came here for Danny.'

She clasped her cold fingers behind her back and said lightly, 'To take him to the Dairy Queen. We could all go after the dishes are done.'

'Julie, I warned you not to see me as a challenge.'

'It's a warning I'm choosing to ignore.'

'You'll get hurt if you do. Because I won't change.'

'I don't believe that.'

'Then you're being very foolish,' he said shortly.

They were facing each other like adversaries across the width of the table. 'You say you admire my honesty, yet you don't like it when I'm honest,' Julie cried with the courage of desperation. 'I've discovered something about you the last few minutes—that you're a man of passion and deep feelings . . . and I'm not talking about sex. You can't hide from me any more, not like you did at the dance last week. I've found you out.'

He pounded his fist on the table with a force that made the glasses rattle. 'I'm not going to get involved with you—do you hear me?' he exploded, and wondered who he was trying to convince, her or himself.

Julie's impulse was to run. She stood her ground and said, 'You asked me once if I loved my husband and I gave you a truthful answer to what was a hard question. Now I'm going to ask you a hard question. Did you love your wife, Teal? Did you love Elizabeth?'

Tension ripped along his nerves. 'I don't want to talk about Elizabeth. Not to you or to anyone else.'

In pure anticlimax Danny called down the stairs, 'Is that you, Mum? Come on up and see our fort in the attic.'

Julie let out her pent-up breath, rubbing her hands down the side of her skirt. 'I'll be back in a minute,' she said. Then she walked past Teal and into the hallway.

The house had the gracious proportions of an earlier generation, the banisters polished oak, the high ceilings decorated with ornate plaster moldings. But again she noticed the absence of paintings or plants that might have given life and form to the empty corners.

She climbed the stairs, smiling up at Danny, who was hanging over the railings. He said, 'Wait there a minute; I've got to tell Scott you're coming.'

He disappeared. She was standing on the second floor, and right in front of her was the open door to Teal's bedroom. A sweater she recognized was flung over one corner of the big bed.

Drawn by a curiosity she could not have denied, Julie stepped closer and looked inside. Tall windows overlooked the back garden, the leaves of the trees making a verdant network through the sheer curtains. The walls were white, the expensive bedspread and the plush carpet a light blue, while the furniture was made of pale pine.

She was suddenly cold, chilled to the bone, not even the surface untidiness of the room giving her comfort. Because this was the room Teal had shared with

Elizabeth? Was that what was wrong—she was jealous of a dead woman? Or was it something deeper than that?

Her eyes wandered around the room. There were photographs of Scott on the dresser, and a formal portrait of a young woman with her hair pulled back severely from a face that had an austere beauty. Then, her breath catching in her throat, Julie noticed something else. In front of the portrait, in a tiny crystal vase, was the pink rosebud she had given Teal last week. It was drooping now, the petals rusted round the edges. But he had taken the trouble to put it in water, and he had kept it in his bedroom.

Why? Why on earth had he done that?

CHAPTER SEVEN

'WHERE are you, Mum?'

Guiltily Julie backed out of Teal's bedroom. After following Danny up a narrow flight of stairs, she found herself in a roomy attic that would have been any child's delight. She crawled into the fort on her hands and knees, tested out the camp bed and consumed emergency rations consisting of dry cookies and lurid pink fruit punch. As she extricated herself from the door flaps, she said, 'I want to help your dad clean up the kitchen, Scott. Then I'll take you both for an ice-cream—would you like that?'

They would. Quickly she ran downstairs and into the kitchen. Teal had put on a shirt and was rinsing off the dishes in the sink. 'I'll help,' she said, and started stashing mugs and glasses in the dishwasher.

He was scrubbing at a plate with fierce energy. She gathered up the knives and said in a conversational tone of voice, 'You kept my rose.'

Teal jammed a plate in the rack and said in utter fury, 'Do you always go snooping in other people's bedrooms?'

'I wanted to see if it was as colorless as the rest of the house.'

'I had nothing to do with decorating this place—Elizabeth chose the color schemes when we moved in eight years ago.'

'Oh,' said Julie. 'You haven't changed a thing since she died?'

'No,' he said curtly.

Because he was overwhelmed with grief and couldn't bear to undo his wife's handiwork—was that the reason? If only she knew the answer to that question, she might understand what made Teal the way he was.

'Why did you keep the rose?' she asked in a small voice.

Teal stared at the water gurgling down the drain. He could follow the letter of the agreement and fob her off with an easy answer; or he could opt for the truth.

He said, 'Giving me that rose was important to you—it didn't seem right just to turf it.'

Almost inaudibly she answered, 'Thanks, Teal—that was sweet of you.'

He looked over at her. She was placing spoons in tidy rows in the cutlery basket and looked deep in thought. Forks followed the spoons into the basket, then she picked up a cloth to wipe the table.

'You know what?' she said suddenly. 'I think we need to renegotiate the agreement. I'm getting tired of fighting all the time.'

Speaking the truth could get to be a habit, Teal thought wryly. 'The only way we won't fight is if we never see each other.'

'What a pessimist you are.' Handing him the last dirty plate, Julie said, 'It's very simple. I want sex and you don't. I did my best to shake you up with the dress I wore to the dance, but that backfired—you accused me of sleeping with Nick and you didn't take me to bed to prove your manhood. You were right—it's the wrong plot. You're the most strong-willed man I've ever met and I can see it's useless for me to try and change your mind.'

She put a couple of clean knives away in the drawer and added, puzzled, 'Why do you keep the bicycle-repair kit in with the cutlery?'

'That's Mrs Inkpen. Her method of tidying up is to sweep everything off the counters into the nearest drawer. Don't change the subject.'

Julie laughed. 'I bet I'd like Mrs Inkpen—her filing system is the very antithesis of a lawyer's. Now, where was I?'

'You were talking about sex. You want it and I don't. Are you referring to sex with me, by the way?'

'Absolutely,' she said, wiping the counter with a flourish. 'I've never gone to bed with anyone except Robert...my upbringing left me with certain principles, one of which was called fidelity. But to get back to the agreement. Celibacy is an "in" word in all the magazines these days, and I'm sure it won't hurt me. So I suggest we change tack. No more kisses. No more close dancing. Let's just have some fun.'

'Fun?' Teal repeated quizzically.

'Mmm...like taking the boys to the Dairy Queen. Going to the beach with them, or for bicycle rides. That sort of thing.'

'You figure we wouldn't scrap that way?'

She wrinkled her nose at him. 'Well, it's worth a try, don't you think? considering we've got more than two months before the agreement runs out.'

Deliberately testing her, Teal let his gaze linger on her face and said huskily, 'That outfit you're wearing—it makes your eyes look as blue as the sea.'

'That's just the sort of thing you shouldn't do,' she cried. 'When you look at me like that—as if I'm the only woman in the world—all I want to do is make wild, passionate love with you. I wore this skirt because I was trying to cover as much of my anatomy as I could.'

'Julie, you could wear a canvas tent and still cause a traffic jam.'

'You've got to stop saying things like that,' she ordered. 'The new agreement won't allow for them. No sex. Not even a breath of it.'

'We'd be like brother and sister?' he remarked innocently.

Not all Julie's powers of imagination could picture Teal as her brother. 'That's how we'd behave,' she said firmly, and waved a slotted spoon at him. 'It's summer, Teal, and the boys are off school! Let's get out and enjoy ourselves, that's all I'm saying. After all, if we go to the Dairy Queen and the beach, people are bound to see us together—which is the whole point, isn't it?'

Quickly she stopped speaking as Danny and Scott rushed into the kitchen. Danny said, 'Are we going to get ice-cream, Mum?'

'Are you coming with us, Dad?' Scott cried.

Knowing how much was resting on his answer, Teal said, 'Sure, I'm coming . . . give us five minutes to finish the dishes.'

With loud whoops the boys took off into the garden. Teal attacked the pile of saucepans while Julie, for once, said nothing. When the last pot had been put away, Teal ran upstairs to change into a pair of jeans and Julie went outside.

Dusk was falling, the garden full of mysterious shadows. She was going to the Dairy Queen with Teal and Scott and Danny, she thought, and felt happiness well up in her heart.

Teal joined her on the step. 'Ready?'

'Could we stop off at my place so I can get my purse?'

'I'll treat you.'

'I'd rather pay for myself, Teal.'

'No scrapping, remember?' he said with a lazy grin.

'That doesn't mean you're always going to get your own way,' she announced. 'This isn't about me losing my independence.'

'Tonight it is,' he replied, putting his hands on her shoulders to turn her around and steer her in the direction of the car.

'No sex', she had said blithely a few minutes ago. What a joke, she now thought. When I'm within a mile of this man I can't keep my mind out of the bedroom. I'm the one who's going to have to learn about control.

The Dairy Queen was crowded. They bought their ice-cream and drove home, sitting at the picnic table under the maple tree. Moths danced around the porch light as the boys delved into their sundaes enthusiastically, Danny waving his spoon as he told his mother about the new additions to the tree house.

'Oops!' he said suddenly. 'I got chocolate on your sweater, Mum.'

Julie looked down. 'Darn...it's brand-new. I'll put some cold water on it,' she said, pushing herself up from the table.

'I'll get a clean cloth for you,' Teal said, following her into the kitchen and opening one of the drawers. He turned on the cold tap, wetting the cloth, and said, 'Hold still.'

The chocolate had landed just above her left breast. He held the soft knit fabric away from her body and scrubbed at it, his dark hair only inches from her face. No sex, Julie thought frantically, and all the while her eyes, greedy for him, were noting the arch of his brow, the strong jut of his cheekbone under the tanned skin, the slight shadow of his beard along his jawline. Then he looked up. His hands stilled. 'You're not remotely like a sister to me,' he said.

She could feel his breath on her cheek. 'The boys will be wondering what we're up to,' she answered weakly.

He let go of her sweater. Beneath it her nipples had hardened; dry-mouthed, he said, 'I think I got most of the chocolate out.'

The stain was the last thing on her mind. Heat scorching her cheeks, Julie stepped back and said over-loudly, 'Celibacy is an entirely viable option and will no doubt build strength of character.'

In a strained voice Teal said, 'You've met lots of men the last few months... why me?'

She remembered the chill that had struck her bones in his bedroom and let the words spill out. 'There's a place I find myself in sometimes—after all, who doesn't?—a place of loneliness where I know that, no matter who I'm with, I'm all alone. But you, I think, live in that place. Nearly all the time.'

'So you feel sorry for me,' he said harshly.

'Oh, no, it's not that simple. It's as though I can't help myself, Teal, as though something about you calls to me instinctually.' She hugged her breasts, feeling the wet fabric cling to her skin. 'Let's drop the subject, okay? You've made it abundantly clear you don't want to make love with me, and talking about it just gets me all riled up.'

'I'm beginning to realize that being chased by Janine and Cindy Thurston and Carole was an exceedingly simple form of existence compared with being in the same room with you,' Teal responded tersely. 'We'd better go back out—the ice-cream will have melted.'

Like me, Julie thought, and in a swirl of skirts ran outside. So far her renegotiated agreement didn't seem to be meeting with much success. It was probably a measure of the naïveté Robert had often accused her of that she had suggested it in the first place.

Glumly she took a mouthful of chocolate and runny ice-cream, and half an hour later was back in her own house with Danny.

On Thursday evening at eight o'clock Teal drove into Julie's driveway on his bicycle, Scott and Danny close behind him. Julie had worked from seven until seven; he had it in his mind to take her for a drink downtown and then suggest to her that they all go to the beach on Saturday. For fun. As he leaned his bicycle against the fence, the boys took off into the garden to dig for worms; Teal had promised to take them both fishing the next day. He knocked on the back door and heard Julie call in a distracted voice, 'Come in.'

He walked into the kitchen, which looked rather worse than his had a couple of days ago. Then Julie came in from the living-room. Her hair was damp from the shower, she was wearing faded, very tight-fitting jeans and a sloppy sweatshirt, and she looked as distracted as she had sounded.

'Teal,' she said. 'How are you? I——'

Then an older woman, elegantly clad in a crisp linen suit and immaculate white pumps, tapped her way into the room on Julie's heels. Julie shot a hunted look round the kitchen and said, 'This is Teal Carruthers, Mrs LeMarchant; he's a friend of mine. Teal, I'd like you to meet my landlady, Mrs LeMarchant . . . she's here for a visit.'

'How do you do, Mr Carruthers?' Ethelda LeMarchant said, managing in one glance to make Teal aware that his hair needed combing and his shirt was missing a button.

He shook hands, hoping there wasn't any bicycle grease on his fingers, exchanged some small talk with her and heard her say, 'Well, I must be going . . .'

The back door burst open and the boys raced in. Danny was dangling a plump, shiny worm in one hand, scattering mud on the floor with the other. 'Look at this one, Mum,' he cried. 'It's the biggest worm I ever saw. Can I keep it in my bedroom?'

'Say hello to Mrs LeMarchant, Danny,' Julie said faintly. 'And this is Scott Carruthers, Teal's son.'

Neither boy could have been called clean. Mrs LeMarchant acknowledged them with chilly politeness, said, 'Perhaps we can get together for tea sometime this week, Mrs Ferris, to talk over the lease . . . a pleasure to have met you, Mr Carruthers,' and headed for the back door. As the screen shut behind her and her steps clicked down the driveway, Julie sat down on the nearest stool, buried her face in her hands and burst into tears.

Teal took an instinctive step toward her. But Danny beat him to it. The little boy dropped the worm on the counter and made a bee line for his mother, flinging his arms around her and burrowing into her body. 'It's okay, Mum—you don't have to be scared of worms; they're not like rats.'

Julie wrapped her arms around him and sobbed harder. 'It's n-nothing to do with the worms, Danny.'

Scott looked aghast at the sight of a grown-up weeping; his mother would never have cried in front of him, Teal was certain. He said calmly, 'Tell you what, boys—why don't you turn on the television in the living-room? There's a nature show on Channel 19. I'll make Julie some tea and find out what's upsetting her.'

Julie looked up, her face blotchy with tears, and dropped a kiss on her son's blond curls. 'That's a g-good idea,' she snuffled. 'I'll be all right in a few minutes, Danny. Truly it was nothing to do with you.'

Danny butted his head against her sleeve and said with a fierce protectiveness that brought a lump to Teal's throat, 'I love you, Mum.'

She swiped at her nose with the back of her hand, giving him a singularly sweet smile. 'I love you, too. I know I'll feel better if I talk to Teal for a while, so off you go. But put the worm in the jar with the rest of them, or it'll dry out.'

After Teal had filled the kettle, he rinsed out a couple of mugs in the sink and put teabags in the pot. Then he pulled Julie to her feet, deliberately drawing her against the length of his body. 'Tell me what's the matter.'

For once she didn't feel like arguing. Instead she put her arms around his waist and sagged against him with a deep sigh. 'You feel good. Sort of solid. Like that old maple tree in your back garden by the picnic table.'

Her damp hair, which was tickling his nose, smelled fragrantly of shampoo. 'No sex', she'd said. But her weight, warm and entrancingly soft, was pressed into his body, and he was almost sure she wasn't wearing a bra. He said, feeling not at all like a chunk of wood, 'Tell me why you were crying.'

'I had a horrible day at work,' she mumbled. 'Everything went wrong that could go wrong. One of the interns botched a prescription and tried to blame me, I dropped a bag of lipids and it burst all over my brand-new shoes, a patient we thought had stabilized had to go back to ICU—and that was only the morning. This afternoon I had to do rounds with Dr Reid, and you know how I feel about her. Then an hour before my shift ended they brought up three new patients and the man in 326 had a heart attack.'

As she gave a reminiscent shudder Teal said comfortingly, 'One of those days when you should have stayed in bed.'

'You said it. After I got home I was just getting out of the shower when my landlady dropped in. I didn't think she was arriving until the weekend, and I'd planned to clean the house from end to end. But it's a disaster area right now. Einstein's shedding, Danny's toys and my sewing are spread all over the living-room carpet—and you can see the kitchen; your Mrs Inkpen would have a field day. The worm on the counter was the finishing touch.'

'You're paying rent, Julie; you've got a right to be untidy. And it's not very ethical of her to drop in unannounced.'

'Oh—I hadn't thought of it that way.' She looked up, her pulse leaping at the concern in his face. 'I'm paying eight hundred dollars a month. That's over a dollar an hour—you're right, I should be able to be messy. Although she did ask me to keep the house in apple-pie order.'

'An apple pie isn't a particularly tidy dish,' Teal commented.

'Pastry flaking all over the place.'

'Juice bubbling over the oven.'

Julie smiled, reluctantly edging free of his embrace. 'I feel better—thanks for the use of the shoulder.'

'Any time,' Teal said, and discovered with a twinge of pure panic that he meant it. 'We came to see if Danny could go fishing tomorrow morning,' he added hurriedly. 'And I thought the four of us might go to the beach on Saturday.'

'You're taking tomorrow off?' she asked in surprise.

He grinned. 'I won my case.'

'The one with the boy? Oh, Teal, I'm so happy for you!'

This time Julie threw her arms around him rather than sagging against him; but there was the same delicious sense of holding all the softness, energy and warmth of a woman who was fully alive. She was laughing up at him, a laughter all the more precious for her recent tears. Julie knew what emotions were all about, he thought dazedly. She lived them.

Not like Elizabeth.

The renegotiated agreement was about fun, not sex. The devil with the agreement, Teal thought, pulling her hard to his chest as, with a distinct lack of anything that could be called technique, he kissed her open mouth. A tiny shock ran through her. The long curves of her body, the yielding sweetness of her lips excited him beyond measure. He forgot that their two sons were in the next room and that he'd promised to keep his distance, forgot that he'd sworn, two years ago, never to lose control of his sexuality again. He forgot everything but his own primitive hunger for the woman in his arms.

Her tongue danced with his. His hand found the swell of her breast through the loose folds of her sweater and he discovered that he was right—she wasn't wearing a bra. With a fierce impatience he fumbled for the hem of the sweater, and then felt, under his palm, the smooth warmth of her belly.

She strained closer to him, her fingers tangled in his hair. 'Julie...' he said exultantly and blindly reached for the firm rise of her breast under her sweater. As she shivered with pleasure, making a tiny sound in her throat, he found himself looking straight into her eyes, smoke-blue eyes that were ablaze with passion.

With his free hand he smoothed back her hair, saying in a choked voice, 'You want me, Julie...you really want me,' and even as he spoke wondered how he had found the words through the turmoil of emotion in his chest.

She took his palm and pressed it to her side, so that he could feel the heavy pounding of her heart. 'Of course

I want you,' she whispered. 'What is it, Teal? Why do you even need to say that?'

He couldn't begin to tell her; the phrases wouldn't formulate themselves, and the words caught in his throat. Helplessly he buried his face in the shining weight of her hair, feeling its dampness cool against his cheek. She said so softly that he had to strain to hear her, 'You can tell me, Teal—you can trust me.'

'If I trusted anyone, it would be you,' he muttered.

'When you're ready, you will tell me.'

Was it that simple? Surely not... it couldn't be. He said in a clipped voice, knowing he was running away, 'The boys will be wondering what's going on.'

Nothing could be further from Julie's mind than the boys. 'You've done it again,' she cried. 'It's as though you drop a barrier between us—like one of those portcullises clanging to the ground in a moldy old medieval castle. I hate it when you do that!'

From behind the barrier Teal watched anger and distress battle in her face. 'I can't help it—it's the way I am,' he said in a raw voice. 'I've told you over and over not to see me as a challenge.'

So he had. With a wordless exclamation of disgust she pulled free of him. 'What's this about going fishing tomorrow?'

He outlined his plan for Danny to sleep at his house with Scott, so that they could leave early in the morning. 'I'll put the canoe on the car tonight, and take them to a lake I know where you can almost always catch some trout. I'll take good care of Danny, Julie.'

'I trust you absolutely with my son,' she said.

But not otherwise ... was that the unspoken corollary? Teal didn't want to ask: he'd had enough emotion for one night. He wanted to be in the green simplicity of the woods, a fly rod in his hands. Miles from this

woman who made nonsense of the way he had lived his
life for the last two years.

Two years? More like eight.

Or thirty-four.

And that, less that twelve hours later, was where Teal
was. He and the boys fished from the canoe for a couple
of hours, then he took them to shore and made breakfast
over a camp stove. The boys then wandered along the
rocky shore of the lake with their spinning rods while
he fished a stillwater.

The mosquitoes were bad. Maybe it was time to head
home, Teal thought, and tramped through the bushes
toward the cove where Scott and Danny were fishing.
He was screened from them by a thicket of alders, where
yellow-throated warblers were singing with piercing
sweetness and frogs were croaking in ponderous bass
notes; through the coarse-leaved branches he heard Scott
say, 'Do you think they'll get married?' and stopped dead
in his tracks.

'Who?' Danny said. 'My mum and your dad? Nope.
Pass me that lure, Scott.'

'The one with the yellow tassle? Why won't they get
married? I think it's a neat idea.'

With the air of one pronouncing the final word Danny
said, 'I heard my mum tell my dad once that she hated
being married and she'd never do it again.'

There was a silence while Scott thought this over. A
mosquito whined in Teal's ear, and he knew he should
push through the bushes and interrupt a conversation
he was not meant to overhear. Scott said, 'They've got
an agreement. Dad told me about it.'

'That's just so Mum doesn't have to date all those
other guys that were bugging her.'

In a puzzled voice Scott said, 'Then why were they kissing each other in the kitchen last night?'

'You can kiss someone without getting married,' Danny said scornfully.

'Maybe they'll have a baby,' Scott offered.

Danny said, not sounding so sure of himself, 'You gotta do more than kiss to make a baby. It's like those dogs we saw in the playground.'

'Oh,' said Scott. 'That's weird.' There was another silence before he went on with the kind of dogged persistence that was part of his character, 'Still, I'd like them to get married—I really like you mum.'

'Hey!' Danny yelled. 'I've got a strike! Look, it's a real fish.'

'Keep your rod up,' Scott cried, and shouted for his father, the prospect of landing a trout diverting him from the intricacies of sex and marriage.

Teal pushed through the bushes, making rather a lot of noise, and helped Danny land a seven-inch brook trout. 'Good for you,' he said warmly, ruffling the little boy's hair, touched by his excitement. He had grown very fond of Danny, he realized, cutting a forked alder twig so that Danny could carry the fish. He certainly could no longer avoid the fact that the bonds among the four of them—he, Julie, Scott, and Danny—were becoming increasingly interwoven in a way that at some deep level made him profoundly uneasy.

Tomorrow, Julie's day off, they were all going to the beach. All four of them.

Not a wise move.

However, making a mockery of Teal's doubts, the sun was shining brightly the next morning. He was a few minutes late leaving his house; Julie was outside the bungalow waiting for him, and when she saw the black

BMW she stepped into the road, saucily raising her skirt above her knee and striking a provocative pose, her thumb raised like a hitch-hiker.

He laughed out loud, wondering if she'd ever lose the capacity to surprise him. A passing delivery truck blasted its horn, the driver shouting an appreciative comment out his window, and in a swift surge of possessiveness Teal thought, Back off, buddy, she's mine.

She wasn't his. He was a fool to think that way.

He pulled into her driveway, composed his face and climbed out of the car. Julie sauntered toward him, wearing her turquoise skirt, this time with a halter-top whose brevity raised Teal's blood-pressure several notches. He said equably, 'Good morning,' and by a considerable exercise of will did not take her in his arms.

Scott leaped out of the car, threw himself at Julie and hugged her, then ran up the back steps into the house to find Danny. Teal said flatly, 'Does he always do that?'

'That's the first time.' She grimaced. 'Do you think we should renegotiate the renegotiation?'

'I'm a pretty good lawyer and I haven't got the first idea how to go about that,' Teal said with an underlying savagery that frightened her.

'We're heading into some deep waters, Teal.'

He couldn't agree more. 'Let's head for the beach instead. I don't want to have to deal with agreements and negotiations today—it's my day off.'

She smiled, shaking off her unease and lifting her face to the heat of the sun, her hair swinging loose on her shoulders. 'You're right—it's a wonderful day!' she said.

Her beauty, so vivid and inescapable a part of her, always had the power to catch Teal off guard, and now filled him with a fierce and nameless yearning that penetrated all his defenses. Turning away from her so that she couldn't see his face, he opened the trunk of the car and went into the house to get their gear.

They stopped for ice-cream on the way to the beach, and as soon as they arrived the boys stripped off their T-shirts and ran for the ocean. Julie spread her towel on the white sand, looking around her contentedly. 'This is heaven,' she said. Then, trying not to feel self-conscious, she dropped her skirt to the sand, following it with her top.

Her bikini was also turquoise; the stretch marks on her belly, because they made her less than perfect, because they stemmed from another man's child, caught at Teal's heart in a complicated mingling of tenderness and jealousy. Suddenly tired of running from his emotions, he said huskily, 'Lie down and I'll put some suntan lotion on your back.'

As her eyes met his, between them blazed all the complexities of unassuaged desire. She said, 'Only if you'll let me do the same with you.'

'I don't think I've got the will-power to deny you anything right now,' Teal said.

'Then it's too bad this is a public beach,' Julie replied stringently and lay face down on the towel, her cheek resting on her linked hands, her eyes closed.

Keeping a weather eye on the boys, who were frolicking at the water's edge, Teal began smoothing the lotion over her shoulders. Her bra-strap was in his way. He unlinked it, his imagination running riot, and let his palms slide over the curve of her ribcage. The suntan lotion was an excuse; he was honest enough to admit that—an excuse to allow his hands to explore her nakedness for the first time, tracing the concavity of her waist and the soft swell of her hips. His knees brushing her legs as he knelt beside her, he smoothed the pale skin of her inner thigh.

Julie reared her head and in a strangled voice said, 'I could, right now, pull you down on top of me and ravish you in full view of everyone else on the beach, including our two sons—I've never in my life been tempted to behave like that! It's not just me, is it, Teal? Please tell me it's not just me...that you feel the same way.'

She had twisted to face him, grabbing at her bra to cover her breasts. There was real anguish in her face.

'Why do you think I'm kneeling down?' he answered with a crooked smile that didn't reach his eyes. 'To hide the all too obvious evidence that I want you just as much as you want me.'

She glanced downward and blushed scarlet. 'Oh. That's good.'

'Good?' he repeated testily. 'Who are you kidding? It's uncomfortable, it's frustrating, and it scares the living daylights out of me.'

'That, also, is good—it's past time you admitted to some feelings!'

'I've admitted to more in the last six weeks than in my entire life,' he retorted, then could have bitten off his tongue for saying something that, indirectly, was so revealing of his marriage.

She gave him a long, thoughtful look. 'That's the truth, isn't it? You've kept everything to yourself ever since you were little.'

'This is a day off, Julie,' he said tightly. 'No agreements, no negotiations—and no psychoanalysis.'

'And no sex?' she flashed.

He suddenly laughed, a laugh that came from deep in his chest and snapped the tension between them. 'I'd be a blatant hypocrite if I agreed to that.'

A reluctant smile tugged at her mouth. 'Me, too,' she said. After fumbling with the catch on her bra, she scrambled to her feet. 'Now it's your turn,' she added.

Teal lay down, carefully, on his stomach. The first touch of lotion was cool on his skin. But Julie's hands were warm and he closed his eyes, aware through every nerve in his body of the pressure of her palms as they roamed across his shoulderblades and down his spine. No sex? he thought wildly. That was the joke of the century.

'The boys are coming,' she said. 'On the run.'

In a flurry of sand Scott skidded to a halt beside his father. 'When are you guys coming swimming?' he demanded.

'The waves are great!' Danny puffed, and mischievously laid an ice-cold hand on Teal's leg. Teal yelped. Danny and Scott screamed with laughter.

Julie said with a diplomacy that she was sure Teal would appreciate, 'I'll come with you—give your dad a minute or two to relax first.'

Right, Teal thought ironically, glancing over his shoulder as the two boys grabbed Julie's hands and ran down the beach with her. Whenever he was away from her, it seemed entirely possible to keep matters between them at the level of fun. But the minute he touched her that particular three-letter word was immediately replaced by another. A far more potent one, he thought wryly, rolling over onto his back.

He was out of control.

Out of control, and no way back.

Monday was Julie's birthday. She drove home slowly, giving herself time to bridge the gap between the hospital and home. She had brought two striploin steaks and the makings of a salad for supper; her parents would phone, and her sisters, and she would have to battle the usual homesickness that birthdays seemed to engender. She was twenty-nine, she thought, turning down her street. Next year she'd be thirty. And ten years ago she had married Robert.

None of these thoughts was particularly happy.

Cheer up, Julie, she chided herself. Twenty-nine's not old, and it'll be nice to spend a quiet evening with Danny. You're the luckiest woman in the world to have such a wonderful son.

She slowed for her driveway, then ground her gears in sheer surprise. The whole front garden was filled with pink plastic flamingoes circling a sign that said 'Happy 29th, Julie'. They were very ugly flamingoes. Smiling foolishly, she parked the car and climbed the back steps.

Einstein was sitting on the porch looking extremely bad-tempered, a big pink bow attached to his collar. He hissed at her as she opened the door.

The kitchen was full of balloons, pink and white and red. 'Happy birthday, Mum!' Danny cried. Scott jammed a paper hat on her head, yelling, 'Surprise, surprise!' and Teal stepped forward and kissed her on the mouth, putting a glass of champagne in her hand.

Her eyes awash with tears, she sat down on the nearest stool, gave them all a wobbly smile and took a big gulp of champagne. 'I didn't expect this at all,' she quavered. 'Who's responsible for the birds on the front lawn?'

'Einstein is,' Danny giggled. 'We're going out for supper downtown; Teal's taking us. And then we have to come back here for your presents.'

She looked over at the man leaning on the counter; she could still feel the warm pressure of his lips on hers. This was his doing, she knew it. 'Thank you,' she said and raised her glass in a toast to him.

He smiled back, a smile that warmed his eyes and reminded her irresistibly of the tang of the ocean and the heat of the sand and the smooth slide of a man's hands over her bare back. The gate to the castle was finally opening, she thought. But would she be invited to enter? And if invited would she have the courage to walk through the doorway?

She had hated sex with Robert.

As the bubbles of champagne exploded in her throat, she made a pledge to herself. Before she was thirty, she wanted Teal to be her lover. She had no idea how she was going to bring that about, but she wanted it more than she had even wanted anything for any of her birthdays.

She was more sure that she might succeed than she had been a couple of weeks ago; but she was still far from certain.

CHAPTER EIGHT

THE birthday party was still very much on Teal's mind a few days later as he sat in his study trying to concentrate on his latest brief. Doodling with a pen on his legal pad, he remembered how Julie had thrown herself into the celebrations with all the zest of a child. She had changed from her trim white uniform into a sundress that had made his head swim and she had thoroughly enjoyed her meal in the restaurant.

Danny had saved up his money to buy her a cake; it had been adorned with livid green and orange icing and twenty-nine red candles and had, predictably, made her both laugh and cry. Teal had arranged for two sitters, and after the boys were in bed had taken her dancing in a bar downtown.

He hadn't ravished her on the dance-floor under the strobe lights. But it had been a near thing. And he had limited himself to one kiss on her doorstep when he had taken her home, although it had been an intense, prolonged and passionate kiss that had led, also predictably, to another of the many sleepless nights he'd been having lately.

He couldn't go on like this.

But if he and Julie became lovers—a step that in itself broke him out in a cold sweat—the boys would be bound to find out. And then Scott, if not Danny, would be marching the pair of them up the aisle complete with Mendelssohn and white roses.

It was ironic, he thought, that Danny had overheard Julie's aversion to remarrying. He, Teal, had no idea whether she still felt that way. It didn't really matter. His own aversion was more than enough for the two of them—although he sincerely hoped that Scott didn't know he felt that way.

He looked down at the pad of yellow paper, where unconsciously he had been drawing a series of squares and rectangles, rigid, geometric figures with no curves, no flow or spontaneity. His pen had scored the paper deeply enough to tear it.

It would be simpler if this were just about him and Julie. But there were four people involved. If not six, he added unhappily, thinking of the handsome, debonair actor who had been married to Julie, and of Elizabeth, his own wife, who in her way had been as rigid and unspontaneous as the figures he had drawn.

The past had happened. He couldn't erase it, much as he might want to. Perhaps, he thought moodily, drawing a big bunch of balloons floating above the largest square, it had taken Julie's arrival in his life to make him realize how deeply he had been scarred by his marriage. To hear how loudly, to use her phrase, the portcullis had clanged shut.

What was he going to do?

He was not a man used to being at a loss. At work he made dozens of decisions daily, using his intelligence and an intuition gleaned from experience. And nearly always they were the right decisions. Yet now he felt paralyzed, his intelligence battling his intuition with a ferocity that immobilized him. Rational thought told him to run a mile from the woman with the tumbled hair and the smoke-blue eyes. Intuition said, Stay; she's important to you. Vital. If you run from her, you'll never get a second chance.

With deep relief he heard the thud of Scott's steps on the oak stairway; it never failed to astonish him how much noise an eight-year-old boy could make. 'I'm in the study,' he called, and shoved the legal pad in the drawer of his desk.

'Dad, could you take me to the store? I want to get some sugar. Danny and I are going to sell lemonade 'cause we need the money to get a model airplane set.'

'We'll take our bikes,' Teal said, standing up and stretching the tension from his shoulders. The exercise would do him good, and maybe when he got back he'd be able to concentrate on his job rather than his sex life.

His non-existent sex life.

And whose choice was that? No one's but his.

'I wonder what's taking Scott so long?' Danny said restlessly. He had been painstakingly squeezing lemons into a big pitcher, had emptied both ice trays into the juice and now needed the sugar.

'Maybe his dad couldn't take him right away,' Julie said soothingly. She had just gotten home from work. She'd had a relatively peaceful shift and had been able to catch up on some paperwork, and tonight she planned to go to bed early in the hopes of catching up on her sleep. The trouble was, she didn't want to sleep alone any more. She wanted Teal beside her in the bed.

As she got a mug out of the cupboard and plugged in the kettle, Danny's voice broke into her train of thought. 'Can I take my bike and see if Scott's home yet?'

'Sure. Stay on the sidewalk, though.'

She made her favorite Earl Grey tea. Taking the mug out on the back porch, she pushed Einstein off the lawn chair, much to his displeasure, and sat down. He immediately jumped up in her lap and the tea slopped over the arm of the chair, just missing her thigh. She hastily put the mug down on the small plastic table beside her and rubbed Einstein's ears, a move that never failed to reduce him to bleary-eyed ecstasy. Julie liked Einstein. He knew what he wanted out of life and did his utmost to ensure he got it.

'I wish I could catch Teal as easily as you catch birds,' she told him, kneading his fur.

Einstein blinked complacently.

Danny peddled up the driveway and let his bike fall against the fence. 'He's not home yet,' he said disconsolately. 'His dad wouldn't have taken him for ice-cream without me, would he?'

'I'm sure he wouldn't, Danny...maybe they met someone they knew at the store. Do you want me to go over to the playground with you while you're waiting?'

Danny brightened. 'We could play catch with my new baseball glove.'

He ran inside to find it. Julie sipped her tea, stroking Einstein's fur. While she was more than happy that Danny and Scott were such close friends, at times she worried a little that they were too close. Too dependent on each other for everything.

Danny came outside brandishing his glove and she drained her mug. 'I'll have to get my sneakers,' she said. 'Two seconds.'

She went inside, found her sneakers in the very back of her closet, and was tying the laces when the telephone by her bed rang. She picked up the receiver and said, 'Hello?'

There was a pause, then a small voice said, 'Julie?'

'Yes, it's Julie...is that you, Scott? Speak up, dear, I can hardly hear you.'

'Julie, my dad...' His voice trailed away altogether.

Gripping the receiver, filled with a sudden cold terror, Julie said sharply, 'Scott, where are you? What's wrong?'

Voices spoke in the background. Then a woman said, 'Is that Julie Ferris?'

In an agony of impatience Julie said, 'Yes . . . please tell me what's wrong.'

'It's Rita Glassco, from Emergency. Scott's father was hit by a car; he's being looked at now. Possible head and chest injuries, not sure what else. Scott wanted to phone you.'

Julie liked Rita, who was also a single parent. 'I'll be there as soon as I can,' she said rapidly. 'Rita, would you let me speak to Scott again, please?' After a pause she heard the sound of Scott's breathing. 'Scott,' she said as forcibly as she could, 'Danny and I will come right away—we'll be there in ten minutes. And Scott, your dad will be all right, do you hear me?'

'Yeah,' he said, sounding anything but convinced.

Julie grabbed her purse, ran for the back door and quickly explained to Danny what had happened. 'Hop in the car while I lock up.'

She drove the shortest route to the hospital, agonizing over every red light, blasting her horn at a couple of tourists who couldn't decide which lane to take and ended up blocking both. But finally she pulled up in the nurses' parking lot. Taking Danny's hand firmly in hers, she ran to the emergency department.

It was in its usual state of controlled chaos. Rita was talking on the phone at the main desk, and when she saw Julie gestured to the second waiting-room. Julie hurried down the hall and walked into the room. Several people were sitting in the chairs lined up against the wall; but she had eyes only for Scott. He was hunched over, staring at the scuffed toes of his Adidas sneakers with a dull misery that frightened her out of her wits. He looked like a child who had totally lost hope.

Teal wasn't dead . . . he couldn't be.

'Scott, we're here,' she said.

He looked up and in one convulsive movement flung himself at her. She staggered under his weight, knelt on the floor and wrapped her arms around him, holding him hard; he was trembling all over. Gathering Danny into her embrace as well, she asked urgently, 'Have you seen your dad yet, Scott?' He shook his head. 'Have they said what's wrong with him?' His dark hair, so like Teal's, rubbed against her cheek in denial.

'I know the nurse at the desk—let's go find out what's happening,' she said.

But he clutched her all the harder. It didn't take much sensitivity to realize that he was terrified of what he might hear; as, indeed, was she. 'We'll all go together,' she said. 'Come on, love.'

He glued himself to her side and allowed himself to be steered to the main desk; Rita put her hand over the receiver of the telephone and said hastily, 'They were taking Mr Carruthers up to X-Ray, and they'll bring him back to Room 9... Sorry, sir, you were saying?'

Room 9 was empty. Julie stood irresolutely in the hall. She could go up to the X-ray department or she could wait here. Then her dilemma was solved for her. A stretcher was wheeled round the corner. The man on it was Teal.

His eyes were closed and his face drained of color. The skin had been scraped from one cheek and all down his arm. His chest was bare. Then, in sheer terror, she saw that one of the doctors accompanying the stretcher was Nick.

Nick was a neurosurgeon. Neurosurgeons were only called in for serious injuries.

I love Teal, she thought with the clarity of true despair. I love him... he can't die.

Nick looked up, saw her standing there and came toward her, giving her the intimate smile he bestowed on all women who were over sixteen and under sixty. 'Julie, what a nice surprise . . . what are you doing here?'

Torn by a paralyzing fear, fury that Nick could be so callous, and the sheer wonder of her discovery, she faltered. 'Teal . . . what's wrong with him?'

'What are you talking about?'

'For God's sake, Nick—this is Teal on the stretcher,' she cried. 'Tell me what's wrong with him—I have to know!'

'Oh, he's not my patient,' Nick said casually.

'He's *not*?'

Nick grabbed Julie's sleeve. 'You look like you're going to faint...here, sit down.' He turned to the intern. 'What's the problem with Carruthers?'

'Concussion, three broken ribs, contusions and bruising,' the intern replied. 'He'll be here for a day or so.'

'Nothing serious,' Nick remarked. 'You surprise me, Julie; that evening at the symphony benefit I got the impression you and Teal were antagonists more than lovers.'

Ignoring Nick, she grasped the intern's white sleeve and said over-loudly, 'That's the truth? You're not hiding anything?'

'You can see the chart,' Nick interposed in an annoyed voice.

Aware that she was behaving very unprofessionally, Julie stooped down by Scott and said in the same loud voice, 'He's all right, Scott. He'll be in hospital for a couple of days and then he'll be home.'

But Scott was staring at his father's motionless form on the stretcher and gave no evidence of having heard her. 'He's not dead,' she said violently. Scott gave her a blank look and said nothing. Desperate to get through to him, Julie took the boy's hand in hers and laid it on Teal's bare chest. 'See,' she said, 'he's breathing; can you feel it?'

Teal's torso was rising and falling slowly and steadily. Scott's lashes flickered. He said in a thin voice, 'He's not dead?'

'He's breathing, sweetheart,' she repeated forcefully. 'He's going to be all right.'

In the same emotionless voice Scott said, 'I thought he was dead. Like my mum.'

Julie's face contorted with compassion. Having no idea what to say, she put her arms around Scott and held him as tightly as she could, feeling tears of relief and pity stream down her cheeks, and wishing Scott would cry as well.

Nick said officiously, 'You'll have to move, Julie; you're blocking the corridor.'

The attendant was wheeling the stretcher down the hall, the intern briskly walking alongside it. Half carrying Scott, Danny trailing along behind her, Julie followed the little cavalcade into the treatment-room. The intern said, 'The orthopaedic resident will be along to tape him up. Then we'll get him a room upstairs. Shouldn't be too long.'

'Do you know what happened?' Julie asked.

'Car went through a stop sign and ran into his bicycle.' The intern shrugged. 'He was lucky—could have been a lot worse.'

He could have been killed, Julie thought, and felt the same fierce upwelling of terror and love in her breast. If she had ever pictured falling in love again, she had envisioned a moonlit night and sweetly scented summer roses and herself in a filmy dress with flowers in her hair. Not blue jeans and a bare hospital room and two frightened little boys as her companions.

The intern left the room. Julie sat down on the only chair, pulled Scott on to her lap and held Danny in the circle of her other arm. 'Broken ribs are painful, but not serious, Scott,' she said. 'The doctors'll probably keep your dad in hospital a couple of days because they like to watch a concussion. Truly he'll be all right.'

Scott's eyes were glued to the motionless figure on the stretcher, and she wasn't at all sure that he had heard her. 'I wouldn't lie to you, Scott!'

Without turning his head, he said with stony politeness, 'The policeman told me my mum would be all right.'

Julie's mouth tightened. How had Elizabeth Carruthers died? Why had there been a policeman—had it been another accident? Absently stroking Scott's rigid shoulders, she knew she lacked the courage to ask him. If indeed he would answer, which she doubted.

She smiled down at Danny. 'Are you okay?'

He gave her a wordless nod. Concentrating on calming her own churned-up emotions, Julie held both boys close and waited. A nurse rushed in, checked Teal's vital signs and left, all without saying a word. Twenty minutes later the resident walked in. He had dark circles under his eyes and rumpled red hair, and had once had a long conversation with Julie in the cafeteria about white-water canoeing, a sport to which he was addicted.

'Julie—what are you doing here?' he asked.

I'm in love with the man on the stretcher ... 'Teal Carruthers is a—a friend of mine, Steve,' she said, and rubbed her chin on Scott's head. 'This is his son.'

Steve had unclipped the X-rays and was holding them up to the light. 'Clean breaks,' he said. 'He looks in good shape, shouldn't take overly long healing...he'll be okay, sonny.' And he gave Scott a tired grin.

Scott stared back expressionlessly. Julie sighed. It was a good thing she had the next three days off; Scott was obviously going to need a great deal of attention.

After Steve had taped Teal's ribs with casual expertise, he said, 'Do you know if they've got him a room yet?' Julie shook her head. 'I'll check at the front desk for you; the place is a madhouse tonight. See you, Julie.' He directed another smile at Scott. 'No bicycle riding for your dad for a while,' he said, scribbled some notes on the chart, and left the room.

An hour later Teal had been transferred to a private room on the fifth floor. The move had made him restless; his eyelids were flickering and he was trying to speak, although Julie couldn't catch what he was saying. It was getting late; she should take the boys home and put them to bed. But she was reluctant to leave until Scott had at least seen his father recover consciousness.

She leaned over the bed and said softly, 'It's all right, Teal...we're here.'

He moved his arm, his hand searching for a hold on the smooth white coverlet. As pain convulsed his features, his eyes flew open, looking straight at her. His irises opaque with bewilderment, he whispered, 'Julie?'

But before she could reply his confusion was ripped aside by an overriding terror. 'Scott—where's Scott?' he burst out, trying to push himself up from the bed. But the effort was too much for him. With an animal sound of pure agony he collapsed back on the pillow.

Feeling as inept as a student on her first night on the wards, Julie put her palm on his chest and said clearly, 'Scott's right here—he wasn't hurt at all. Do you hear me, Teal? Scott's here by the bed.'

Teal's chest was heaving as he fought the pain down, his struggle so apparent and so intense that Julie felt tears crowd her eyes. She blinked them back; this was no time for her to cry. Then he opened his eyes again. She hitched Scott halfway up the metal railings on the bed and watched Teal's vision focus on his son, a frown of fierce concentration furrowing his brow.

'Scott,' he said hoarsely. 'I was so afraid you'd been hit...'

Scott shook his head. Although Julie could feel that the boy was trembling again, his face gave nothing away. Teal's eyes had flooded with tears of weakness; Scott's were dry. She said with a calmness she was far from feeling, 'I'll take him to my place until you're home... I don't have to work so I can look after him through the day as well.'

'Thanks,' Teal muttered. With an obvious effort of will he looked straight at his son. 'I love you, Scott,' he said.

The effort had exhausted him; his eyes closed. Julie, who would have given a great deal to have Teal say those words to her, said quietly, 'Scott, if you're ready to leave, I think we should go. Your dad needs all the rest he can get and he knows you're all right now. Why don't we go home and I'll make you both some hot chocolate before you go to bed?'

Scott wriggled free, sliding to the floor. 'Okay,' he said in a dull voice.

'We can phone first thing in the morning to see how he is,' she added, wishing she knew what was going on in his head.

'You can sleep in my bed if you want,' Danny offered. Scott smiled minimally, slipping his hand into Julie's, and walked out of the room without a backward look. Julie asked the floor nurse to let them know if there was

any change in Teal's condition, then took the boys home.
She made up the other bunk bed in Danny's room, found
Scott a pair of Danny's pajamas, added extra marsh-
mallows to the hot chocolate and read several chapters
from one of the more soothing of her son's eclectic collection of books.

Danny fell asleep. She tucked Scott in, kissing him
goodnight. 'I'm in the next room if you need me and
I'll leave a night light on in the hall. Sleep well,
sweetheart.'

After pulling on a pair of cotton pajamas, Julie went
to bed herself. She had expected to lie awake worrying
about Teal, and must have fallen instantly into a deep
sleep; the next thing she knew she was lying wide-eyed
in the darkness wondering what had woken her. Then
she heard it again: a child's thin cry of terror.

She was out of bed in a flash and into the adjoining
bedroom. Danny was peacefully asleep, burrowed under
the covers, Einstein curled into his knees. But Scott was
thrashing under the sheets, whimpering in his sleep. Julie
took him by the shoulders. 'Wake up—you're having a
nightmare, Scott.'

His head jerked up and he grabbed her, clinging to
her as though he would never let go, his thin little body
shaking violently. It took Julie a minute to realize that
he was crying; with a pang of acute pity she heard the
words that he was mumbling into her shoulder over and
over again, 'I want my mum, I want my mum...'

Instinctively she gathered him into her arms and lay
down beside him, pulling the blankets round him. He
cried for a long time before, between one breath and the
next, he fell asleep. Julie lay still in the darkness.
Somehow she had to find out what had happened to
Scott's mother.

Nor did she change her mind in the morning. The boys hadn't been up for half an hour before Scott picked a fight with Danny and was openly rude to her when she intervened, behavior so unlike him that she was non-plussed. Yet when they approached the main door of the hospital that afternoon, Scott was clutching her hand so tightly he was hurting her.

Teal was propped up in bed when she led the boys into his room. Conquering the urge to throw herself at him as Scott had thrown himself at her, she said with commendable lightness, 'Your face looks like you col-lided with a dump truck, not a car. How are you feeling?'

'Like I collided with a dump truck,' he said with a careful smile. 'Whatever else you do, don't make me laugh. Hi there, Danny. Scott, how are you doing, son?' He patted the bed. 'Why don't you climb up here so I can give you a hug?'

Julie took Danny to the cafeteria for an ice-cream, and when she went back upstairs asked both boys to wait in the recreation-room down the hall because she needed to talk to Teal. Although he looked worn out when she went back in, she hardened her heart. Briefly she described how Scott had been behaving. 'So I need to know what happened to your wife,' she finished.

He should have realized Scott would react that way, Teal thought, his helplessness like a dead weight in his chest. Trying to gather his wits through a headache that held his forehead in a vise, he said, 'It was a senseless accident. She slipped on some ice at the edge of the road when she was walking downtown—it was in January—and fell, hitting her head against the curb. She fractured her skull and died of a haemorrhage in hospital.' Playing with the hem of the sheet, he added tersely, 'Scott was with her.'

Teal's explanation made total sense of Scott's behavior. 'So this is the second time,' Julie whispered. 'Of course he didn't believe me when I kept telling him you'd be all right. And of course he's having nightmares.'

'He is?' Julie nodded. Unable to restrain his frustration, Teal said, 'It's hardly fair to expect you to cope with all this, Julie. He's not your child—why should you be saddled with him?'

She felt as though Teal had struck her in the face. 'Surely you'd do the same for me.'

'It's still not right—especially on your days off, when you need your rest.'

'I'm not complaining, Teal,' she said, an edge to her voice. 'I needed to know what happened to Elizabeth so I'd know best how to deal with Scott's fears. That's all.'

He hitched himself higher in the bed, gasping from the pain in his ribs. 'I'm not saying I don't appreciate what you're doing—naturally I'm very grateful to you.'

Gratitude was not high on the list of emotional responses Julie wanted from Teal. But she shouldn't lose her temper with a man who had three broken ribs and a concussion. A man she loved.

'Thank you for telling me about Elizabeth,' she said stiffly. 'Do you want me to bring Scott in again this evening?'

The vise had tightened around Teal's temples, and he hated feeling so powerless. 'I could call Marylee . . . perhaps she could take Scott for a few days.'

'Don't you trust me?' Julie grated.

'This is about imposition. Not about trust.'

'Teal Carruthers,' she seethed, 'you're being about as obtuse as a man can be—which is pretty damned obtuse. I'm happy to look after Scott. Nor do I feel as though you're imposing him on me. Have you got that straight?'

'We'll discuss this later when I'm capable of stringing more than two sentences together,' he snarled.

She stalked to the door. 'I'll bring Scott in at seven this evening. Your problem is that you can't stand being indebted to me.'

That she was totally accurate didn't help at all. 'If I could stand upright, you wouldn't get away with walking out on me!'

She poked her head back in the door. 'Try me,' she said, and blew him a kiss. She was behaving very childishly. But there was a certain satisfaction in such behavior; which was maybe why children did it.

Scott had another nightmare at three o'clock the next morning. Again Julie woke him. As he huddled in her arms, she said gently, 'Your dad told me what happened to your mother—no wonder you were so scared when the car hit his bicycle. Why don't you tell me how it happened?'

The words spilled over one another. 'We were driving down the street and this neat black sports car was speeding at the intersection. Dad yelled at me to brake, so I did. He braked too, but the car ran into him anyway. The police said afterwards the man in the sports car had been drinking; that was why he didn't see the stop sign. Dad hit the road and there was all this blood and people standing around watching, and then the ambulance and the cruiser came and they took me to the hospital, too. That's when I phoned you.'

'You did absolutely the right thing,' she said. 'It must have been terrifying for you, Scott... Why don't you try and sleep now, and you'll feel better in the morning?'

'I was real scared,' he confessed, shoving his head under her chin.

Within moments he was asleep again, curled up against her with a trust that touched her to the heart. If she loved Teal as woman to man, she was beginning to love Scott as a mother loved a son.

What had Teal said? 'He's not your child'...

No wonder those words had hurt so much.

Her pledge to become Teal's lover now seemed rather infantile. She still wanted to make love to him; that hadn't changed. But she wanted far more than that. She wanted Teal to trust her, to let down his guard and shed his control once and for all.

She wanted a lot. The sun, the moon and the stars, she thought ruefully. The whole man and no half-measures.

Julie spent the next morning cleaning and tidying Teal's house. Then from her garden and his she purloined as many flowers as she could, putting vases of brightly colored blooms in his bedroom and the living-room and the kitchen. Scott trailed around after her, talking non-stop as though to make up for his silence the last two days. Just before lunch Teal came home.

Julie had picked him up at the hospital and driven him back to his house. He negotiated the back steps and sat down on one of the kitchen chairs to catch his breath, saying shakily, 'I feel like an old man of ninety. At this rate it'll take me fifteen minutes to make it to my bedroom.'

Scott grinned at him. 'Julie's getting lunch for us and she's cooking supper too. She made gumdrop cookies yesterday and today she vacuumed the whole house. That was nice of her, eh, Dad?'

Julie winced; she wanted no more remarks about impositions. 'It gave me an excuse not to invite my landlady over for tea,' she said.

Teal looked around, his eyes brushing over the big bouquet of shasta daisies and dahlias on the table; they couldn't by any stretch of the imagination be called colorless. 'Mrs Inkpen could learn a thing or two from you,' he said, and pushed himself up from the table. 'It's ridiculous, but I need to lie down. Will you come up with me, Scott?'

'Sure, Dad. But then I have to help Julie set the table.'

The two of them disappeared in the direction of the stairs. Looking bored, Danny sprawled himself across the nearest chair. Julie started making sandwiches. She wasn't imagining things: ever since the accident Teal had been avoiding anything that could be construed as intimacy with her. He didn't want to be beholden to her. He resented her cheering up Elizabeth's kitchen with a few flowers.

Perhaps he didn't want her here at all.

Just because she loved him, it didn't mean he loved her.

Scott took up a lunch tray, staying there while Teal ate, and trotted back down with the empty tray an hour later. 'Dad's going to have a sleep,' he reported. Julie took the boys swimming all afternoon, delaying her return as long as she could.

When she got back, Scott vanished upstairs again, Danny played listlessly in the garden, and she baked chicken legs and made a salad. This time she took the tray up herself. Teal was dozing in the big bed, the breeze wafting the curtains like sails catching the wind. Scott was curled up on one corner of the bed, reading. 'I've brought your supper, Teal,' she said.

His eyes jerked open. He had been dreaming about her; she had been driving him along a country lane in a black sports car, so fast that they were out of control. Pulling his body up in the bed, feeling sweat break out on his forehead, he wished passionately that anyone but Julie were bringing him his supper.

'Thanks,' he said briefly.

'Your supper's downstairs, Scott,' she said.

'I want to eat with my dad.'

'Let him eat up here, Julie—it's one less for you to worry about.'

Danny was missing Scott's company, but Julie was darned if she was going to say so. She prepared another tray, and after she had taken it upstairs she and Danny ate at the picnic table under the maple tree. Danny picked at his food and she had little appetite; she felt ill at ease, her senses overly alert like those of an animal waiting for a storm.

When Danny disappeared into the tree house, she went inside to clean up the kitchen. Scott brought the trays down, lingering by the sink as she rinsed off the plates. She understood why he had been staying so close to Teal ever since the accident, and was searching for the words to explain that Danny was feeling abandoned when Scott said, 'I gotta favor to ask.'

'Sure,' she said, smiling at him as she reached for the detergent.

'A big favor. A real big one.'

He was looking very serious. More cautiously she said, 'If I can.'

'I want you to marry my dad.'

The plastic bottle of detergent slipped from her fingers and thumped to the floor. She said blankly, 'I can't do that, Scott.'

'Why not?'

Because he hasn't asked me. She picked up the bottle and turned on the tap, her mind going round in circles.

'Marriage is a big step,' she hedged. 'I'm divorced and your dad's widowed, so we've both been hurt . . . we're not ready to get married again.'

'Danny and I have seen you kissing Dad—so you must like him.'

'I do like him. But you can't marry everyone you like.'

His jaw set in a way she recognized, Scott said, 'You mean you don't want to marry him.'

The sink was on the verge of overflowing. Julie grabbed for the tap and knew that if she were truthful she'd say, If he loved me, I'd marry him . . . if he'd stop being so controlled and let his feelings out, I'd marry him. Instead she said, 'I can't answer that, Scott. I know you don't understand, and I hate it when adults tell children they'll understand when they're older . . . but that's what I'm saying.'

Scott was rhythmically kicking the leg of one of the chairs, his face stormy—the storm she had been subconsciously waiting for, Julie realized with a sinking heart. 'It's all your fault!' he blurted. 'I like it when you're here; it's like you're my mum, and I don't see why you won't marry my dad!'

Tears were hanging on his lashes. Feeling her way, she asked, 'Have you spoken to your father about this?'

Glaring at her, he said rudely, 'Why should I? It's your fault, not his—Danny told me you wouldn't get married ever again. I wish you'd never come here!'

He ran outdoors, slamming the screen door behind him. Julie took a step after him, then halted in frustration. It was better to leave him on his own for a while; he obviously wasn't in the mood to listen to reason. So she started cleaning up the dishes, her heart like a chunk of ice in her breast; although normally nimble-fingered, she broke a glass and chipped a plate. Finally, with immense reluctance, she went upstairs.

Teal was standing by the bureau in his bedroom, trying to get his arms into a cotton shirt. As she moved to help him, he said shortly, 'I can manage.'

Her nails digging into her palms, she said, 'Teal, don't you think it would be better if I slept on the couch downstairs tonight? You're still pretty shaky on your feet.' She managed a credible smile. 'Your own personal nurse.'

It was the last thing he wanted. 'That's not necessary, Julie; I'll be fine. Anyway, you have to go to work tomorrow, don't you?'

'I could leave from here.'

Not looking at her, he said, 'Go home and get some rest—you must need it after the last couple of days.'

Everything Julie had done since his accident had been motivated by love. But she couldn't tell him that. 'You're shutting me out again,' she said.

'I'm beginning to think I *was* crazy to suggest that damned agreement. You were right—there are four of us involved here, not two, and there's a huge potential for hurting the boys.'

What about me? she wanted to scream. With careful restraint she said, 'What are you getting at?'

He straightened, knowing he didn't have the energy for any kind of a showdown. 'Nothing other than that I think you should go home tonight.'

If she lived up to her reputation for honesty and courage, she'd be telling Teal that she was in love with him—and knew she couldn't do it. Steeling herself, Julie asked, 'Is it Elizabeth who's in the way—because you still love her?'

He said violently, 'I don't want to lie to you, Julie—will you for God's sake leave it alone?'

Too proud to cry in front of him, she said quietly, 'I'm sorry... I guess I should have called Mrs Inkpen to come here today. I'll take Danny home now.'

She turned away from him and walked down the oak stairs, blind to the evening light that fell softly on the burnished wood. Picking up her handbag from the counter, she put her sweater round her shoulders because she was cold. Then, as shrill voices penetrated her distress, she realized that the boys were arguing outdoors. Through the open screen she heard Scott cry, 'It's all your mother's fault—she's the one who won't marry my dad!'

'It isn't her fault,' Danny retorted.

'It is so!'

'I bet your dad hasn't asked her. It's the man who's supposed to do the asking.'

'She'd say no even if he did,' Scott threw back. 'You told me she would. You told me she didn't like being married to your father and she didn't want to get married ever again.'

Frozen to the spot, Julie heard Danny say sulkily, 'I bet your dad could change her mind if he wanted to.' And then she heard something else: Teal's footsteps coming into the kitchen. Wishing him a thousand miles away, she stood as still as a post.

'It's not his fault,' Scott yelled. 'It's your mum who won't get married.'

'Shut up!' Danny screeched, and to her horror Julie heard a sudden thud and then bodies scuffling in the bushes. Jerked into motion, she ran outside and down the steps. Grabbing at the nearest body, she hauled Scott off. He was sobbing, like a stuck record, 'I hate you, I hate you...'

Danny picked himself up, flailing at the air with his fists and hitting his mother instead of Scott. 'I don't want to be your friend any more,' he cried. 'I hate you, too!' Then he turned and ran down the driveway as fast as he could.

From the door Teal ordered, 'Come inside right now, Scott. Julie, you'd better go after Danny—I'll talk to you later.'

She shot a quick glance at the man standing on the porch. His face was set in grim lines, the scrapes and bruises on his cheek making him look like a stranger, someone she'd never known and never would know. Pivoting, she ran after her son.

Danny had headed straight home and was banging in futile rage on the back door. Julie pulled out her keys and said, 'Stop it, Danny—it's okay to be angry but you don't break things. Go indoors and we'll talk when you've calmed down a bit.'

Danny ran for the stairs, scooping up Einstein as he went. Julie locked the back door, sank down on the nearest stool and put her head down on the counter. She had done the stupidest thing in the world: for the second time in her life she had fallen in love with a man who was unreachable. And, once again, her son was paying the price.

CHAPTER NINE

Two hours later the telephone rang. Danny was in bed asleep, worn out by emotion. Einstein, who had allowed himself to be hugged for the better part of an hour, was now outdoors hunting mice. Julie had changed into her housecoat and poured herself a glass of wine in an attempt to relax. That she was now regarding a telephone as if it were a boa constrictor loose in her bedroom proved the futility of her efforts.

Gingerly she picked up the receiver. 'Hello?'

'It's Teal. How's Danny?'

'Asleep. And Scott?'

'The same. Marylee phoned an hour ago—she came into town today and heard about the accident. Scott and I are going back to the cottage with her tomorrow morning to spend a few days there. It'll give me the chance to recuperate and the boys the chance to cool down. So I'll call you when we get back.'

Julie said, quite rationally, 'Do you think that's a good idea?'

'Obviously—or I wouldn't be doing it.'

'You don't think that you're running away from conflict?'

Teal didn't want her opposing the only course of action open to him. 'Our two sons need to learn that they're not the ones calling the shots.'

Also quite rationally, Julie decided to lose her temper. 'So who is calling the shots, Teal? Your parents, who didn't want you? Your wife, who's been dead for two

151

years? Or you, who's scared to death to trust in your emotions?'

'Don't push me, Julie!'

'You're the one who's doing the pushing—pushing me away! You do it all the time.'

Out of some deep place he hadn't even recognized Teal said bluntly, 'When I come back, I think we should end our agreement.'

The words were like a death-knell. Julie's temper died, and into the vacuum rushed terror and despair. Drawing on every scrap of her pride—an emotion a long way from either honesty or courage—she said, 'Fine. Have a good time at the cottage. Goodbye.'

She put the phone back on the hook. After pouring the wine down the bathroom sink, she went to bed and cried herself to sleep.

The next few days were among the worst in Julie's life. Teal's absence made her feel as if one of her limbs had been amputated: she was left with pain and the ghostly memory of what had been.

Adding to her distress, she had to work three straight shifts, which meant leaving Danny with a sitter at a time when he badly needed to be with her; the sensation this gave her was of being torn in two, one part doing her best for her patients, the other frantic to be home with her son. Danny moped around the house, missing Scott, and, so she discovered on the third night, missing more than Scott. She was drying his hair before he went to bed when he said out of the blue, 'Teal's just like my dad.'

Julie's hands stilled. 'What do you mean?'

'He's gone away. Like my dad always did.'

Tears filmed Julie's eyes; she had been crying a lot the last few days. And how could she deny what Danny was saying? It was true. Robert had spent very little time at the old house on the shore. His career had always taken precedence over his family, a career that had progressed steadily from small local theaters to the lights of Broadway. And she now knew that Melissa also had kept him away.

That Danny was suffering as deeply as she galvanized Julie into action. She said, 'Danny, I've got the next four days off. If we can get reservations, would you like to go to Prince Edward Island? We could go to the beach, and see *Anne of Green Gables*, and go to all the amusement parks.'

'When?'

'Tomorrow,' she said recklessly.

'Yeah,' he said, with the first sign of interest he'd shown in anything since Scott had gone away.

As though it was meant to be, everything fell into place. Julie paid for the cottage with the money she had been saving for a down payment on a house, and they caught the ferry to the island the next morning. Danny met other children at the cottages and at the beach, he loved the musical about the little orphan girl with red hair, and three days into their holiday Julie arranged a switch of shifts by long distance so that they could stay an extra day.

Danny looked like a different boy by the time they caught the ferry home. On the outskirts of Halifax they picked up Einstein at the kennels where he had been boarded, and twenty minutes later turned into their driveway.

Einstein had not appreciated his stay at the kennels. He spat at Danny when the boy opened the latch on the cage, and streaked for the bushes in the back garden. Crouched under the lilac, he growled at them, his tail lashing. No doubt he'd dig up some of her flowers in revenge, Julie thought, wishing she could find this funny, and climbed out of the car, stretching her limbs.

She and Danny began carrying their cases and gear into the house, which smelled empty and deserted and gave her very little sense of having come home. None of the messages on her answering machine was from Teal, and her mail was a collection of bills and fliers. Crushed by disappointment, she fought back tears.

What would she do if ending the agreement meant Teal never wanted to see her again? It was the question she had struggled with all the time she was away; the only answer she had reached was that she didn't think she could bear it.

She went back outside to untie the lobster pot they had bought from a fisherman near Souris. She was wrestling with the knots when, with a screech of brakes, a black car pulled up at the end of the driveway. Scott hurtled out of the front seat and ran toward them. He stopped short a couple of feet from Danny, who was trying to do up Einstein's cage again, and said in a rush, 'I'm sorry I was mad at you—I don't hate you. Can we be friends again?'

Danny stood up, his grin exposing a new gap in his teeth. 'Yeah...let's go play in the tree house.'

They ran back down the driveway, Danny yelling on the way, 'Hi, Teal!' Then they were gone and Julie was left with a dark-haired man striding toward her, dressed in an immaculate grey business suit. He must have just come from work, she thought, and wished she didn't look so crumpled and wind-blown.

As he got closer, she saw something else: he was in a towering rage. His face still had not entirely healed, giving him the air of a high-class gangster; she quelled any impulse she might have to giggle. He gripped her by the elbow and said, 'Where the *devil* have you been?'

'I left a message on your machine—we went to PEI.'

'You were supposed to get back yesterday!'

'I changed shifts with one of the other nurses so we could stay another day.'

'Did it occur to you to let me know?'

'No,' she said baldly, 'it didn't. You're the one who doesn't want to get involved—remember?'

'It's too late,' he grated. 'I *am* involved. Whether I want to be or not. The last twenty-four hours have been the longest of my entire life. You'd had a car accident. You'd been abducted. You'd met someone else and married him. For someone who deals in facts, my imagination's had a field day.'

Julie's heart was beating as fast as Einstein's when he was stalking a bird. 'You sure don't look very happy about being involved.'

Biting off the words, he said, 'I was involved once before. It caused me one hell of a lot of grief.'

'Elizabeth . . .'

'Right—Elizabeth. Congratulations, Julie.'

Julie wanted to ask whether he meant grief literally, or whether he had meant misery; the distinction was all-important. She said, 'So what are you going to do about me, Teal?'

'I know what I want to do.'

She remembered those horrible days before she had gone away, and the many hours of her holiday she had spent sunk in despair. 'We both know that,' she stormed. 'You want to end the agreement. Run away and hide so you won't have to change. Well, go ahead. Do it. *I* won't stop you!'

'I want to go to bed with you,' Teal said.

Her jaw dropped. *What*?'

With savage self-contempt he added, 'You'll laugh at me if I say it would take less courage to jump off a hundred-foot cliff.'

Feeling as stunned as if she were the one with the concussion, Julie said, 'No, I won't laugh.'

'Would you go to bed with me, Julie? Would you do that?'

She was still not quite sure she could believe the evidence of her own ears. 'We'd have to end the agreement,' she said foolishly. 'It said no sex.'

'That agreement was one of the stupidest moves I've ever made in my whole life.' He tightened his grasp on her arm. 'For heaven's sake say you'll do it.'

She gave him a small smile. 'I brought you back a present,' she said. 'You can open it when you get home—although make sure Scott's not around. It's my answer to your question.'

Teal scanned her face. He didn't see how a present was much of an answer, and he was desperate to know he hadn't lost her. With a muffled groan he pulled her toward him, lowered his head and began kissing her. For a moment she resisted him. But then to his infinite joy she kissed him back, her body curving to fit his in a way that inflamed him. He muttered against her lips, 'The answer's yes, isn't it? Tell me it's yes...'

She wound her arms around him, felt him flinch with pain and said, horrified, 'I forgot about your ribs—I'm sorry!'

'I forget about them too, until they remind me. You still haven't said yes.'

She reached up and kissed him very explicitly. 'Trust your senses, Teal,' she said.

He hadn't lost her; she still wanted him. Almost dizzy with relief, Teal said, 'Why can't I open your present in front of Scott?'

'Wait and see,' she said with a mischievous grin.

'When are your next days off?' he demanded.

'Not for five days. I owe Shirley a shift.'

'I've waited thirty-four years...why does five days sound like forever?' he said. 'I'd better head home, Julie, and see what the boys are up to.'

'I'm glad they're friends again.'

'Not half as glad as I am.' He kissed her again. 'I don't deserve this—I was a fool to tell you I wanted to end the agreement.'

'It hurt. A lot,' she said honestly.

He had known for weeks that he had the power to arouse her; he had been hiding from the knowledge that he could also hurt her. All the old fears twanged along his nerves. Take her to bed first, Teal, he told himself, and worry about feelings afterwards.

'Have you eaten?' he asked. 'Let me go home and change, and the four of us could go out for dinner.'

'Yes,' said Julie, and smiled at him.

'Every time I'm away from you I forget how beautiful you are,' Teal said roughly, lifting the weight of her hair in his two hands and holding it away from her face. 'I always doubt that you can possibly be as beautiful as I remember.'

Mesmerized by the wonderment in his gray eyes, Julie knew she had been right to risk bringing him home a gift. She smiled at him again, letting her happiness shine in her face.

He said huskily, 'When you look at me like that, everything seems so simple,' and gave her another lingering kiss, nibbling at her lower lip. 'I must go home—how long before you're ready for dinner?'

'Give me an hour.' She stepped back, took a large gift-wrapped box out of the back seat of her car and passed it to him. 'I hope this is what you want,' she said very seriously.

'Why don't I open it right now?'

'Oh, not out here,' she answered in quick alarm.

'Then I'll open it as soon as I get home. See you around seven.' Tucking the box under his arm, he walked back to his car and drove off, waving at her as he went.

Teal wanted to go to bed with her. Maybe as soon as next weekend.

He was involved. Whatever that meant.

Teal drove straight home. The boys were in the tree house. Going up to his bedroom, he undid the ribbon on the box and tore off the flowered paper. Then he opened the lid.

One by one he spread the contents of the box on his bed. A pretty home-made candle. A tape of 'Lara's Theme'. A filmy blue nightgown that made his heart thump in his chest. And finally, attached to a cardboard backing, an advertisement for a cottage by the sea, complete with fireplace and king-sized bed. On the card inside the box Julie had written, 'This gift is for us to share . . . but only if you want to.'

He was a grown man, he thought numbly. Grown men didn't cry.

Of all the tangled emotions clogging his throat, wonderment and fear were the two uppermost. For Julie's real gift was, of course, herself.

At ten past seven Julie was tapping on Teal's door, wearing a flounced skirt and a ruffled top, her hair loose on her shoulders. Scott opened the door. 'Hi, Julie,' he said and hugged her. 'I missed you.'

She hugged him back. Then Danny came running in, Teal following at a more leisurely pace on his heels. She loved both boys and at the moment would have wished them to be anywhere else but here. The gift which had caused her so much heart-searching now seemed the height of temerity; she was chasing Teal, just like all those other women.

Teal crossed the kitchen floor, kissed her firmly on the mouth and said, 'Ready, guys?'

Julie ushered their two sons out to the car, wondering why falling in love was considered a desirable state of mind. All it was doing to her was tying her stomach in knots.

They ate at a neighborhood steak house and went back to Teal's afterwards. As he poured two brandies, the boys went outside to play flashlight tag in the back garden. Teal raised his glass and said quietly, 'I'd like to share your gift, Julie.'

Her heart gave a panic-stricken lurch. 'Oh,' she said, 'that's nice.'

'If you're free in five days, why don't I make reservations at that new resort that's near Chester? It's only an hour from the city and they have chalets with fireplaces right by the beach.'

'That sounds lovely... but what about the boys?'

While he'd been waiting for her Teal had thought this out. 'Marylee has often offered to take Scott for me. I could ask her if Scott and Danny could stay at the cottage for a couple of days.'

'If she doesn't mind, that would be ideal,' Julie said, and listened to the thrum of her pulse in her ears. This had been her idea in the first place... why was she feeling so afraid?

'Great. I'll call for reservations first thing tomorrow.'

Julie took a big mouthful of brandy and let it burn its way down her throat. She loved Teal. They would have two days together in a secluded cottage with the sound of the sea as their only companion. They would make love, and maybe she would find out what it was that had distanced him so drastically from his sexuality and his emotions. There was no need for her to worry.

She asked some questions about the resort and checked on his calendar to make sure which days she had off. Then the boys came running in, hot, breathless and in dire need of something to drink, and shortly afterwards Julie took Danny home.

As she undressed that night before going to bed, she looked down at herself, her nightgown dangling in one hand. Privately she had always thought her breasts were too full; and there was no question but that her pregnancy had marked her body. Robert had lost interest in her sexually very early in the marriage, although it was only on his last visit to the old house on the shore that she'd discovered he had been having an affair with Melissa for years. If she, Julie, hadn't been woman enough to hold Robert, why should she be able to satisfy a man as complicated as Teal?

She should never have given the gift to him. It was asking for trouble.

Before he left the house the next morning, Teal made reservations for two nights in one of the seaside chalets at the resort. He gave out his VISA number and put down the phone. Not giving himself time to think, he dialed Marylee's number and explained what he wanted.

'We'd be delighted to have the boys,' she said warmly. 'In fact, I was thinking of phoning you. I'm taking Sara and Jane horseback riding after supper this evening, and I thought Scott might like to go, too. Why don't you ask Danny? That way he could meet me and the girls, and he wouldn't be coming to stay with total strangers.'

Inwardly blessing her for her tact and kindness, Teal said, 'That's sweet of you, Marylee...I'll ask Danny. What time?'

'I'd pick them up at six. We wouldn't be home before nine—the stables are out of town; is that too late?'

'I'll call Julie and check with her—I shouldn't think so. Thanks, Marylee...I'll see you at six.'

The die was cast, he thought, putting down the phone. Julie's shift today was seven to seven; he'd phone her from work. He pulled on his jacket, automatically shielding his ribs, and went downstairs to say hello to Mrs Inkpen.

Julie sounded harassed when he spoke to her. 'That's fine,' she said. 'Danny went riding in PEI and loved it. Would you give her whatever money she needs and I'll pay you back...? Okay, Shirley, I'll be right there...I've got to go, Teal, bye.'

Today was Monday. On Saturday he was going to spend two days with the woman he had just spoken to. Two days and two nights, he thought with a dry mouth. Two nights alone with Julie...

His secretary knocked on the door. 'Come in,' Teal said, and with relief submerged himself in the business of the day.

Sharp at six Marylee picked the boys up. Danny was ready and waiting, a plastic bag of carrots tucked under his arm for the horses. Probably Julie's entire supply of carrots, Teal thought drily, waving goodbye and then walking back into his empty house.

Because Mrs Inkpen had done her usual sweep, it was extremely tidy. The flowers Julie had brought had long ago died; as he wandered restlessly from room to room, he decided she was right—the house was colorless. Bleak. Bare. He had never liked minimalist art, so why was he living in a home so denuded of vitality?

So expressive of Elizabeth.

He paused in front of a black and white photograph that had been one of her favorites. An old man was sitting alone on a park bench with a crowd of blank-faced and anonymous people streaming past him. No connections anywhere, Teal thought. Only loneliness and isolation.

But surely Julie was different from everything this photograph expressed. Julie danced as if there were no tomorrow, as if the very essence of joy surged through her veins.

How would she make love? The same way?

On Saturday he'd find out. He'd committed himself to doing so.

Grown men weren't supposed to feel afraid, either.

He collected a bundle of Scott's dirty clothes and started a wash. He made himself a salad and ate it staring out at the garden. He'd feel better if he could mow the lawn or prune the shrubs; but his ribs were still too painful for that. He tried to work, but the tangle of legal words couldn't hold his interest. Finally, at quarter-past eight, he left the house and walked over to Julie's.

He could tell her about their reservations, and that Marylee would keep the boys.

There were lights shining in her windows and through the screen door he could hear Bette Midler singing about the wind beneath her wings. He rang the bell.

Julie came running through the kitchen and unlatched the door, her face alight with pleasure. 'Hi, Teal—come in.'

She was wearing the cut-off denim shorts and halter-top that she had been wearing the first time he had met her. Her legs seemed to go on forever. He said, feeling his blood thicken in his veins, 'I hope you don't mind my dropping in—I wanted to tell you about the reservations.'

Mind? Just the sight of him had made Julie feel as buoyant as one of her birthday balloons. 'It's nice to see you,' she chattered. 'I'm trying to tidy up Danny's room. Three dried-up worms in the pocket of his jeans and I've just found a dead mouse under the bed. Einstein's contribution. You know how I feel about rodents. Yuk.'

It would be all right, Teal thought. She was as different from Elizabeth as she could be. 'Danny's T-shirts always look as though he's slept in the ditch,' he said. 'I'll get rid of the mouse for you if you like.'

'Grab a beer from the fridge and I definitely do like.'

He uncapped the beer and followed her down the hall. Her room was across from Danny's. In a quick glance he saw a bed with a rose-pink spread heaped with lacy cushions, and curtains splashed with exotic tropical flowers. It was a double bed.

Danny's room was decorated in reds and blues; picking his way past the vacuum cleaner and the clothes hamper, he put his beer on the bookshelves and eased himself under the bed. Luckily, for the sake of his ribs, the mouse was within reach. As Julie wrinkled her nose in disgust, he walked past her and went outside to bury it in the garden.

After scrubbing his hands in the kitchen, he went back to the bedroom. Julie had turned off the vacuum cleaner. Picking up the hamper, she headed for the door. But she tripped over the cord, and a motley collection of shorts and socks fell on the floor. 'Darn,' she said, and put the hamper down.

Teal stooped to help her pick up the clothes. They both reached for the same sock, his hand overlying hers. He found himself gripping it, seized by a tension he couldn't have put a name to, and looked up, his eyes meeting the mysterious smoke-blue of hers. And then his gaze dropped, lingering on her cleavage, on the fullness of her breasts under the blue fabric.

'Julie...' he said hoarsely, and leaned forward to kiss her.

Her mouth was soft, welcoming him. Bracing his knee on the carpet, he pulled her closer, teasing her lips open with his tongue. Her skin smelled of soap and her shoulderbones felt fragile under his palms. This is right, he thought dimly. It has to be right.

'Come to bed with me, Julie—now,' he muttered. 'I don't want to wait until the weekend. We've waited long enough.'

'Yes,' she said.

Awkwardly he got to his feet, clasping her hand in his as she led him across the hall. She pulled back the spread, revealing sheets with the same wild pattern of flowers, and then stood still, looking unaccustomedly unsure of herself. Teal unbuttoned his shirt, hearing the tape on his ribcage rasp against it as he pulled it off. Then he eased her top over her head, baring her breasts. His hands not quite steady, he stroked each one to its tip, feeling them tighten at his touch.

And then his control broke. He pulled her down on the bed with him, seeking out her mouth, the curves of her breasts, tangling his legs with the length of hers. Clumsy with haste, he tugged at the zipper on her shorts and shoved the denim down over her hips, intoxicated by the silken warmth of her flesh. It had been too long, he thought, too long since he'd been with a woman, and God, how he wanted her.

As he twisted to get out of his own shorts, his ribs screamed a protest. He ignored them, too intent on plundering all the sweetness of her mouth, his hips already moving against hers as he pressed her down into the mattress. The softness of her breasts crushed to his chest pushed him deeper into the heated, frantic spiral of desire. His heartbeat was pounding in his ears, the blood surging through his body, and his whole world had narrowed to a woman's body on a bed, a woman whose legs had opened to him and whose hips were moving under his in a rhythm too provocative to be denied.

With his fingers he sought out the wetness between her thighs, and in passionate gratitude thrust into her, groaning deep in his throat as she enveloped him. He could feel the pressure mounting unbearably, the throbbing seizing him in its ancient impulsions; before he was ready for it he spilled within her in a tumult of release that took the breath from his body and left him, drained, in that place that was like death.

His eyes were closed and all around him was blackness, desire was gone as if it had been slashed from him with a sword. He was alone, as he had been alone all his life.

Fighting for breath, his head hanging low, he felt words begin to swirl in his brain, words that only served to deepen his isolation; for Julie had been right to guess that he'd lived in a place of loneliness for as long as he could remember. He'd married Elizabeth to get out of it; and instead had found himself mired deeper than before. There was no surcease, he thought in despair. None. The love stories of the world which spoke of unions beyond the physical were just that: stories. Fabrications to console against the darkness of the human spirit.

He pushed himself up on his elbows, feeling the air cool against his skin where Julie's body had warmed him. This is Julie, he thought. Julie lying beneath me. But, the way I treated her, she could have been anyone.

And then, with an irony that he couldn't possibly have explained to her, he realized that he had done nothing to protect her against a pregnancy.

He rolled off her and said in a voice devoid of emotion, 'I shouldn't have done that—I didn't stop to think.'

She was lying very still, the curves of her body gleaming like pearl in the dusky evening light. It took him a moment to see that she was crying, slow, silent tears seeping down her cheeks. She looked bereft. Stunned. Like a woman who had just been told her beloved was dead, he thought—and wondered where such an image had come from.

Elizabeth, once he had climaxed, had wanted nothing more from him. But Julie was weeping. Through the black loneliness Teal felt the first faint stirrings of a feeling different from despair.

In a voice she scarcely recognized as her own, Julie said, 'What shouldn't you have done?'

'I shouldn't have made love to you.'

'You didn't.'

Her honesty flicked him on the raw. Anger was an emotion he knew; gratefully he embraced it. 'That's right—I didn't. You could have been anyone—which is the reason I've been fighting you off all summer.'

She sat up on the bed, ignoring the tears hanging on her lashes, her nostrils flared. 'Oh, so now it's my fault?'

He hauled himself upright. 'No, damn it, it's my fault! Why the devil do you think I wanted the agreement in the first place? To keep me out of situations like this, of course.'

'You don't have to swear,' she snapped.

He raked his hair back from his forehead. 'You have my full permission to cancel out of this weekend.'

She said levelly, 'I wanted to make love with you more than anything else in the world. But all I feel now is used. Used and tossed aside.'

'That's all I'm capable of giving!'

'Then you're just like Robert,' Julie said.

He felt as if she'd hit him in the ribs with the bedpost. 'You hated sex with Robert.'

'That's right.' Her fists clenched impotently, she said, 'What's the good of my being beautiful and sexy-looking? So what if every date I have wants to take me to bed? It doesn't do me any good—no one ever sees me as a real person. Sex is using people—just like you used me.'

Utterly appalled, Teal whispered, 'Julie, I'm sorry...'

He wasn't sure she'd even heard him. She went on in the same dead voice, 'If you can't give more of yourself than you just did, I'm not going anywhere with you this weekend.'

The stab of pain in Teal's chest had nothing to do with his ribs. He said clumsily, 'I hurt you—I didn't mean to do that.'

If anything, she looked even more stricken. 'This is the end, isn't it? We're through with each other.'

She was sitting only inches from him, naked, her hair tumbled on her shoulders, her cheeks drained of color. For the second time in minutes Teal's breathing stopped in his throat; into the silence the antique clock in the living-room began to chime.

Julie's eyes widened in shock. 'It's nine o'clock,' she gasped, scrambling off the bed and reaching for her clothes. 'Marylee will be bringing the boys back any minute.'

He took her by the arm. 'We can't leave this——'

'Teal, the boys will be home soon,' she repeated furiously. 'They sure don't need to find us in bed together;

they're confused enough as it is. Let go of me! And for heaven's sake put something on!'

His clothes seemed to be scattered all over the floor; he had no recollection of how they'd got there. As Julie fled from the room, he began to get dressed, struggling to sort out his feelings even as his fingers wrestled with the buttons on his shirt.

Out of his confusion one thought surfaced. He couldn't walk out of this house and never hold Julie in his arms again. He couldn't bear that.

He followed her down the hall to the bathroom, where she was splashing cold water on her face, and said hoarsely, 'We've got to talk——'

'I don't think so,' she said tightly. 'Sometimes actions speak louder than words.'

'I'm not leaving you like this!'

'You don't have any choice. I'm going outside to wait for Danny, and I'm certainly not going to be in the middle of a fight with you when he arrives.'

What was wrong with him? He felt tongue-tied, his brain reduced to mush. Mr Chief Justice Mersey wouldn't recognize him, Teal thought fleetingly, and in the mirror saw a stranger looking back at him, a man he scarcely recognized.

Julie had already gone down the hall. Trying to get a grip on himself, Teal went outside. She was sitting on the only chair on the porch, Einstein clutched to her breast; two pairs of eyes, one smoke-blue, the other amber, regarded him with equal animosity. Her fingers were clenched in Einstein's fur, and he could see the hammer-beat of her pulse at the base of her throat.

She was certainly angry with him, Teal was in no doubt about that. But beneath a surface bravado he sensed that she was also frightened. Terrified out of her wits. Praying that he was right, he announced with all the violence of suppressed emotion and no diplomacy whatsoever, 'I'll pick you up on Saturday after lunch.'

'I'm not going.'

'Yes, you are! You were crying, Julie—what I do matters to you; I'm finally starting to figure that out. All I'm asking for is a second chance—I promise there'll be no repeat of what happened tonight.'

Rubbing Einstein's skull with fierce concentration, Julie said raggedly, 'What if you really are like Robert? I couldn't bear to go through that again.'

Teal put all the force of his personality into his words. 'I'm not—I swear I'm not.'

'I don't know anything any more,' she said hopelessly, her shoulders drooping.

Behind him a car turned into the driveway. Teal said urgently, 'You're going with me on the weekend, Julie.'

Not looking at him, she muttered, 'All right—I'll go.'

Light-headed with relief, Teal turned around as the four children erupted from the car, and somehow managed to conduct a coherent conversation with Marylee in the kitchen. There was no further opportunity to speak to Julie alone, nor did he try to engineer one. Half an hour later he and Scott walked home together.

He had Julie's promise that she'd go away with him on Saturday.

The rest was up to him.

CHAPTER TEN

TEAL and Julie arrived at the resort late in the afternoon. Julie had worked an overnight shift and had gone to bed at seven-thirty that morning to get some sleep. At least, that had been the theory, she thought as Teal parked in front of a log-faced chalet and she climbed out of the car. She had been too on edge to sleep well, and now was a mass of nerves.

The chalet was surrounded by fragrant balsam fir and silver-trunked birches, through which she glimpsed the vibrant blue of the sea. The waves sloshed against the rocks with a repetitive, soothing rhythm, while the boughs of the trees swayed back and forth in the breeze. She and Teal were enclosed in a small private world, and as she filled her lungs with the salt air she felt a slight lessening of the tension that had been with her ever since she'd allowed Teal into her bed last Monday night.

Why had she done that? And why had she let him talk her into coming here?

'What a beautiful place,' she said banally.

Teal was getting their cases out of the back seat. He could only lift with one hand; she grabbed her own bag, waited as he unlocked the door of the chalet and followed him inside.

At any other time the room would have delighted her. A bouquet of garden flowers stood on the coffee-table in front of the stone fireplace, the picture window overlooked the ocean, and the bed—a very large bed—had an attractive forest-green spread that blended with the lighter green carpet.

170

Teal put his case down and went back outside, returning a moment later with the gift box she had given him. Without saying a word he placed the candle beside the bed, put her nightgown on the pillow and inserted the tape of 'Lara's Theme' into his portable tape deck. The plaintive melody filled the room. He said quietly, 'Come to bed with me, Julie.'

Instinctively he had done exactly the right thing. How could she go for a walk with him along the shore, or play tennis, or have a drink at the bar in the main lodge when part of her craved to be held by him and the rest of her wanted to run a mile from the big bed?

She smiled with stiff lips and picked up the blue nightgown. 'I won't be a minute.'

The bathroom was luxuriously appointed. Julie undressed, slid the gown over her head, brushed her hair loose and sprayed on some of her most expensive perfume to give herself courage. Courage. She was beginning to hate that word.

She met her eyes in the mirror. I love Teal, she thought. I love him. Everything will be all right.

When she went back into the room he had drawn the curtains and stripped to his briefs. The candle was burning with a pure, still flame by the bed. She had no idea what he was thinking, still less what he might be feeling. She was walking into the unknown, toward a man who in so many ways was still a mystery to her, and held tightly to the surety of her love.

Teal watched her come toward him. Even in the small light that the candle cast he could see the outline of her body beneath the filmy blue gown. She was walking tall, all her courage in her eyes; she deserved another orchid, he thought. A whole bouquet of orchids.

Since Monday he had rehearsed any number of fancy speeches and romantic gestures that he'd hoped would please her. As she stopped in her tracks four feet away from him, he forgot them all and said harshly, 'I don't understand why you're here, Julie—not after the way I've treated you.'

She gave him a blank look. 'Because I love you, of course. Hadn't you figured that out?'

Teal felt as though she'd punched him in the gut; at his involuntary indrawn breath his ribs knifed a protest. 'No,' he said in magnificent understatement, 'I hadn't figured that out.'

'Well, now you know.'

She wasn't nearly as at ease as she was trying to sound; a muscle was twitching in her jaw and her eyes were looking anywhere in the room but at him. These tiny betrayals filled Teal with the same emotions he'd felt when he'd first held Scott in his arms: both an overwhelming tenderness at the mystery and wonder of another human being, and a sense of the utter incommunicability of that tenderness.

He closed the distance between them, resting his hands lightly on Julie's shoulders. 'I've done nothing to warrant that.'

'Love isn't earned,' she said helplessly. 'It just is.'

'And what about lovemaking?'

Feeling absurdly shy, Julie slid her hands up Teal's chest, playing with the edge of the tape on his ribs as she sought for words. 'I'm no expert,' she said. 'Far from it. I—I guess what I want is togetherness. No barriers. No separations. The two of us as close as we can possibly be.' Very carefully she pressed down on the corner of the tape, where it had come unstuck. 'I might as well tell you I have no idea how to go about that.'

Neither did he. But, as her perfume drifted to his nostrils, one thing was crystal-clear to him. Julie was open to him. As open as Elizabeth had been closed. Although he could easily have given these words a sexual connotation, he didn't mean them that way. He was important to her, he thought painfully. What he did could affect her, for better or for worse.

This wasn't just about his hang-ups. Julie had her own demons as well. She was a woman whose beauty touched him to the heart; yet this beauty had never brought her the sexual pleasure to which she was entitled.

If he was here to be healed, so also was she.

He said at random, 'Last time I did nothing to protect you from pregnancy.'

'I'm on the Pill because I've been having trouble with my periods,' she said, and crinkled her nose at him. 'Just as well, wouldn't you say? I don't think, right now, that we need the complication of a baby.'

His voice sounding strange in his ears, Teal said, 'We're here for us, then. Just us.'

'No "just" about it,' she said vigorously. 'Of course we're here for us—who else would we be here for?'

Forcing himself to lower the first of the barriers, knowing he was stepping from long-familiar territory into the unknown, Teal took a deep breath and said, 'The only reason Elizabeth wanted to go to bed with me— ever—was to get pregnant.'

The shock of his disclosure ran through Julie's body. For a moment she scarcely believed it, so alien was it to the way she felt about Teal. But then, meeting his eyes, she saw that it was indeed true. She said strongly, 'I'm not Elizabeth. I want you—right here and now—for yourself.'

Blushing, but refusing to let her eyes drop, she rested her hands on his shoulders, molding the strongly carved muscles. 'Your body is beautiful to me, Teal.' A tiny smile tilted her mouth. 'You wouldn't believe some of the dreams I've had about you.'

It never occurred to him to disbelieve her. Like a man learning a new skill, his first movements tentative and uncertain, he reached out one hand and traced the planes of her cheekbone and the gentle inward line of her cheek. 'I never could reach Elizabeth,' he confessed. 'Not once in seven years of marriage, not even when Scott was born, did she share herself with me. Her core, her essence—she kept those to herself and wouldn't let me in.'

'The place of loneliness,' Julie said softly.

He nodded, grateful for her understanding. 'You're very different from her. I need you, Julie.'

He had never thought to say those words to a woman—and found he had spoken them almost naturally, for their time had come. Julie felt tears film her eyes. In a choked voice she said, 'As we're into confessions, Robert never needed me—or Danny—any more than Elizabeth needed you. Our whole marriage was an act, a sham from beginning to end. For him it was like a dress rehearsal where he could practise extending his emotional range—he used to pick fights with me and then stand back and watch my reactions as though I were a bug on a pin. I hated it!'

Teal didn't even have to think about his next words. 'You're absolutely real to me, Julie. Yes, I find you beautiful—heart-stoppingly beautiful; I'd be a liar if I pretended otherwise—but it's your courage and passion and honesty that——' His voice faltered, then gained strength. 'That I'm in love with.'

She blinked. 'What did you say?'

'I'm in love with you,' Teal said. Throwing back his head, he gave an exultant laugh. 'What a fool I've been! It's been staring me in the face ever since I met you. Julie, darling, dearest Julie, I love you.'

His movements not at all uncertain of themselves, Teal took her face in his hands and kissed her. She looked dazed, her body tense with shock, so that she felt like a mannequin in his arms; he set out to show her that he'd meant every word he'd said. Gentling his kiss, he let his lips play with hers, brushing against them as delicately as the touch of a butterfly, his tongue teasing their softness until he felt their first, almost shy response.

Her palms glided down his chest. 'Am I dreaming?' she whispered. 'Did you say you loved me?'

Laughter warming his voice, Teal said, 'Sweetheart, despite having worked the night shift, you're wide awake. And yes, I do love you.'

'I love you, too!' Julie exclaimed. In all her fantasizing about the weekend, she had not once dreamed of hearing Teal say those words. She looped her arms around his neck, her eyes dancing. 'You know what? I'm not nearly as scared as I was five minutes ago.'

Teal had never thought laughter could be a part of lovemaking. 'You're not begging for mercy? Julie, you disappoint me.'

She let one hand wander further down his body. 'It's not mercy I'm begging for, Teal Carruthers.'

'Are you telling me I talk too much?' he growled, steering her toward the bed, pulling back the covers and lying down beside her on the cool sheets. He said, no longer laughing, 'We have two days together. Two whole days. We have all the time in the world to learn how to please each other.'

'There's nothing I would rather do,' Julie said.

The intensity that was so much a part of her shone from her eyes, and in them, mysteriously, he caught a gleam of the same blue that was at the base of the candleflame. Although his heart was racing and he desired her as fiercely as a caged man craved freedom, he deliberately restrained himself. Because Julie wanted something from him. Something far more complex than the

child Elizabeth had wanted. Julie wanted all of him, body
and soul, his emotions, his laughter and his tears. She
wanted intimacy—the one thing Elizabeth had shunned.

He began stroking the length of her body under the
filmy nightgown, learning the flow from breast to waist
to hip to thigh, the geography of flesh and bone that
was Julie. He took the weight of her breasts in his hands,
teasing their tips to hardness, intoxicated by the sensual
slide of the pale blue fabric over her skin, now hiding,
now revealing. He buried his face in the shining fall of
her hair, ran his mouth down her throat to the rise of
her breast, tasting her, and then let his fingers drift between her thighs, tangled in the slippery folds of her
gown.

Her indrawn breath echoed his own. He looked up.
Although she had been lying still, it was as far from the
stillness of passivity as it could be. Her eyes, brilliant
with desire, were trained on his, and the soft, voluptuous curve of her mouth spoke volumes; for a moment
that was out of time her image filled his vision and he
knew he would never forget this instant when, unful-
filled, he was certain he could both find and give
fulfillment.

She leaned forward, pulling the nightgown over her
head in a graceful flash of bare arms, her nakedness
touching him to the core. Then she reached over and
pulled his briefs down over his hips. 'Lie still, Teal,' she
whispered. 'It's my turn.'

He lay back on the sheets, aware with some distant
part of his brain that she wanted him to expose his vulnerability as much as his body. Lying down beside him,
her breasts moving gently in the candlelight, she touched
him with hands and mouth and body until he thought
he would die with the pleasure of it. And finally, as he
had been longing for her to do, she slid her thighs be-

tween his and with the fingers of one hand encircled the hardness that was all his pent-up need of her.

He groaned her name as the dark throbbing spread to encompass his whole body. 'Not yet, Julie—not yet,' he muttered, and rolled over, remembering at the last moment to protect his ribs. Parting her thighs, he began playing with her with an exquisite gentleness; she was as sleek and wet as a sea creature, her body arching with pleasure like a dolphin's in the waves of the ocean. As she pulled him closer, forgetting to be gentle, he felt a flood of primitive power that he could so move her. She was his. His mate. His woman. His love.

In her eyes and in the long line of her throat he sensed the storm gathering within her, and knew that his one desire was to release that storm. Bringing all his imagination and his new-found love to the task, he watched her throw her head back, her belly a taut curve.

Then suddenly she broke, crying out his name over and over again in a litany that filled Teal with a strange mixture of pride and humility. As she collapsed in his arms, her breathing as rapid as a child's, he felt again that upwelling of tenderness. But this time he could communicate it: he had the words. The simplest, most profound words in the language.

'Julie, I love you,' he said.

Her lashes fluttered open. She took his palm and laid it against her breast so that he could feel the triphammer of her heartbeat, and whispered, 'Dearest Teal . . . I love you, too.'

For a few moments she was still, lost in the place to which he had taken her. He let his mouth drift over her drowned face and the sweet curves of her body, content to wait for her because there was all the time in the world and she was his, his beautiful Julie.

His head was resting on her breast. Toying with the silky thickness of his hair, Julie murmured, 'I feel very happy.' She let her hands wander the length of his spine, almost idly at first. Then they moved lower, to his hips and buttocks. Suddenly her body twisted, and with a blatant eroticism that seared Teal like fire she pulled him on top of her, opening her legs to gather him in. 'Now,' she said fiercely. 'Now, Teal.'

He thrust deep into her body, rearing up on his elbows to drink in all the fleeting expressions on her face. 'I don't want this to be over,' he said roughly.

She arched her hips under him and his face convulsed. 'Teal,' she said, 'this is just the beginning ... I'm not going to go away. Not if you don't want me to.'

Open to him. Wanting him. 'I don't want you to go away. Ever,' he said, and lowered his weight on her, kissing her with a passion that had lain dormant within him for years. It had taken Julie to release it, he thought. The gift she had really given him was himself. His true self. The man he had always had the potential to be.

Fueled by gratitude and love, guided by a new-born intuition of what pleased her, he roamed her body; and all the while he moved inside her, wanting fervently to give her pleasure.

In a broken voice he hadn't heard before, she said, 'Please, Teal ... oh, please.' Only then did he let go, allowing the urgent demands of his body to overwhelm him and trusting that somehow that was what she wanted too.

She cried out, sharp and fierce as a seabird; he emptied within her even as the tension in her body throbbed its way to satiation. One flesh, Teal thought. So that's what that means. I never knew.

His chest was heaving, and the beating of his heart could have been her own. He smoothed her hair back from her face and said, struggling for breath, 'What I feel now is the very opposite of loneliness.'

She wound her arms around him. 'When we're truly together, how can we be lonely?'

The candle was still burning by the bedside. His voice husky with emotion, Teal said, 'You've given me the most wonderful gift in the world.'

She smiled at him, snuggling a little closer, and rested her cheek on his shoulder. Within minutes she was asleep. But Teal stayed awake, listening to the peaceful rhythm of her breathing, letting the joy and trust that she had brought him settle quietly in his heart.

They made love again when Julie awoke, ordered Room Service for dinner because neither of them wanted any company other than their own, played in the Jacuzzi after they had eaten, and somehow found themselves locked in an embrace against the bathroom door. Julie started to giggle. 'You're a sex maniac,' she said.

'Are you complaining?'

With an abrupt change of mood she said seriously, 'I've loved every minute we've spent here.' Her brow wrinkled. 'I've seen a side of you I only caught glimpses of before—I wasn't always sure it existed because you were so controlled. So determined to keep me at a distance.'

In less than eight hours in a chalet by the sea Teal knew his whole life had shifted. He took a fleecy towel from the pile on the shelf and started drying Julie's body, already so well-known to him, so endlessly a source of delight.

He said soberly, 'Elizabeth's dead, and I sometimes think her loneliness must have been as great if not greater than mine...although I'll never know that now.

'I loved her when we married. I knew she wanted children, and that was fine with me. I soon found out that she didn't like sex, but I was young and I figured that would change with time. Scott was born, and from the first moment I saw him I loved him and understood that with him, at least, I didn't have to feel alone. Because you were right—my parents didn't want me; I was just a pawn in their ongoing battle.'

He smoothed the towel down her hips. 'Elizabeth wanted another child. Right away. I went along with that; I thought a daughter would be lovely. But it didn't happen. A year went by, then two. Elizabeth started going to doctors and, because I knew how important it was to her, I went too. There was nothing wrong with me, I was told. Somehow—and this was her word—the fault was hers.'

His hands grew still. The bathroom door was made of pine; he focussed on the knots and whorls in the wood and went on with his story.

'She was desperate, so we tried everything, going from clinic to clinic and doctor to doctor. Elizabeth had never liked being touched; in bed she never let herself go—she was afraid to, I think. All her energy was focussed on getting pregnant—so sex became totally mechanical, tied to temperature and position and timing. No spontaneity, and certainly no love. I got so I loathed it.'

He grimaced. 'Sometimes I wanted to leave her. But how could I when her need was so enormous and when we had Scott to bind us together? And then, of course, she died.'

He pushed himself back, bending his neck to relieve the tightness of his muscles.

'I grieved for her. Of course I did; we'd lived together for seven years and she was the mother of my son, and if I'd fallen out of love with her she was still my wife and far too young to die. But mingled with the grief was tremendous guilt that I'd failed her by never being able to reach her—somehow I should have been able to do so.

'I think the worst thing of all, though, buried underneath everything else, was a feeling of relief.' He suddenly banged his fist against the door-frame, glad of the pain. 'Sheer, simple relief. How could I admit that to anyone? I've never told another living soul, not even Bruce and Marylee.'

But he had told her. Instantly certain that it had been the guilt and the relief, rather than the grief, that had kept him so distanced, so far away from her, Julie said, 'You must have tried to reach Elizabeth.'

'Yeah, I tried. And I failed.'

'She has to bear some of the responsibility for that.'

'Lovemaking didn't reach her and Scott's birth made no difference, so I tried anger—but she wouldn't fight with me,' he said, running his fingernail down the pine panels. 'She just retreated into silence. A silence that could go on for days. God, how I hated that.'

'No wonder you shied like a half-broken horse every time a woman talked commitment.' Julie reached up and lightly touched his mouth. 'The agreement makes a lot more sense now.'

'Logically it made sense.' He smiled crookedly. 'From the moment I first saw you I think my subconscious knew I needed you…and the agreement was how it went about getting you.'

Julie said forthrightly, 'You've broken the pattern of your marriage with me. We've never been either silent or superficial with each other—no matter how hard we tried.'

'It was your honesty that first attracted me.' For the first time since he had started talking to her, Teal smiled. 'Well, that and your cleavage.'

She laughed, letting the towel slide to the floor. 'Let's go to bed.'

'Again?' Teal said. 'I'm not the only sex maniac around here.'

'Beds can be for sleeping, too.'

He said, because he knew it was important, 'I'm glad I told you about Elizabeth . . . I wanted you to understand. And I want you to feel free to talk about Robert— he's Danny's father, he exists. And I do want us to break the patterns, Julie. You're far too important to me for it to be otherwise.'

She gave him an impish smile. 'I don't hate sex any more.'

'I rather noticed that.' He let his eyes travel the length of her body with a leisurely sensuality. 'What was that you said about sleeping? I'm not sure sleep is my main priority right now.'

'I'm used to night shifts,' Julie said, tangling her fingers in his body hair. 'Let's light a fire in the fireplace.'

'And then we'll light another one in the bed,' Teal said.

Which they did.

Teal pulled up by his house at seven on Monday evening, an hour later than had been planned. Marylee's car was already in the driveway. 'Back to normality,' he said as the boys raced down the steps to meet them.

'I feel as though we've been away for weeks,' Julie responded, and opened her door for Danny's hug. 'Hello, sweetie, how are you?'

Marylee came wandering down the steps. 'Did you have a good time?' she said innocently.

Julie blushed. Teal said with considerable panache, 'Superb. How was the cottage?'

'Wonderful. They want to go back next weekend—if you're interested.'

Julie blushed even redder; amused, Teal came to her rescue. 'I'm sure that could be arranged,' he remarked. 'Want to carry my bag in, Scott?'

'What was the resort like, Julie?' Marylee asked. 'I've heard the beach is beautiful.'

Julie hadn't gone near the beach. 'The dining-room was very attractive,' she said weakly.

'The rocks were gray, the sea was blue and the beach was made of sand,' Teal said. 'Come on in for a drink, Marylee.'

They drank vodka and orange under the maple tree, after which Marylee left. The boys had a tendency to hover; apart from the hours she spent at work Julie was almost never away from Danny. 'I think you missed us,' she said.

The boys exchanged a conspiratorial glance. 'Sort of,' Danny said. 'We got a surprise for you.'

'Yeah,' Scott said. 'In the basement.'

Teal raised his brow. 'Is the lawnmower broken again?'

'Nope.' Scott looked over at Danny, who was stifling a giggle. 'Hurry up and finish your drink, Dad, so we can show you.'

Teal tossed back the last of his vodka. 'Let's go.'

They all went inside. At the top of the basement stairs the boys stood back and Danny said, 'The surprise is in the corner by the furnace—you'll really like it. But you both got to go and see it. Together.'

'Does it bite?' Julie said suspiciously.

This time Scott was the one to collapse into giggles. 'It's okay, Mum,' Danny said kindly. 'Anyway, Teal'll protect you.'

'You haven't come up with a stray dog, Danny? You know Mrs LeMarchant won't let us keep a dog.'

'Go see,' Scott said with another fit of laughter.

Julie gave Teal a mystified look. Teal shrugged his shoulders; he had no more idea than she what this was about. 'After you,' he said.

She went down the stairs cautiously. The basement was full of shadows and very untidy: Mrs Inkpen clearly didn't make it this far. Crossing the floor, she headed for the far corner, Teal close on her heels. Then she heard the door at the top of the stairs slam shut and the metallic screech of the bolt. Teal said, perplexed, 'What are those two up to?'

Julie didn't like basements. Fire in her eye, she marched back up the stairs and said, 'Danny, let us out of here.' The only response was more laughter. She rattled the handle, but the door held firm.

'Did you look by the furnace?' Danny asked.

From the bottom of the stairs Teal called, 'Come and look at this, Julie. I think we've been handed an ultimatum.'

She tramped down the steps. 'Does your basement have rats?' she asked militantly.

'I've never seen one,' Teal answered, grinning at her. 'Once Einstein moves in, we certainly won't have any.'

She frowned at him, her hands on her hips. 'I know you didn't get too much sun the last two days because we never went out in it,' she said. 'What are you talking about? Danny wouldn't part with Einstein.'

'Darling Julie, I think I must have told you I loved you at least once an hour on the hour the whole time we were away. But do you know what I didn't do?'

'Take me for a walk on the beach,' she said promptly.

'I didn't ask you to marry me.'

In the light filtering through the small windows set high in the cement walls Julie could see that he was smiling; but his eyes were intent on her face, and the expression in them made her knees weak. 'You scarcely had time,' she said. 'I kept hauling you off to bed.'

'Will you marry me, Julie?'

She smiled back. 'You must love me if you're willing to take on Einstein.'

'Answer the question, Mrs Ferris,' he ordered in his best courtroom manner.

'Yes, Teal, I'll marry you. I'd really like to. Although we'll have to draw up a new agreement—one that includes sex.'

'I'll make it a priority.' He took her in his arms and kissed her at some length. 'What an innovative and enjoyable way to seal a contract,' he murmured. 'I can't have you disliking lawyers if you're going to marry one.'

Feeling joy bubble up within her, Julie said, 'So what was the boys' surprise?'

From his trouser pocket Teal took out a much creased piece of paper. 'We want you to get maried,' Scott had printed in big red letters. 'We'll let you out wen you agre.'

Underneath, Danny's neater script said, 'Bread and water by the furnace. There's no rats, Mum. We checked.'

She said severely, 'I'm greatly disillusioned. You're only asking me to marry you to avoid a diet of bread and water.'

'Actually I'm hoping that if they live together your son's ability to spell will rub off on mine,' Teal replied.

Then, as she had freed him to do, he gave all his emotions free rein. 'I love you, I need you, I want you,' he said. 'Which has nothing to do with our two sons or with bread and water. As well you know. We could get a special license and get married by the end of the month.'

'Okay,' said Julie.

'Good,' said Teal, and kissed her again. 'Now shall we let the boys know? Or should we let them suffer for a while?'

She glanced around her. 'Even though from now on I'll feel differently about basements, having been proposed to in one, I'm not averse to vacating it as soon as possible.'

He took her by the hand and led her up the stairs. 'We're going to get married,' he said loudly. 'You can let us out now.'

'That didn't take long,' Danny said through the door. 'We were going to starve you into submission, like that movie we saw with all the old knights and barons.'

'That's neat!' Scott crowed. 'Where's the key, Danny?'

'You've got it.'

'No, I don't, I gave it to you.'

'It's not in my pocket.'

'Maybe it's on the picnic table.'

'We'd better go look.'

In the cramped space at the top of the stairs Teal took Julie into his arms. 'We might as well enjoy ourselves while we're waiting,' he said.

Four weeks later Einstein took possession of Teal's garden. He liked it better than the one he had just left; it definitely had more possibilities.

JAYNE ANN KRENTZ

Lady's Choice

Travis Sawyer has a plan for revenge. Juliana Grant has a
plan too—she has picked Travis as Mr Right. When
Travis takes over the resort in which Juliana has invested
her money, Juliana takes matters
into her own hands.

*"Jayne Ann Krentz is one of the hottest writers
in romance today."*—USA Today

1-55166-270-1
AVAILABLE FROM MARCH 1998

Catherine Coulter

Afterglow

Chalk-and-cheese lovers Chelsea Lattimer and
David Winter finally find happiness after a series
of disastrous relationships—thanks to their
match-making friends.

Afterglow is a wonderful romantic comedy from
New York Times bestselling author Catherine Coulter.

1-55166-472-0
AVAILABLE FROM MARCH 1998

JANICE KAISER

FAIR GAME

Dana Kirk is a rich and successful woman, but someone
wants to kill her and her teenage daughter. Who hates
her enough to terrorise this single mother? Detective
Mitchell Cross knows she needs help—
his help—to stay alive.

*"...enough plot twists and turns to delight
armchair sleuths"*—Publishers Weekly

1-55166-065-2
AVAILABLE FROM MARCH 1998

SUSAN WIGGS

The Lightkeeper

Lighthouse keeper Jesse Morgan's reclusive life is
changed forever when he finds Mary Dare washed up on
the shore one morning—unconscious and pregnant.
She's keeping a secret—one that puts them both in
terrible danger.

"A classic beauty and the beast love story...
A poignant, beautiful romance."
—bestselling author Kristin Hannah

MIRA®

1-55166-301-5
AVAILABLE FROM MAY 1998

DEBBIE MACOMBER

The Playboy and the Widow

A confirmed bachelor, Cliff Howard wasn't prepared to trade in the fast lane for car pools. Diana Collins lived life hiding behind motherhood and determined to play it safe. They were both adept at playing their roles. Until the playboy met the widow...

"Debbie Macomber's stories sparkle with love and laughter..."
—*New York Times* bestselling author, Jayne Ann Krentz

MIRA®

1-55166-080-6
AVAILABLE FROM MAY 1998

INTERNATIONAL BESTSELLING AUTHOR

Karen Young

Good Girls

When they were good...

Jack Sullivan is an ambitious and painful presence in
the lives of three prominent Mississippi women.
He made Suzanne a prisoner of violent memories,
used Taylor as a lonely trophy wife and drove
Annie's mother to suicide. When Jack is murdered,
each wonders who finally pulled the trigger...

"Karen Young is a spellbinding storyteller."
—Romantic Times

MIRA®

1-55166-306-6
AVAILABLE FROM MAY 1998

LINDA HOWARD

WHITE LIES

Escorted by the FBI to her ex-husband's bedside, Jay Granger is unprepared for her reaction. *He* doesn't remember a thing, but his effect on her is immediate and undeniable. Is this the man she married...or a total stranger?

"Howard's writing is compelling"
—Publishers Weekly

1-55166-274-4
AVAILABLE FROM APRIL 1998

NORA ROBERTS

Hot Ice

She had the cash and the connections. He knew
the whereabouts of a fabulous hidden fortune. It
was a business proposition, pure and simple.
Now all they needed to do was stay one step
ahead of their murderous rivals.

*"...her stories have fuelled the dreams of
25 million readers"*—Entertainment Weekly

MIRA®

1-55166-395-3
AVAILABLE FROM APRIL 1998

MARY LYNN
BAXTER

Raw Heat

Successful broadcast journalist Juliana Reed is caught
in a web of corruption, blackmail and murder. Texas
Ranger, Gates O'Brien—her ex-husband—is the only
person she can turn to. Both know that getting out
alive is just the beginning...

*"Baxter's writing...strikes every chord within
the female spirit."*
—Bestselling author Sandra Brown

1-55166-394-5
AVAILABLE FROM APRIL 1998